TECHNICAL
WRITING

TECHNICAL
WRITING

John M. Lannon
Southern Vermont College

Little, Brown and Company
Boston   Toronto

Library of Congress Catalog Card No. 78–71864

ISBN 0-316-514330

10   9   8   7   6   5   4   3

HAL

Published simultaneously in Canada
by Little, Brown & Company (Canada) Limited

Printed in the United States of America

for Leslie

Preface

TO THE INSTRUCTOR

This text provides a clear and workable approach to technical communications for both students and instructors. Intended specifically for heterogeneous classes, it speaks to a diversity of student interests. The principles of effective technical writing are applied in a wide variety of assignments, from brief memos and summaries to detailed formal reports. Sample situations parallel those that both two- and four-year students will face in college and on the job.

The text is organized in four major parts. Part I treats technical writing as a deliberate act of communication for a definite purpose to a specified audience. It explains the meaning and purpose of technical writing through a comparison and contrast with the kinds of writing done in traditional composition courses. Contents include suggestions for audience analysis and for achieving effective technical style.

Part II covers various rhetorical and organizational strategies for reaching one's audience. Specifically, it explains how to achieve economy, clarity, precision, and control in technical reporting, and how to collect and record information from various sources.

Part III applies the earlier concepts and strategies to reporting situations typically encountered in college and on the job. The kinds of tasks covered include résumés, memos, letters, proposals, progress reports, mechanism descriptions, instructions, lab reports, analytical reports, and oral reports. Each assignment is prefaced by a full explanation of its underlying rhetorical purpose and principles.

Appendixes include a detailed handbook section for easy reference and an explanation of brainstorming techniques as a prewriting strategy.

The rationale for the sequence of chapters and their individual development is based on five assumptions:

1. That students need intensive practice and guidance in the *process* of writing — in approaching the material, in planning, in writing, and in revising. Thus, they should not simply be told about this process; they must be shown the nitty-gritty of the "why" and "how to" in actual practice.

2. That, often, the only significant difference between freshman/sophomore and junior/senior students is in their respective levels of specialized knowledge. Otherwise, juniors and seniors generally face the same difficulties in planning, writing, and revising as their younger counterparts.

3. That the proliferation of technical writing courses has led to classes that are grouped heterogeneously. This assortment of people with varied backgrounds and interests calls for examples and illustrations that are broadly engaging so that all students will study them with interest.

4. That a frequent and most difficult challenge in report writing is in writing for a nonspecialized audience.

5. That there are nearly as many approaches to the teaching of technical and business writing as there are instructors teaching these courses, and that some schools regard report writing as a lower-level course, and others, as an upper-level course. Therefore, flexibility in a textbook is crucial.

In line with these assumptions, the text follows a cumulative skills pattern, moving from the short, early assignments of summaries and definitions to the formal analytical report with all supplements — an assignment which applies most skills developed earlier. However, within this structure, each chapter is self-contained for maximum flexibility in planning individual courses.

Ample exercises in each chapter span a wide range of practical applications at various levels of challenge and complexity. Thus the instructor who wishes to spend more time on certain chapters, such as those dealing with letters or informal reports, will find plentiful resources. Timely examples and models are drawn mostly from student writing, cover a wide variety of technical and business fields, and are intelligible to students in all majors.

Individual chapters move from theory to practice by:

1. defining each assignment in detail.

2. explaining its purpose and usefulness to students, whose implied question is "why are we doing this?"

3. discussing the specific criteria that the completed assignment should satisfy — with an emphasis on rhetorical purpose.

4. providing model assignments (usually student written) with explanations, discussions, and marginal commentary.

5. giving step-by-step guidelines in planning, organizing, and writing the assignment for a specified audience with specified needs.

6. providing a checklist to be used by students to evaluate and revise the assignment or to serve as an editorial guide in proofreading the work of peers.

The emphasis throughout is on the *process* of writing. Students are carefully guided in organizing and developing their materials systematically: they learn to move from theory to model to statement of purpose to outline to completed assignment. The importance of an Introduction-Body-Conclusion structure is stressed repeatedly to show that the structure of any piece of writing parallels the structure of the basic paragraph.

The book should be easy to teach and learn from, whether your approach is basic or accelerated. The instructor's manual contains sample syllabi and suggestions for implementing either approach. All materials in the text and manual have been used with success at both the community college and university levels, with lower- and upperclass students in just about every conceivable major. Besides helping students organize and control their writing, this text should help them think of writing as a process of applied rhetoric instead of mere mechanical transcription.

My thanks to many friends and colleagues for their help. W. Keats Sparrow of East Carolina University, David Fear of Valencia Community College, Gregory Cowan of Texas A & M University, and Raymond Dumont, Jr., of Idaho State University read the rough manuscript and provided advice and encouragement. At Cape Cod Community College, Admont Clark helped greatly with revisions, Judith Barnet provided important samples, and Dennis Martin class-tested various chapters. At the University of Idaho, Teoman Sipahigil provided much-needed materials and Charles (Skip) Stratton gave generous advice based on his seasoned experience, provided full access to his vast inventory of sample papers and materials, and helped me through many difficult spots. My chairman, Daniel Pearlman, was a steady source of encouragement.

Special thanks to Richard S. Beal of Boston University, whose rigorous and inspired guidance is in large part responsible for whatever is good in this book, and to Gene Krupa of the University of Iowa. Without his talent, advice, and effort, major sections of the final draft might never have materialized.

From Katherine Carlone, Charles Christensen, Sheryl Gipstein, Barbara Sonnenschein, and Jan Young of Little, Brown and Company, I received generous and gracious support throughout this project.

TO THE STUDENT

This text is designed to give you practice in the kinds of writing you will do in college and on the job. Specifically, you will learn to collect useful information, to interpret it, and to present your findings in letters and reports that readers will find informative and clear.

An essential ingredient of good writing is a clear sense of direction — knowing why you are writing, for whom you are writing, and where you are going. In each assignment, you will identify your audience's needs and your writing goal before putting words on paper. Then you will make a clear plan for achieving your goal by developing a detailed outline. Using your outline as a roadmap, you will write the report, concentrating on its physical presentation (format) and revising to achieve a professional product.

It is hoped you will learn to see the act of writing as a deliberate process. As in other processes, such as accounting or furniture making, the product will only be as good as what has gone into it. And the process of writing involves more than simply putting words on paper, for that is only a small part of "writing." The other parts include thinking about your purpose before you write and refining the product after you have written. Very often, these take more time than the "writing" itself.

By writing with purpose and control you will be able to give readers what they expect: a quality product. This should have an immediate influence on the grades for your papers in various courses. The long-range influence on your career should be obvious enough.

So you will know that it is not "busy-work," the purpose of each assignment is explained. You will usually be invited to choose your own subject to write about.

Most of the sample letters and reports in this book were written by my students. After completing the assignments which follow, they felt better about their writing abilities. I hope you will about yours.

Contents

PART I
COMMUNICATING TO A SPECIFIED AUDIENCE   1

1
Introduction to Technical Writing   2

Chapter Goals   3
Definition   3
Technical Versus Nontechnical Writing   4
The Value of Technical Writing Skills   6
Specific Uses of Technical Writing Skills   8
Audience Needs   9
The Writer's Attitude   9
Chapter Summary   9
Exercises   10

2
Writing for Readers   12

Chapter Goals   13
Definition   13
The Concept of "Audience"   13
Writing for Different Readers   14
Focusing on Your Reader's Needs   17
Writing Clear Factual Prose   20
Chapter Summary   29
Exercises   30

PART II
STRATEGIES FOR TECHNICAL REPORTING   33

3
Summarizing Information   34

Chapter Goals   35
Definition   35
Purpose of Summaries   35
Elements of an Effective Summary   37
Writing the Summary   39
Applying the Steps   41
Writing the Abstract   48
Placing Summaries and Abstracts in Your Report   48
Chapter Summary   49
Revision Checklist   50
Exercises   50

4
Defining Your Terms   56

Chapter Goals   57
Definition   57
Purpose of Definitions   57
Using Definitions Selectively   59
Elements of an Effective Definition   60
Choosing the Best Type of Definition   61
Expanding Your Definition   65
Applying the Steps   68
Placing Definitions in Your Report   72
Chapter Summary   73
Revision Checklist   74
Exercises   75

5
Dividing in Order to Organize   78

Chapter Goals   79
Definitions   79
Using Partition and Classification   80
Guidelines for Partition   82
Guidelines for Classification   87
Applying the Techniques of Division   93
Chapter Summary   94
Revision Checklist   96
Exercises   96

6

Charting Your Course: The Outline   **100**

Chapter Goals   101
Definition   101
Purpose of Outlining   102
Choosing the Best Type of Outline   103
Elements of an Effective Formal Outline   109
Constructing the Formal Outline   114
Using Your Outline to Advantage   118
The Report Design Worksheet   118
Chapter Summary   123
Revision Checklist   124
Exercises   125

7

Researching Information   **128**

Chapter Goals   129
Definition   129
Purpose of Research   130
Identifying Information Sources   132
Taking Effective Notes   155
Planning and Writing the Report   158
Chapter Summary   174
Exercises   174

8

Using an Effective Format and Supplements   **180**

Chapter Goals   181
Definitions   181
Purpose of an Effective Format   182
Purpose of Report Supplements   183
Creating an Effective Format   188
Composing Report Supplements   192
Chapter Summary   215
Exercises   215

9

Visual Aids   **218**

Chapter Goals   219
Definition   219
Purpose of Visual Aids   219
Tables   221

Figures   223
Chapter Summary   236
Revision Checklist   237
Exercises   237

PART III
SPECIFIC APPLICATIONS   241

10
Writing Effective Letters   242

Chapter Goals   243
Definition   243
Purpose of Letters   244
Elements of an Effective Letter   245
Writing Various Types of Letters   260
Writing the Résumé and Job Application Letter   268
Supporting Your Application   284
Chapter Summary   291
Revision Checklist   292
Exercises   292

11
Writing Informal Reports   298

Chapter Goals   299
Definition   299
Purpose of Informal Reports   299
Choosing the Best Report Form for Your Purpose   300
Composing Various Informal Reports   301
Chapter Summary   332
Revision Checklist   335
Exercises   335

12
Writing a Description   340

Chapter Goals   341
Definition   341
Purpose of Description   342
Making Your Description Objective   347
Elements of an Effective Description   351
Organizing and Writing Your Description   353

Applying the Steps   363
Chapter Summary   375
Revision Checklist   376
Exercises   376

13
Explaining a Process   380

Chapter Goals   381
Definition   381
The Purpose of Process Explanation   381
Types of Process Explanation   382
Elements of Effective Instructions   384
Organizing and Writing a Set of Instructions   390
Applying the Steps   396
Elements of an Effective Process Narrative   396
Organizing and Writing a Process Narrative   405
Applying the Steps   406
Elements of an Effective Process Analysis   406
Organizing and Writing a Process Analysis   416
Applying the Steps   416
Chapter Summary   428
Revision Checklist   429
Exercises   430

14
Analyzing Data and Writing the Formal Report   432

Chapter Goals   433
Definition   433
Purpose of Analysis   434
Typical Analytical Problems   435
Elements of an Effective Analysis   438
Finding, Evaluating, and Interpreting Data   441
Planning and Writing the Formal Report   445
Applying the Steps   453
Chapter Summary   507
Revision Checklist   508
Exercises   509

15
Oral Reporting   512

Chapter Goals   513
Definition   513

Purpose of Oral Reports   514
Identifying the Best Type of Formal Report   515
Preparing the Extemporaneous Delivery   517
Delivering the Extemporaneous Report   524
Chapter Summary   526
Revision Checklist   527
Exercises   528

Appendix A
Review of Grammar, Usage, and Mechanics   529

Appendix B
The Brainstorming Technique   597

Index   601

TECHNICAL WRITING

I

COMMUNICATING TO A SPECIFIED AUDIENCE

1

Introduction to Technical Writing

CHAPTER GOALS

DEFINITION

TECHNICAL VERSUS NONTECHNICAL
WRITING

THE VALUE OF TECHNICAL WRITING
SKILLS

SPECIFIC USES OF TECHNICAL WRITING
SKILLS

AUDIENCE NEEDS

THE WRITER'S ATTITUDE

CHAPTER SUMMARY

EXERCISES

CHAPTER GOALS

Upon completing this chapter you will understand:

- The general meaning and purpose of technical writing.
- The major differences between technical and nontechnical writing.
- The importance of developing your technical writing skills.
- The connection between the kinds of writing you will do here and the kinds of writing you will do on the job.
- The importance of writing for a specific audience.
- The emphasis on *objective* writing that will characterize each of your assignments.
- The importance of your attitude as a writer.

DEFINITION

In technical writing a person reports factual information objectively for the practical use of his or her readers, often for a specific reader. This information is usually specialized. It is based on one's experiences, observations, and interpretations within a specific area of knowledge. The purpose of technical writing is always to inform. Often it provides facts that help the reader answer a question, solve a problem, make a decision, or the like. Such writing does not seek to entertain or appeal to emotions, but to inform objectively. The quality of any piece of technical writing depends on how objectively and clearly it presents the information that readers will need.

TECHNICAL VERSUS NONTECHNICAL WRITING

Poetry and fiction are not technical writing because they are expressions of imagination and personal feelings.[1] Poets or novelists describe *their own* way of seeing a subject. Each describes his or her private world, not the world of demonstrable fact. Consider, for example, this poem by Tennyson:

THE EAGLE: A FRAGMENT

He clasps the crag with crooked hands;
Close to the sun in lonely lands
Ringed with the azure world, he stands.

The wrinkled sea beneath him crawls;
He watches from his mountain walls
And like a thunderbolt he falls.

Although the eagle is often the subject of scientific and technical studies, here it is not described factually. Instead, it is described metaphorically (in emotionally or imaginatively suggestive terms): claws become "crooked hands"; the blue sky becomes "the azure world"; the sea is "wrinkled" and it "crawls"; "like a thunderbolt he falls" in his rapid dive for prey. Clearly, the poet is describing *his own* imaginative perception of the eagle. He is obviously impressed by the bird's majestic and solitary nature ("Close to the sun in lonely lands"). He writes the poem to evoke the same awe in the reader. Such a description is not technical writing because it is not an objective recording of facts. Other poets could describe the eagle in countless other ways, depending on their own feelings.

The nonfiction essay is also not technical writing because an essay, by definition, presents the writer's personal opinions. Consider, for instance, this single-paragraph essay about the eagle:

The eagle is the *most noble* bird. This large and *impressive* creature perches on the highest cliffs, scanning the earth below. Against the light of the sun he presents a *dignified* silhouette, commanding *full sway* over his world from his solitary perch. On sighting his prey he dives with *swift* and *deadly accuracy, sure* and *self-reliant*. The eagle's *majestic demeanor, independence, pride,* and *invincible spirit* all symbolize basic American values. Thus it is no surprise that this *awesome* bird was chosen as the national emblem of the United States.

---

[1] The ideas developed in this section were inspired by Patrick M. Kelley and Roger E. Masse, "A Definition of Technical Writing." *The Technical Writing Teacher* 4 (Spring 1977): 94–97.

It is highly subjective; again, the writer describes his own perception of the bird. Notice the number of judgmental terms (in italics). Any factual information contained here is subordinate to the writer's opinions. Because many of his opinions might not be shared by other people, this writer's description is not technical. (Another writer, for example, might see the eagle as cold and brutal, or as ugly and dumb, or as just another bird to be hunted.)

In contrast to these nontechnical versions, here is a technical description of the eagle:

Eagle, a large diurnal bird of prey that has been a symbol of power and courage since ancient times. The eagle is found throughout the world except in Antarctica and on a few remote oceanic islands. The bird is characterized by stout legs, strong feet with sharp talons, and a strongly hooked bill that is nearly as long as its head. The eagle has large, broad, strong wings, with ragged rounded tips, and a broad tail that in flight is spread like a fan. The female is larger than the male. The bird's eyes are highly developed, and there are two focusing points (fovea) in each eye, so that it has binocular vision for distance sighting. The various species prey on mammals, reptiles, or fish. The pursuit flight is either a swooping down or direct diving on the prey. The eagle kills with its talons and dismembers with its bill. The nest, a huge bulky structure of sticks lined with grass or moss, is usually built on a cliff, but some species nest in trees.

The name eagle is derived from the Roman name for the golden eagle, *Aquila chrysaëtos*. This species, a typical eagle, was formerly found throughout most of the northern hemisphere. It is nearly extinct in most of the British Isles, and is now very rare east of the Rocky Mountains in North America. The adult golden eagle is blackish, with a golden wash on the back of the neck, and white at the base of the tail and in the wings. The legs and feet are feathered, but the toes are not. The golden eagle is 30 to 40 inches long, and its wingspan is 6 to 7 feet. It feeds chiefly on such small mammals as rodents, but a group will attack animals as large as antelopes. When living prey is scarce, the golden eagle feeds on carrion. A variety of golden eagle, *Aquila chrysaëtos canadensis,* is still found in remote mountain areas, foothills, and plains from northern Canada and Alaska south to the Gulf states and northern Mexico.

The bald eagle, *Haliaeetus leucocephala,* is named for its snow-white head. One of the sea eagles, it nests along fresh or salt waters in polar regions of the northern hemisphere, throughout most of the United States, and south into Mexico. In recent years the number of bald eagles has been much reduced, and they are now most numerous in Alaska. The adult is blackish brown, with a snow-white head and tail. The bald eagle has unfeathered feet and toes. It is 30 to 40 inches long, and it has a wingspan of 6 to 8 feet. It feeds mainly on fish; however, it catches very few itself, either pirating its food from other birds or picking up dead fish on the shore. In 1782, Congress adopted a design displaying the bird for the Great Seal of the United States, and the bald eagle became the national bird.

The harpy eagle is perhaps the most powerful of the eagles. It preys on animals as large as the sloth.

The eagle is classified in the order Falconiformes, family Acciptridae.[2]

This is technical writing because it contains purely factual information, presented objectively. All data can be checked and verified by anyone, and would be likely to change only after new scientific findings. As an expression of fact instead of opinion, this version gives the reader dependable information, which can be used to support solid interpretations, conclusions, and recommendations. The singular purpose of any piece of technical writing is to provide hard information (fact); the earlier versions we presented provided mainly soft information (opinion).

We have just seen that an object such as the golden eagle can be the subject of poetry, general descriptive writing, or technical writing. Therefore, technical writing is defined not primarily by its subject but by the author's point of view. A technical subject is specialized — usually mechanical or scientific (e.g., a description of screw-thread gaging techniques). But many technical subjects — like the golden eagle — can also be discussed from nontechnical points of view. On the other hand, almost any subject, overtly technical or not (except, perhaps, political or religious convictions), can be discussed from a technical point of view, based objectively on facts. Here, interpretations and conclusions are supported by demonstrable and convincing evidence, as in a study of the feasibility of opening a small business in your home town. Your responsibility as a technical writer is to observe, interpret, and report — all from a technical point of view.

Examples of technical writing are found in most good textbooks, where the authors communicate specialized information uncolored by their attitudes or opinions. Other examples include assembly instructions for a stereo system, a car's service manual, a recipe for clam chowder, a police description of an accident, encyclopedia entries, and course offerings listed in your college catalog. Each of these messages reports facts, without personal opinions, for the reader's practical use.

THE VALUE OF TECHNICAL WRITING SKILLS

Your ability to communicate useful information will increase your chances for a successful career. As jobs become more complex and specialized, the demand

[2] Reprinted with permission from *Collier's Encyclopedia*. © 1971, Crowell-Collier Educational Corporation.

for effective communication increases. In fact, roughly 85 percent of communication in the working world is carried out in writing. Therefore, not many of us can ignore the need to write well.

Top corporation administrators consistently rank communications skills as one of their highest priorities in evaluating job candidates and employees. Here are some of their comments:

– "Certainly it is not necessary that every man we hire be a finished public speaker or writer, but it is necessary that he be able to communicate.... Some of the reports that I have had occasion to read over the years would curl your hair, and as for oral presentation — many of them can charitably be called atrocious."

– "One of the chief weaknesses of many college graduates is the inability to express themselves well. Even though technically qualified, they will not advance far with such a handicap."

– "The ability to read and comprehend what one reads and the ability to translate orally are essential to communication. Communication is essential to controlling and directing people, and people (with the help of machines, but, I repeat, *people*) get the job done.... A man who can use good, plain, understandable English is worth more to me than a specialist."

Many employers are convinced that you can be trained on the job to perform specific tasks but, after college, you cannot be trained to communicate well. One company official even concludes, "If a candidate does not have basic speaking and writing skills at age twenty-one, he is a lost cause."[3] To sum up, your communications skills have their final chance for development during your college years; they will not appear magically later in life.

The message embedded in these brief quotes is clear: technical expertise, motivation, and creativity alone are not enough. At the very least, you will need to be a "part-time" technical writer. And without the ability to communicate, you may not get far.

A prospective employer will first judge your writing skills by the quality of your application letter and résumé. If you are hired by a large organization, your retention and promotion may depend on decisions made by executives you have never met. In this case, the quality of your letters, memos, progress reports, work orders, requisitions, recommendations, and written instructions will be regarded as an indicator of the overall quality of your work. This is hardly the time to let your competence be buried beneath carelessly written reports. Good writing skills give you an advantage in any field. And as you advance in your field, your ability to communicate will increase in importance while your

---

[3] These quotations are from Linwood E. Orange, *English: The Pre-Professional Major,* 2nd ed. (New York: MLA, 1973), pp. 4–5.

reliance on your technical background may correspondingly decrease. The higher your professional goals, the better communications skills you will need. In short, your value to any organization will depend on how well you can convey to others what you know.

SPECIFIC USES OF TECHNICAL WRITING SKILLS

> Because modern society is becoming increasingly technical, scientists, doctors, engineers, and a wide variety of other technical persons must keep informed of new advances being made by others working in their fields. A discovery made by one scientist may directly affect a problem on which a scientist in another state or country might be working. Instruction manuals must be developed to explain the operation and maintenance of the increasing number of machines in industry, business, and homes. New developments in technical fields are constantly affecting modern living and must be reported and explained to the businessman affected by them and to the general public. People are interested in learning about new inventions, drugs, or equipment which will affect their lives.[4]

The application of writing skills extends into many fields, including the health and social sciences, agriculture, law enforcement, engineering, and business. Almost anyone in a responsible position will write accounts of his or her activities and findings, often daily.

Police and fire personnel write detailed incident or investigation reports which must be clear enough to serve as evidence in court. Nurses and medical technicians keep daily records that are crucial to patient welfare. Medical personnel also compile and present research data on various health questions. Executive, medical, and legal secretaries need to write clear and precise memos, letters, minutes, and reports. Managers write memos, personnel evaluations, requisitions, and instructions. Contractors and tradespeople write detailed proposals, bids, and specifications for prospective customers. Moreover, they often trace, identify, and report sources of malfunction in structures or machinery. Engineers and architects plan, on paper, the structural details of a project before contracts are awarded and actual construction begins. They must also communicate with members of related fields before presenting a client with a detailed proposal. For example, the architect's plans are reviewed by a structural engineer who certifies that the proposed structure, as designed, will

---

[4] Quoted from "Writer, Technical," *Occupational Brief*, No. 178 (Moravia, New York: Chronicle Guidance Publications, Inc., 1969). This edition was revised in 1974 and is available from Chronicle Guidance Publications, Inc., Moravia, New York 13118 for one dollar a copy.

stand without collapsing. You should not assume that the writing challenge ends with your last composition course. In fact, it only begins here.

AUDIENCE NEEDS

Whenever you write technical reports you write for a specific audience, translating and interpreting data so they can be understood and used. Depending on your working situation and the purpose of your report, your audience may vary. Sometimes you will write for colleagues whose level of technical understanding is higher than or equal to your own. At other times you will write for administrators who are technically informed, but not expert, in your subject. Much of your reporting may be aimed toward readers outside of your organization who have little or no technical understanding. Your report may be read by one person or by dozens. In each case you will need to make your message clear and appropriate for a specific level of technical understanding. Requirements and techniques for reaching your audience are discussed in Chapter 2.

THE WRITER'S ATTITUDE

Writing ability is not genetically or magically acquired; nor is it a talent that develops automatically as you study other subjects or do your job. Any literate person can become an effective writer. Writing is a skill — like typing, bricklaying, tennis, or brain surgery — to be developed, refined, and perfected by long hours of practice, self-discipline, and revision.

Above all, good writing is the product of your motivation and willingness to endure the sweat and frustration that accompany any worthwhile effort. Avoid the unfortunate assumption made by one of my students: "I don't need to worry about writing well because I plan to have a secretary who will take my dictation and write for me." Recalling the executive comments earlier in this chapter, we might reasonably conclude that a person with the attitude of my student will have contact with the secretary only each afternoon as he empties her wastebasket! Remember that your skill in report writing is as important as any other skill that you will ever need to develop.

CHAPTER SUMMARY

Technical writing reports factual information objectively for the reader's practical use. The information reported is often specialized — coming from the writer's experiences, observations, and interpretations within a particular area of knowledge. Nontechnical writing is subjective, emphasizing soft information (opinion). Technical writing is objective, emphasizing hard information (fact). To write technically means to express a technical point of view — a view based on demonstrable and convincing evidence — toward just about any subject, technical or not.

Roughly 85 percent of communication in the working world is carried out in writing. Therefore, at the very least, you will need to be a "part-time" technical writer. In fact, your value to any organization will depend mainly on your ability to communicate what you know.

Technical writing skills have application in countless career fields. In all cases, your own job-related writing will be based on observable facts instead of sheer opinion. Whenever you communicate these facts you write for a specific audience, translating and interpreting data for your reader's use. Depending on your working situation and the purpose of your report, your reading audience may be experts, technically informed readers, or laypersons. In each case, you will need to address a specific level of technical understanding.

Think of technical writing as a skill — one that is as important as any other you will ever develop.

EXERCISES

1. In class: Politics and religion are emotionally charged subjects that are generally discussed from a nontechnical — that is, subjective — point of view. Identify specific topics within these subjects that might be discussed from a technical point of view.

2. Controversial subjects like abortion, euthanasia, the Equal Rights Amendment, marijuana laws, and the gun-control issue usually elicit discussions that are based on emotions and opinions. How could these subjects be discussed from a technical point of view?

3. Write a one- or two-paragraph nontechnical description of your classroom as a physical space. Let your reader know how you *feel* about this room. Next, write the same description from a technical point of view, based purely on demonstrable facts. Finally, write one paragraph explaining the changes you made in moving from sample 1 to sample 2.

4. Locate a one- or two-page example of technical writing in your library. Make a photocopy and bring it to class. Be prepared to explain why your selection can be called technical writing.

5. Interview a family friend or relative who works for an organization or who is self-employed. Choose a person who has a responsible, attractive, and

well-paid position. Ask your respondent to describe in detail the kinds of writing that he or she does on the job. Write a brief report of your findings.

6. (a) In a brief essay, describe the kinds of "part-time" technical writing you expect to do in your career field. Why will you write technical reports, and for whom will you write them? (b) In another brief essay, describe the specific skills you hope to gain from your technical writing course. How do you plan to apply these skills in your own career?

2

Writing
for Readers

CHAPTER GOALS

DEFINITION

THE CONCEPT OF "AUDIENCE"

WRITING FOR DIFFERENT READERS
  The Expert
  The Technically Informed Reader
  The General Reader

FOCUSING ON YOUR READER'S NEEDS
  Reader Identification
  Purpose of the Request
  Readers' Technical Knowledge
  Needed Details
  Sample Situations

WRITING CLEAR FACTUAL PROSE
  Avoid Pretentious Language
  Avoid Jargon
  Be Concrete and Specific
  Avoid Overly Complex or Overly Simple
    Sentences
  Use Active and Passive Constructions
    Selectively
  Be Concise
  Avoid Bias
  Proofread and Revise Carefully

CHAPTER SUMMARY

EXERCISES

CHAPTER GOALS

Upon completing this chapter you will understand:

- Why the concept of "audience" is crucial.
- The importance of writing specifically for your reader.
- The differences between the expert, the technically informed reader, and the general reader.
- How to categorize your readers and adjust your writing to their knowledge and needs.
- How to use guidelines for writing factual prose that is simple, direct, economical, and clear.
- How to recognize poor writing and revise it to get your message across.

DEFINITION

All writing (at least all the writing we discuss in this book) is for readers. Whatever you write is effective only if your reader understands it. Because readers vary widely, think first about the reader's needs whenever you pick up a pencil.

THE CONCEPT OF "AUDIENCE"

Because people have different backgrounds, an idea that makes perfect sense to you might be meaningless to someone else, unless you explain it properly. The idea, then, is only as good as the message conveying it. Your job is to connect with your audience, which, for our purposes, consists of one or more readers.

All good practical writing connects with its readers by recognizing their differences in background and their specific needs. There are plenty of examples all around us of the differences in audience knowledge and needs. Watching the TV football game with friends who know all about the game is certainly a different experience from watching it with someone who doesn't understand it at all. Explaining how to repair a leaking faucet to someone who has no mechanical ability and has never fixed things around the house is different from explaining the same task to a do-it-yourselfer. The kinds of explanation you find in *Popular Mechanics* differ from the kinds in your biology or physics textbook. In each case, the audience's needs must be satisfied if the message is to make sense.

Most writing is intended *to be used*. Whether you are giving instructions, describing a product, reporting research findings, or explaining a process, you become the teacher and the reader becomes the student. The reader's needs for an understandable message are no different from your own. For example, if Chapter 1 of your introductory math textbook covered differential equations (which belong in advanced calculus), you would rightly conclude that the author had ignored your needs. For your purposes, the book would be useless. An effective message is tailored to its specific audience.

WRITING FOR DIFFERENT READERS

When you write for a close acquaintance — a parent, an intimate friend, a fellow camera buff, a classmate in experimental psychology, a fellow dental technician, an engineering colleague — you know a good deal about your particular reader. You automatically adjust your report to his or her knowledge and needs. But often you might have to write for much more vaguely defined audiences of people you hardly know. This is particularly true when writing for or addressing large audiences — when you are writing for a particular magazine or professional journal, for example, or when you are called on to explain your company's health insurance program to representatives of many different departments. In such situations, where you have only general knowledge about the background of your audience, it is helpful to think of your audience as belonging mainly to one of three groups: experts, technically informed readers, or what we can call general readers.

The Expert

When you write for experts (persons with the most technical knowledge in their field) you don't need to simplify and interpret. Here, for instance, is an account of emergency room treatment given to a heart attack victim written for the medical expert:

> Mr. X was brought to the emergency room by ambulance at 1:00 A.M., September 27, 1977. The patient complained of severe chest pains, shortness

of breath, and dizziness. Auscultation and electrocardiogram revealed a massive cardiac infarction and pulmonary edema marked by pronounced cyanosis. Vital signs were as follows: blood pressure, 80/40; pulse, 140/min.; respiration, 35/min. Lab tests recorded a wbc count of 20,000, an elevated serum transaminase and a urea nitrogen level of 60 mg%. Urinalysis showed 4+ protein and 4+ granular cast/field, suggesting acute renal failure secondary to the hypotension.

The patient was given 10 mg. of morphine stat, subcutaneously, followed by nasal oxygen and a 5% D & W IV. At 1:25 A.M. the cardiac monitor recorded an irregular sinus rhythm, suggesting left ventricular fibrillation. The patient was defibrillated stat and given a 50 mg. bolus of Xylocaine IV. A Xylocaine drip was started, and sodium bicarbonate was administered until a normal heartbeat was established. By 3:00 A.M., the oscilloscope was recording a normal sinus rhythm.

As the heartbeat stabilized and cyanosis diminished, the patient was given 5 cc of Heparin IV, to be repeated every six hours. By 5:00 A.M. the BUN had fallen to 20 mg% and the vital signs had stabilized as follows: blood pressure, 110/60; pulse, 105/min.; respiration, 22/min. The patient was now conscious and responsive.

Written at the highest level of technicality, this narrative is only meaningful to the trained medical person. The writer assumes that his reader has the knowledge needed to understand the message.

Other messages written for experts appear in many of the specialized journals in your library's periodical section. For example, a researcher in forestry might publish an article in *The Journal of Wood Technology* describing the results of a new seeding technique, and express most of that message in charts, graphs, curves, and equations. Unless these data are translated into simpler terms they will mean nothing to the nonexpert.

The Technically Informed Reader

The technically informed reader knows more than the layperson but less than the expert. This person's needs are the most difficult to identify. A first-year medical student, for example, can be called technically informed, but so can the second-, third-, and fourth-year student. Obviously their levels of understanding differ. Therefore, when you write for technically informed readers, assume that they know less instead of more; explain and interpret your data.

Here is a partial version of the earlier report. This time it is written for medical technicians, nursing and medical students, and medical social workers — all informed but not expert.

> Examination by stethoscope and electrocardiogram revealed a massive failure of the heart muscle along with fluid build-up in the lungs, which produced a cyanotic discoloration of the lips and fingertips from lack of oxygen.

The patient's blood pressure at 80 mm Hg (systolic)/40 mm Hg (diastolic) was dangerously below its normal measure of 130/70. A pulse rate of 140/minute was almost twice the normal rate of 60–80. Respiration at 35/minute was over twice the normal rate of 12–16.

Laboratory blood tests yielded a white blood cell count of 20,000/cu. mm (normal values: 5,000–10,000) indicating a severe inflammatory response by the heart muscle. The elevated serum transaminase enzymes (only produced in quantity when the heart muscle fails) confirmed the earlier diagnosis. A blood urea nitrogen level of 60 mg% (normal values: 12–16 mg%) indicated that the kidneys had ceased to filter out metabolic waste products. The 4+ protein and casts reported from the urinalysis (normal values: 0) revealed that the microscopic kidney tubules were degenerating as a result of the lowered blood pressure.

The patient was immediately given morphine to ease the chest pain, followed by oxygen to relieve strain on the cardiopulmonary system, and an intravenous solution of dextrose and water to prevent shock.

This version explains and interprets all the raw data. Because exact dosages are not meaningful to the nonexpert they are not mentioned. However, normal values of lab tests and vital signs can be used for comparison and interpretation. (The expert would know these values as well as the significance of specific dosages.) The kinds of medication would be especially significant to the lab technician, because some medications affect blood test results. To be meaningful to a layperson, however, this information needs further editing, translation, and simplification.

The General Reader

The general reader knows little or nothing of your specialty. Therefore, express your data at the lowest level of technicality. Translate the essential message into everyday English. Here is how the medical report might be rewritten for the layperson. The attending physician might be writing this version for the patient's wife who is out of state or for a jury reviewing a malpractice case.

Both heart sounds and electrical impulses were abnormal, indicating a massive heart attack caused by failure of a large part of the heart muscle. His lungs were swollen with fluid and his lips and fingertips showed a bluish discoloration from lack of oxygen.

The patient's blood pressure was dangerously low, creating the danger of shock. His pulse and respiration were almost twice the normal rate, indicating that the heart and lungs were being overworked in keeping oxygenated blood circulating freely.

Blood tests confirmed the heart attack diagnosis and indicated that waste products usually filtered out by the kidneys were building up in the bloodstream. Urine tests showed that the kidneys were failing as a result of the lowered blood pressure.

> The patient was given medication to ease his chest pain, oxygen to ease the strain on his heart and lungs, and an intravenous solution to prevent his blood vessels from collapsing and causing irreversible shock.

This version mentions no specific medications, lab tests, or normal values because these mean nothing to a layperson. The writer simply describes the chain of events, explaining the reasons for the crisis and for the particular treatment. You will find such general writing in the "Medicine" section of *Time* magazine.

Each of these three versions is useful *only* to readers at a particular technical level. The expert doesn't need the explanations in the last two versions (in fact, he needs the specific technical details found in the first). In contrast, the layperson would find the first version meaningless and the second rough going.

For another illustration of these differences in delivery consider the hypothetical article about forest-seeding techniques mentioned in our section on "The Expert." A less specialized version might appear as a set of instructions for growing trees, in an ecology, agriculture, or gardening magazine whose readers are informed but not expert. Here the scientific findings in the earlier article would be applied to practical ends — with an emphasis on procedure ("how to") instead of theory. An even more simplified version might be found in a magazine with a general readership, like *Outdoor Life*. Instead of discussing scientific and technical details of the seeding technique, this version might show how the new method will help rejuvenate our depleted forests.

In your own job — as doctor, nurse, medical technician, accountant, dental technician, building contractor, banker, sales manager, or whatever — you will be at least a "part-time technical writer." That is, you will need to connect with audiences at various levels. As a building contractor, for instance, you might order "800 board feet of 1×6 no. 2 white pine, rough sawn and kiln dried" from your lumber dealer (a wood expert). For the bank financing the project you might describe the wood less technically as "rough pine interior finish." For the client you might write "new barn board interior walls." Each version is clear and appropriately detailed for its intended audience.

FOCUSING ON YOUR READER'S NEEDS

When you write for a particular reader or a small group of readers, you can focus in sharply on your audience. In that situation, you can ask yourself very specific questions to learn as much as you can about your reader *before* you write.

Who wants the report? Why does he want the report? How much technical knowledge does he have, and how much does he already understand about the subject? Finally, what exactly does the reader need to know?

Reader Identification

Identify the person by name, title, and specialty (Martha Jones, Director of Quality Control, B.S. and M.S. in mechanical engineering).

Purpose of the Request

Find out how your reader plans to use your information. Does he or she simply want a record of your activities or progress? Are you expected to supply only raw data or detailed interpretations and recommendations? Will your reader take some specific action based on your message? Should you provide step-by-step instructions? The more you learn about your reader's specific expectations the better you can tailor your report to be useful.

Readers' Technical Knowledge

A reader who is a colleague in a related project may need only raw data — without interpretations and recommendations — because you both speak the same technical language. A supervisor who deals in several technical areas may need his or her memory refreshed by some explanations of certain data. A manager may have only a general knowledge of your subject and will expect a translation into simpler terms. A client may have no technical knowledge whatever and will expect all data to be spelled out in layperson's language. In short, identify your reader's level of understanding to avoid insulting his intelligence or writing over his head.

Needed Details

In our earlier discussion of medical reports we saw that details of dosage, drug names, and medical terminology are significant to one reader but not to another. The number and kinds of details in your report will depend on what you can learn about your reader and his purpose. Were you asked to "keep it short" or to "be comprehensive"? Can you summarize some parts or does it all need to be spelled out? Is your reader most interested in conclusions and recommendations or does he also want a full description of your investigative procedure? Has he requested a letter, a memo, a short, informal report, or a formal report with all supplements (title page, table of contents, full headings, documentation, appendixes, etc.)? What level of technicality will be most meaningful to your reader?

High Technicality
The diesel engine generates ten BTUs per gallon of fuel as opposed to eight BTUs generated by the conventional gas engine.

Low Technicality

The diesel engine yields 25 percent better gas mileage than its gas-burning counterpart.

Clearly, the first version is meaningful to the expert and perhaps the informed reader, whereas the second makes sense to the layperson. If you are writing for a large audience and are unable to identify all members, write at a low level of technicality. It is safer to risk boring some experts than to write over most people's heads.

Sample Situations

In most jobs you will have to ask the questions in this section often — perhaps daily. Here are two scenarios in which the "part-time technical writer" has to assess his audience's needs carefully.

A DAY IN THE LIFE
OF A POLICE OFFICER

You are a police investigator in the burglary division of a large urban department.

— The local community college asks you to give a lecture describing the various fields of investigative police work during its career week.

— Tomorrow in court you will testify for the prosecution of a felon you have apprehended. His lawyer is known for making police testimony look foolish so you are busy reviewing your notes and getting your report in perfect form.

— You are drafting an article on new fingerprinting techniques for a law-enforcement magazine.

— Your chief asks you to write an instruction manual of investigative techniques to be used by junior officers in your division.

— Next month you will speak before the local chamber of commerce. The subject of your paper will be "Protecting Your Business against Burglary."

A DAY IN THE LIFE
OF A CIVIL ENGINEER

You are a civil engineer in charge of friction studies on various types of road surfaces in a materials-testing laboratory.

— Your vice-president calls to say that your firm is competing for a state contract involving a comprehensive safety study of state highway surfaces. You learn that full reports of your testing procedures, progress, and results are needed before contract negotiations can begin. As engineer in charge you are responsible for the quality of the reports.

— You are asked to write a full set of safety instructions for building crews working on the new bridge spanning the bay. Your instructions will be read by all crew members from supervising engineers to manual laborers.

— At next month's engineering convention in Dallas you will deliver a paper describing a new road-footing technique that reduces frost heave damage in northern states. Your audience will be civil engineering colleagues who are very interested in your information.

— You draft a letter to a colleague you have never met to ask about his new procedure for increasing the durability of road surfaces.

— You are putting the finishing touches on an article for a nationally known magazine. The article describes to a general reading audience the hazards involved in building the trans-Alaskan highway.

In each reporting situation remember that your reader expects *clear* and *useful* information.

Most of your writing in this course — and much of it on the job — will be aimed at the general reader. Whereas in college you write mostly for an audience (your professor) who knows more than you (or at least as much), on the job you will write mostly for an audience who knows less. This is the most challenging kind of writing: to simplify or translate (without distorting) a message that the reader would not otherwise understand.

WRITING CLEAR FACTUAL PROSE

You may write for a broad or a specific audience; for an expert audience or a general one; for a manager you hope to impress or for those who work under you. In each case, your purpose will best be served if you keep in mind certain guidelines for writing clear factual prose.

Avoid Pretentious Language

Some people think that good writing means using sixty-five-cent words. However, the simplest terms are usually the clearest. Use the language that you speak with in the classroom or on the job. Trade down instead of up: find a ten-cent word that will do the job. Say "we tried" instead of "we endeavored." A phrase like "acoustical attenuation for the food-consumption area" is stuffy, pretentious, and confusing. "Sound proofing for the cafeteria" sounds more like a phrase written by a human being. Here are some other examples of overblown prose:

Pretentious Prose

Cross-graded, multiethnic, individualized modular learning program.

Replacement of the weak battery should be effectuated.

In connection with various friction studies in our laboratory, it became of interest for us to investigate road-paving techniques.

The preparation of this report has been highly facilitated by the invaluable advice of Professor Jones who has been of great assistance.

Plain English

A program in which students of all races are encouraged to move ahead at their own speed and grading is geared to each student's learning abilities.

Replace the weak battery.

Our friction studies led us to investigate road-paving techniques.

Professor Jones helped me greatly in preparing this report.

Avoid impressive sounding words. Keep your writing style simple and down-to-earth.

Avoid Jargon

Various professions have developed their own "shorthand" or jargon. Some of these terms do save time (for example, the term "stat" on page 15 means to drop whatever you are doing and deal immediately with the emergency). Most jargon, however, only clouds the message and can be meaningless to insiders as well as outsiders. It is only appropriate when your reader is an informed or expert colleague who uses the same terms routinely. Here are some samples of jargon that are never appropriate.

Jargon

In view of ALRs being used on a one-time-only basis, cost-wise they are impractical.

There is also present the requirement of a fail-safe reentry system design prior to the launching of Explorer II.

Make an improvement in the clerical situation.

For the furtherance of that purpose he accomplished the disbursement of funds to the amount of $6000.

It has the appearance of the tendency to take on the characteristics of a carcinogenic substance.

One must take into consideration the undesirable fact that it is poorly constructed.

Plain English

ALRs are impractical because they are expensive and can be used only once.

We also need to design a fail-safe reentry system before launching Explorer II.

Hire better secretaries. (*or,* Hire more secretaries.)

For that he paid $6000.

It begins to look like a carcinogenic substance.

It is poorly constructed.

Jargon-ridden writing makes you seem as if you are trying to pull something over on your reader or as if you doubt the validity of your own statements.

The following letter, an unfortunate mix of sixty-five-cent words, jargon, and excessive use of passive construction (to be discussed later in this chapter), is similar to one which was actually published in a local newspaper.

> In the absence of definitive studies regarding the optimum length of the school day, I can only state my personal opinion based upon observations made by me and upon teacher observations that have been conveyed to me. Considering the length of the present school day, it is my opinion that the day is excessive length-wise for most elementary pupils, certainly for almost all of the primary children.
>
> To find the answer to the problem requires consideration of two ways in which the problem may be viewed. One way focuses upon the needs of the children, while the other focuses upon logistics, transportation, scheduling, and other limits imposed by the educational system. If it is necessary to prioritize these two ideas, it would seem most reasonable to give the first consideration to the primary reason for the very existence of the system, i.e., to meet the educational needs of the children the system is trying to serve.

Here is the same message translated into plain English:

> Although no studies have defined the best length for a school day, my experience and teachers' comments lead me to believe that the school day is too long for most elementary students — especially the primary students.
>
> We can view this problem from the children's point of view (health, psychological welfare, and so on) or from the system's point of view (scheduling, transportation, utilities costs, and so on). If we consider our most important goals, the children should come first, because the system exists to serve their needs.

Be Concrete and Specific

Choose words that best express your meaning. For instance, don't say "thing" when you mean "lever," "switch," "pencil," or "micrometer." Revise "The person performed the task quickly" to "The technician developed the X-ray in ten minutes." Instead of evaluating a new employee as "nice," "swell," and "terrific," or "lousy," "terrible," and "awful," use precise adjectives like "reliable," "skillful," and "competent," or "untrustworthy," "irritable," and "awkward." The earlier adjectives reveal your attitude toward the person but tell the reader nothing specific about the person himself. The later versions name concrete qualities that a reader will find meaningful.

Although some words may be listed as synonyms in a dictionary or thesaurus, each word contains a different shade of meaning. Thus we can say "I'm slim; you're slender; she's thin; and he's scrawny." Clearly, these words cannot be used interchangeably. The same is true for words like "walk," "ramble," "saunter," and "stroll," or "smell," "essence," "odor," "fragrance," "stink," and "stench." Words that appear to be similar in meaning can create radically different pictures in your reader's mind. Select your terms carefully.

Avoid Overly Complex or Overly Simple Sentences

A short, simple sentence is good for emphasizing an important idea. However, a series of short, choppy sentences is difficult to follow and tedious to read. Your reader struggles to piece related ideas together and you end up looking like a fourth-grade writer.

Overly Simple Sentences

There are some drawbacks about diesel engines. Diesel engines are much noisier than standard engines. They are difficult to start in cold weather. They tend to cause considerable vibrations. They also give off an unpleasant odor. For these reasons many car manufacturers are limiting their diesel models to light trucks only.

Notice the awkward repetitions that short sentences can cause. Here is a more readable and sophisticated version with related ideas combined.

Revision

Diesel engines have some drawbacks. Most obvious are their noisiness, cold-weather starting difficulties, vibrations, and unpleasant odor. Therefore, many manufacturers are limiting their diesel models to light trucks.

Similarly, overly complex sentences — those with too many ideas crammed in — hardly make sense to the reader.

An Overly Complex Sentence

In a smoke-filled room, teary eyes and runny noses occur, and auditory discrimination and visual perception are altered, which is irritating but not associated with any serious disease, except for people with heart and lung diseases who are threatened with major problems from smoke.

Revise this mouthful into more digestible sentences.

> *Revision*
> A smoke-filled room does not only cause teary eyes and runny noses. The smoke also can alter auditory and visual perception. Although the smoke itself does not produce disease, it does pose a threat to people with heart and lung ailments.

Here the major ideas are separated for proper emphasis. In most cases, a combination of simple and complex sentences is best.

Use Active and Passive Constructions Selectively

The active voice is created by an *actor-action-recipient* structure.

> *Actor Action*   *Recipient*
> Joe broke the priceless vase. (*X acts on Y.*)
> *Subject Verb*   *Object*

The passive voice is created when actor and recipient switch positions in the sentence: the recipient is made the subject; a helping verb and a preposition are often added; and the actor becomes part of the prepositional phrase at the end of the sentence.

> *Recipient*   *Action*   *Actor*
> The priceless vase was broken by Joe.   (*Y is acted on by X.*)
> *Subject*   *Verb*   *Prepositional Phrase*

Whichever word (or phrase) is in the subject position receives most emphasis.

> *Active Voice*
> A *low-flying bird* injured Joe.

> *Passive Voice*
> *Joe* was injured by a low-flying bird.

Use the active voice to emphasize the *actor* rather than the *recipient*.

> *Active Voice*
> *Smith Associates* charged us an outrageous fee for their survey.

> *Passive Voice*
> *We* were charged an outrageous fee by Smith Associates for their survey.

In this example the active voice is clearly more effective because it emphasizes the actor. Notice also that the active voice is the more direct expression.
   Use the passive voice to emphasize the *recipient* rather than the *actor*.

Passive Voice
The hijacking story was broadcast by all stations.

Active Voice
All stations broadcast the hijacking story.

Here the passive voice is more effective because it emphasizes the story rather than the stations.

The passive voice is used to achieve an impersonal tone and to emphasize events or results when the actor is unknown, not apparent, or unimportant:

Passive Voice
The victim was badly beaten.

The leak in the nuclear-core housing was repaired within five minutes after it was discovered.

Parts of the plane were found by searchers as far as two miles from the crash site.

In a first-person narrative the passive voice is an effective way to avoid over-using "I" and to vary your sentence style.

When I arrived at the crash site, only burning wreckage could be seen.
        Active   *Passive*

One danger of passive construction is that it camouflages the person responsible for the action.

A mistake was made in your shipment. (*by whom?*)
The girl was kissed. (*by whom?*)
This building was designed poorly. (*by whom?*)
It was decided not to offer you the job. (*by whom?*)
The survey will be done and a report will be sent to you. (*by whom?*)

Don't shirk responsibility by hiding behind the passive. Own up!

We made a mistake in your shipment.
I decided not to offer you the job.

In reporting errors or bad news, use the active voice and you will seem more sincere.

The passive voice is generally a weaker construction, effective only when the fact, result, event, or recipient is of major importance. Otherwise, the active voice is less awkward and more economical. Use the active voice for the most direct expression.

Passive
An offer will be made by us next week.

Active
We will make an offer next week.

Always use the active voice in writing instructions.

Passive
The lid should be sealed.
Care should be exercised.

Active
Seal the lid.
Be careful.

Use the active voice to avoid awkwardness and wordiness.

Passive
I am sure the deadline will be met by us.
It will be expected that you write daily progress reports.

Active
I am sure we will meet the deadline.
We will expect you to write daily progress reports.

As a general rule, prefer the active voice.

Be Concise

A concise message expresses a great deal in a few words. The stress here is on information as well as brevity. A vague message (though brief) is useless.

Brief but Vague
These structural supports are too heavy.

Brief but Well Detailed
These structural supports weigh 300 pounds each, thereby exceeding our specified load tolerance of 200 pounds by 50 percent.

Avoid repetition and wordiness. Prefer one word to two when one will do.

Cluttered
At this point in time I would say that we are ready to move ahead with our project.

Concise
We are ready.

Too many people become experts at "padding" their writing (using word-clutter to fill the page). Some students, for example, find elaborate ways of saying nothing to complete 500-word writing assignments in high school. You too may have practiced the art of stretching — using thirty words when you could have used ten. If you *are* hooked on the habit of making a little go a long way, break it quickly. Eliminate the clutter and don't count words.

Here is a passage that is wordy and has insufficient details:

> *Low-Information Sentences*
>
> *As a final note,* the lawn-tennis court is bounded at each end by a screen. This *high* steel or wooden fence is placed *so that it is* at an *appropriate* distance beyond the baseline *of the court. Its function is significant in that* it prevents the ball from bouncing out of the playing area. The screen *is located so as to* mark the distal boundaries of the playing surface. Each segment *of the screen* is supported by *sturdy* poles *which are* set at *measured lengths.*

The words in italics either cause sentence clutter or are too vague. Here is a version with clutter removed and details of measurement and distance added:

> *High-Information Sentences*
>
> The ends of the lawn tennis court are bounded by a screen. This ten-to-twelve-foot high steel or wooden fence is set 21 feet beyond each baseline. The screen prevents the ball from bouncing out of the playing area and marks the distal boundaries of the playing surface. Each segment is supported by four-inch diameter poles set at three-foot intervals.

Conciseness is rarely achieved in a first draft. Always revise your first draft to refine parts that are wordy, repetitious, or vague.

Avoid Bias

Your job is to report objectively without injecting "loaded" words that reflect personal attitudes. If you are asked to include your interpretations and conclusions, base them on the facts you have discussed earlier. Even controversial subjects deserve objective treatment. For instance, imagine that you have been sent to investigate the causes of an employee-management confrontation at your company's Omaha branch. Your initial report, written for the New York central office, is intended simply to describe the incident. Here is how an unbiased description might read:

> At 9:00 A.M. on Tuesday, January 21, eighty woman employees entered the executive offices of our Omaha branch and remained for six hours, bringing business to a virtual halt. The group issued a formal statement of protest, claiming that their working conditions were repressive, their salary scale unfair, and their promotional opportunities limited. The women's list of demands emphasized affirmative action guidelines, insisting that the company's hiring and promotional policies and wage scales be revised. The demonstration ended when Garvin Tate, vice-president in charge of person-

nel, agreed to appoint a committee to investigate the group's claims and to correct any inequities.

Notice the absence of implied judgments; the facts are presented objectively. A less objective version of the event, from the women's side, might read as follows:

> Last Tuesday, sisters struck another blow against male supremacy when eighty woman employees paralyzed the pin-striped world of solidly entrenched sexism for more than six hours. The organized and articulate protest was aimed against degrading working conditions, unfair salary scales, and lack of promotional opportunities. Stunned executives watched helplessly as the group occupied their offices. The women were determined to continue their occupation until their demands for equal rights were met. Embarrassed company officials soon perceived the magnitude of this protest action and agreed to study the group's demands and to revise the company's discriminatory policies. The success of this long-overdue confrontation serves as an inspiration to oppressed woman employees everywhere.

Notice how the use of judgmental words and qualifiers ("male supremacy," "degrading," "paralyzed," "articulate," "stunned," "discriminatory," etc.) modifies the tone and reveals the writer's personal attitude toward the event. In contrast to this radical bias, the following version reveals a conservative bias:

> Our Omaha branch was the scene of an amusing battle of the sexes last Tuesday, when a Women's Lib group, eighty strong, staged a six-hour sit-in at the company's executive offices. The protest was lodged against supposed inequities in hiring, wages, working conditions, and promotion for women in our company. The libbers threatened to remain in the building until their demands for "equal rights" were met. Bemused company officials reacted to this carnival demonstration with patience and dignity, assuring the militants that their claims and demands — however inaccurate and immoderate — would receive just consideration.

Again, the use of qualifying adjectives and superlatives slants the tone of the report. Let your facts alone influence your reader's attitude.

Proofread and Revise Carefully

We all have to work hard to say what we mean. The first words to tumble out on the page rarely comprise the perfect message. Each word involves a decision, a choice. Even professional writers can spend hours (or days) polishing and refining a few paragraphs. (This book, in fact, was revised several times before it was published.) Leave plenty of time to revise your writing and to proofread carefully your final draft.

When you finish writing a passage go back and read each sentence to be sure that it does the job. Remember that you will often be judged by the quality of your written work. Is each sentence simple, direct, economical, and clear?

Is your spelling correct? Don't be like the applicant for an advertising position who began his letter: "I have broad experience in pubic-relations work." Is your punctuation correct? Have you written "All candidates, who have been selected, will be hired," when you meant to write "All candidates who have been selected will be hired"? Do your word choice, phrasing, and word order express your *precise* meaning? Here are a few examples of hastily written statements that have gone wrong:

> I can't recommend this candidate too highly.

> State law requires that restaurant personnel serve food with a sanitation certificate.

> Our patients are enjoying the warm days while they last.

> I am glad to report that my wife who was reported missing is dead.

> The reason for nominating him was based on the good opinion of myself and Doctor Jones.

> In applying for the job, your company would offer a strong challenge.

> I hope we can discuss the use of our new fertilizer in your office.

Clearly, these inaccurate and embarrassing statements could have been overhauled had the writers taken time to *read* what they had just written. Consult Appendix A and the revision checklists at the ends of individual chapters for detailed help with your own revisions. Remember that clarity is the most important element in your message. Clarity requires self-discipline; it requires that you make your reader's needs your first priority. No matter how important your message, it is useless if not expressed clearly. Your reader should never be left scratching his head, wondering what you meant to say.

CHAPTER SUMMARY

Whenever you write, make your audience your first concern. Assume that your reader will use your information for a practical purpose. Identify your reader as precisely as you can. Are you writing for an expert, an informed reader, or a layperson? For a large, undefined audience, write for the layperson's understanding, with full interpretations and explanations.

Focus your delivery on your readers' needs. Who wants the report? Why do they want it? How much specialized background do they have? What, exactly, do they need to know? Ask yourself these questions whenever you have to be a "part-time technical writer."

Follow these guidelines for writing effective prose:

- Avoid pretentious language.
- Avoid needlessly technical jargon.

– Be concrete and specific.
– Avoid overly complex or overly simple sentences.
– Use active and passive constructions selectively.
– Be concise.
– Avoid bias.
– Proofread and revise carefully.

Remember that the only good message is a clear one.

EXERCISES

1. In a short essay identify and discuss the kinds of job-related writing assignments you expect to face in your career. For whom will you be writing (colleagues, supervisors, clients, etc.)? As an example, include a scenario like those described on pages 19 and 20.

2. Make a list of jargon terms used in your field. Divide your list into effective terms and terms that always cloud the message. Translate the ineffective terms into plain English. Be prepared to discuss your selections and revisions in class.

3. Revise the following sentences to make them more specific.

Example
A storm damaged the building.
Revised: A tornado tore the roof off our Number 2 warehouse.

a. He received an excellent job offer.
b. The group presented its demands.
c. She repaired the machine quickly.
d. This thing bothers me.
e. His performance was awful.
f. The crew damaged a piece of furniture.
g. My new car is disappointing.
h. They discussed the problem.
i. She claimed that he had never phoned her about the deal.

4. Rewrite the following statements in plain English.

a. This writer desires to be considered for a position with your company.
b. At this point in time we cannot agree to your terms.
c. Please refund our full purchase expenditure in view of the fact that the microscope is defective.
d. No decisions will be made until next week as far as the contract is concerned.

    e. There are several banks that can be contacted in terms of obtaining a business loan.

    f. I can wish you no better luck than that you find this job as enjoyable as I have.

    g. Prior to this time we have had no such equipment failure.

    h. In relation to your job, I would like to say that we can no longer offer you employment.

    i. This report is useless as far as I am concerned.

    j. Further interviews appear to be a necessity before we can identify the best qualified candidate.

    k. I suggest that you might want to consider shipping your lobsters by air transport.

5. Locate a two- or three-hundred-word article from your field. (Or select part of a longer article or a section from one of your textbooks.) Choose a piece written at the highest level of technicality that you can understand. Then translate the piece into layperson's language. Exchange translations with a member of your class from a different major. Read your neighbor's translation and write a paragraph evaluating the appropriateness of its level of technicality. Submit to your instructor a copy of your original, your translated version, and your evaluation of your neighbor's translation.

6. Some of the following sentences need to be rewritten in the active or passive voice for better emphasis, less awkwardness, more directness, or greater economy. Make the necessary changes and be prepared to give reasons for each. Mark an E by the sentences that are already effective.

    a. It is believed by us that this contract is faulty.

    b. The tall model wore the $50,000 mink coat.

    c. Joe has been fired.

    d. Hard hats should be worn at all times on this job.

    e. A tornado destroyed our brand-new tractor.

    f. It was decided not to accept your invitation.

    g. A check for full payment will be sent next week.

    h. This package should be kept cool.

    i. A rockslide buried the mine entrance.

    j. Searchers found the victim almost dead.

    k. It is my hope that you succeed.

7. Rewrite the following paragraph in more effective sentences (i.e., an appropriate mix of simple and complex sentences).

    There are two methods that may be used in glazing pottery. The best method is to use underglazes and glazes. Three coats of each are applied. The underglazes designate the color; the glazes give the pottery a shiny finish and a semitransparent color. The underglazes are put on first. They are usually put on with a fine paint brush. The glazes are put on next. A larger brush is usually used for this. The glazes are patted on, whereas the underglazes are brushed on. When glazes and underglazes are used, the pottery must be fired again. This method produces a shiny effect.

STRATEGIES
FOR TECHNICAL
REPORTING

3

Summarizing Information

CHAPTER GOALS

DEFINITION

PURPOSE OF SUMMARIES

ELEMENTS OF AN EFFECTIVE SUMMARY
  Essential Message
  Nontechnical Style
  Independent Meaning
  No New Data
  Introduction-Body-Conclusion Structure
  Conciseness

WRITING THE SUMMARY

APPLYING THE STEPS

WRITING THE ABSTRACT

PLACING SUMMARIES AND ABSTRACTS
        IN YOUR REPORT

CHAPTER SUMMARY

REVISION CHECKLIST

EXERCISES

CHAPTER GOALS

Upon completing this chapter you will know:

- The meaning and purpose of summaries and abstracts.
- The differences between summaries and abstracts.
- How to write a summary of your own work or someone else's and how to evaluate it for effectiveness.
- How to write an abstract.
- Where to place summaries and abstracts in your report.

DEFINITION

A summary is a short version of a longer message which expresses the substance (meaning, emphasis, organization) of the original in a condensed form. Summaries are an economical way to communicate.

PURPOSE OF SUMMARIES

Every effective statement, spoken or written, conveys a message — makes one or more points. Anyone who listens to or reads the statement carefully can extract its important ideas without memorizing the original, word for word. For instance, your notes of a college lecture don't include the lecturer's every word; instead they summarize the main points of the message in a way that you will understand them later. Likewise, in studying a textbook for an examination, you extract the main ideas, deciding which information is important and which is not. In other words, you choose what is essential to your understanding of the subject. From the day you take your first set of notes, your summarizing skills largely affect your academic success. Accordingly, the best students usually are those who take effective notes and who "know what to study" — those who summarize accurately.

Outside of schoolwork you summarize information daily, whether relating an anecdote or describing a recent magazine article you want a friend to read. On the job you will need to write concisely about your work. Perhaps you will record the minutes of a meeting, summarize a conference lecture, news article, or report, or write summaries of your progress on a project. Or you might write proposals for new projects, bids for contracts, or summaries of your research. Also, you will include summaries and abstracts with any long reports you write. When you apply for jobs your letter and résumé will summarize your personal qualities and qualifications. Whether you summarize someone else's information or your own, your job is to communicate the *essential message* — to express the most important information in the least words by accurately condensing the original. The principle is simple: include what your readers need and omit what they don't.

The essential message in any well-written piece is easy enough to identify if we read carefully. Consider this example:

> The lack of technical knowledge among owners of television sets leads to their suspicions about the honesty of TV repair technicians. Although TV owners might be fairly knowledgeable about most repairs made to their automobiles, they rarely understand the nature and extent of specialized electronic TV repairs. For example, the function and importance of the automatic transmission in an automobile is generally well known; however, the average TV owner knows nothing about the function of the flyback transformer in a TV set. The repair charge for a flyback transformer failure is roughly $150 — a large amount to a consumer who lacks even a simple understanding of what the repairs accomplished. In contrast, a $450 repair charge for the transmission on the family car, though distressing, is fairly easily understood and accepted.

Three significant ideas comprise the essential message here: (1) TV owners lack technical knowledge and are suspicious of repair technicians. (2) An owner usually understands even the most expensive automobile repairs. (3) Owners do not understand or accept expenses for repairs and specialized parts needed for their TV sets. A summary of the paragraph might read like this:

> Because TV owners lack technical knowledge of their sets, they are often suspicious of repair technicians. Although consumers may understand expensive automobile repairs, they rarely understand or accept repair and parts expenses for their TVs.

This summary is almost 30 percent of the original length because the original itself is short. With a longer original, a summary might be as short as 5 percent or less. Relative length is secondary to the need to present all significant data contained in the original.

Summaries are important whenever people have little time to read in detail everything that crosses their desks. A summary saves time and helps solve today's massive communications problems by giving readers ready access to important information.[1] Of course, only by reducing length without distorting the original message can a summary be effective.

ELEMENTS OF AN EFFECTIVE SUMMARY

To achieve conciseness, a summary has to be clear, precise, and organized. As a summarizer your job might be compared to that of a United Nations translator. The translator must preserve the *exact meaning* of the original statement in his or her own clear and organized version; like the translator, the summarizer must preserve the exact meaning, but he or she must preserve that meaning while reducing the length of the statement.

The following 235-word summary of a 5000-word report is a good distillation. Although less than 5 percent of the original, the summary contains all the significant points in readable form.

SUMMARY: SURVIVAL PROBLEMS OF TELEVISION SERVICE BUSINESSES

The high rate of business failure among qualified independent TV repair technicians (second only to service station failures) is rooted in a tradition of unsound business management and inadequate communication with customers. Soon after World War II, many radio-mechanic veterans opened radio shops, which were to form the basis of today's TV repair shops. The ensuing rapid technological progress saw these veterans and the newer technicians swept up in a frenzy of too much work and too little time to learn effective business methods. Moreover, the repair technicians' somewhat secretive ways of dealing with customers, coupled with the advent of television and its phenomenal growth, led to customer suspicions that helped form the "TV repairman syndrome." Even the best of today's technicians have difficulty in shaking this image. Accounts of dishonesty and ineptitude, prevalent in the early years, linger on. Expensive repairs to electronic equipment are difficult to explain to the nontechnical consumer who feels that he is the victim of a supertechnology that requires elaborate servicing. Today's technician or shop owner is still hesitant to adopt sound management and collection methods, as well as to inform his beleaguered customers about

---

[1] It is said that one of our recent United States presidents required all significant world information for the last twenty-four hours to be compressed into one typed page and placed on his desk the first thing each morning.

the services he offers. Only when technicians begin to learn improved business methods and sponsor collective advertising to improve their image and better inform the consumer will their chances for survival increase.

The elements that make this summary effective are discussed in detail below.

Essential Message

A good summary answers the reader's implied question: "What point(s) is the original making?" We have just seen that the essential message is the minimum needed for the reader to understand the issue. It is the sum of the significant points — and *only* the significant points — extracted from the original. Significant points include controlling ideas (thesis statements and topic sentences); major findings and interpretations; important names, dates, statistics, and measurements; and major conclusions or recommendations. They do not include background discussions; the author's personal comments, digressions, or conjectures; introductions, explanations, lengthy examples, graphic illustrations, long definitions, or data of questionable accuracy. (These distinctions are illustrated in the example and discussion in the section titled "Applying the Steps.")

Nontechnical Style

Because summaries are written to save the reader's time, more people probably will read your summary than the entire original. Therefore, aim your style at a general reading audience. To ensure clarity, write at the lowest level of technicality. Translate technical terms and complex data into plain English; for example, if the original states: "For twenty-four hours, the patient's serum glucose measured a consistent 240 mg%," you might rephrase: "For twenty-four hours, the patient's blood-sugar level remained critically high." An unclear message is useless. When you do know fairly specifically the kinds of people who will read the report, keep these people in mind. If they are expert or informed, you won't need to simplify as much (as discussed in Chapter 2). However, you are safer to risk oversimplifying than to risk confusing your reader.

Independent Meaning

In meaning, as well as in style, your summary should be clear; it should be a complete logical unit. Your reader should have to read the original only for further details, examples, or illustrations — not to make sense out of your message.

No New Data

Your job is to represent the original faithfully. Avoid personal comments or judgmental statements ("This interesting report . . ." or "I strongly agree with this last point," etc.). In short, write nothing that is not found in the original.

Introduction-Body-Conclusion Structure

A summary is structured like most good writing.

1. It begins with a clear statement of the controlling idea. The thesis statement of the original is rephrased as the topic sentence of the summary.
2. It presents the significant supporting details in the same order as they appear in the original.
3. It closes with a detailed statement of conclusions and recommendations, which refers back to the controlling idea and ties the major supporting details together.

This structure is made coherent, within and between parts, by transitional words (*however, in addition, while, therefore, although, in contrast,* etc.). The summary process is the reverse of the long report or essay process: the essay or report writer develops specific details and examples to support and clarify the essential message; in contrast, the summary writer lifts the essential message out of its context of specific details to make a concise and independent unit.

Conciseness

Because a summary is, above all, concise (saying a great deal in a few words), it must communicate in a fraction of the original length. However, the content of each original differs: some contents are highly technical; some are abstract; some are quantitative, some qualitative; others are argumentative, descriptive or narrative. Therefore, we can't set a rule for summary length. All we can say is that it must be short enough to be economical, and long enough to be clear, complete, and meaningful. It is better to have a long and meaningful summary than a short and meaningless one.

WRITING THE SUMMARY

You will write a summary of your own work only after completing the original. Follow these step-by-step instructions to pare down any longer piece — your own or someone else's — and to polish it to the point of precision:

1. *Read the entire original.* When summarizing another's work, read the entire piece before jotting down a word. In this way you will get a complete

picture. You have to understand the original fully before you can summarize it effectively.

2. *Reread and underline.* Reread the original two or three times, underlining significant points (usually found in the topic sentences of individual paragraphs). If the piece is in a book, journal, or magazine that belongs to someone else, write the points on a separate sheet of paper instead of underlining them.

Try to identify the key sentence, which states the controlling idea of the original. Omit all minor supporting details such as introductions, explanations, illustrations, examples, and definitions.

3. *Edit the underlined data.* Reread the underlined material and cross out needless words. Leave only phrases that you can later rewrite in your own words, combining them into sentences.

4. *Rewrite in your own words.* Rewrite the edited, underlined material in your own words, following the original order of presentation. Include all important data in the first draft, even if you use too many words; you can always trim them later. Avoid judgmental comments ("The author is correct in assuming...") and add no outside data. Your job is to represent, not to amplify, the original.

5. *Edit your own version.* When you are sure that you have everything the reader needs, edit your own version, aiming for the most clarity with the least words.

a. Cross out all your own needless words without compromising clarity. (See Appendix A.) Do not delete "a," "an," or "the" from any of your writing. Express all statements in grammatically complete sentences.

> The summer internship program in journalism gives the ~~journalism~~ student first-hand experience ~~at what goes~~ on ~~within the system of~~ a ~~real~~ newspaper staff.

b. Cross out needless prefaces such as "The writer argues..." or "The researchers discovered..." or "Also discussed is..." Present the information simply and directly.

c. Use numerals for numbers, except when beginning a sentence. (See Appendix A.)

d. Try to incorporate related ideas through subordination within longer sentences. (See Appendix A.)

Choppy Sentences

The occupational outlook for journalists is good. There was a 53 percent increase in journalism jobs between 1947 and 1975. The national job increase was only 41 percent. Indications point to a continuation of this trend. This is partly due to an increase in weekly newspapers.

Revised

The occupational outlook for journalists is good, as evidenced by the 53 percent increase in journalism jobs between 1947 and 1972, in contrast with a national job increase of only 41 percent. Indications point to a continuation of this trend which is partly due to an increase in weekly newspapers.

Notice that five short sentences are combined into two longer ones.

6. Check your version against the original. When your own version is tightened and refined, check it against the original to make sure that you have preserved the essential message, followed the original order, and added no extraneous comments or data.

7. Rewrite your edited version. Rewrite, following an introduction-body-conclusion structure. Add transitional words and phrases to reinforce the logical connection between related ideas (*"X therefore Y"* implies that *X* is related to *Y* in a cause-and-effect relationship).

8. Document your source. If you are summarizing another's work, identify the source in a bibliographical note immediately following the summary, and place directly quoted statements within quotation marks. (See Chapter 7 for documentation format.)

When summarizing your own information, eliminate steps 1 and 8. Otherwise the procedure is identical. You should find this technique immediately useful in preparing for essay examinations.

Because no one enjoys reading disorganized blather, you have a responsibility to your reader to prepare a concise and readable summary. In a sense, a good summary should function like a digital clock: it should save mental operations ("The big hand is on the 2 and the little on the 11; therefore it is 11:10.") by giving an immediate reading. Your readers should get what they need, immediately and effortlessly.

APPLYING THE STEPS

We will now apply the previous steps to an actual summarizing process. Steps 1, 2, and 3 have been completed on the following original article:

BRIGHTER PROSPECTS FOR WOMEN IN ENGINEERING

One of the major deterrents to women considering engineering as a career is the all-male image. This barrier is rapidly disappearing as the engineering image changes from that of a hard-hat roustabout at   Combine as key sentence (thesis).

a construction site to that of a thoughtful, logical individual who is genuinely interested in solving the engineering and social problems which face us today. True, she may still show up at a construction site in her hard hat, but her time is more apt to be spent at a desk working on new solutions. A female engineer — unlikely? Not quite.

Delete example.

Although women make up an unimpressive 1% of the engineering population, their ranks have been growing. The latest Society of Women Engineers survey of schools accredited by the Engineering Council for Professional Development shows that female engineering enrollment increased from 1,035 during 1959–60 to 3,905 during the 1972–73 school year. This increase may not be as large as it appears on the surface. Only 128 schools replied to the 1959–60 survey. But with the advent of the Civil Rights Act of 1964 and, more recently, the implementation of the federal affirmative action program, as well as an increased awareness on the part of the schools, 201 responded last year. However, since the number of female engineering students per school has increased, even as the number of males enrolled at these schools has decreased, there is little doubt that the percentage of women enrolled in engineering undergraduate programs is growing.

Include significant statistic.

Delete data of questionable accuracy.

Include significant finding.

Delete explanation repeating above finding.

JOBS COME FAST, PROMOTIONS SLOWLY

What happens when the newly minted female engineer tries to enter the field? Initially, she is sought after by almost every employer in sight. Once she is on the job, however, things change. On the average, promotions do not come as rapidly for women as they do for men.

Include significant finding.

Discrimination can be a double-edged sword, however, for unlike her male counterpart, the female engineer is highly visible, and if she does an outstanding job, she may very well be rewarded faster than a man would be. If her performance is average or slightly below average, she may be judged in terms of a number of myths. Perhaps chief among them is the notion that men (and women) don't like to work for women. In my personal experience, I have found that people who enjoy their work get it done without any thought to whether their supervisor is a man or a woman.

Delete author's personal comment.

Include significant finding.

Delete author's personal comment.

Some echoes of <u>other misconceptions</u> about women are still heard among engineers, and undoubtedly <u>contribute to the lag in promoting women to top management</u> ranks. <u>Examples</u> of these myths are: (a) <u>a company's public image will suffer</u> if a woman takes over a top management position, because men have traditionally been the corporate leaders; (b) <u>a woman won't travel</u> on sales trips, to plant inspections, to professional conferences and so forth; (c) <u>women don't</u> want to <u>accept responsibility</u>; (d) a woman's <u>family</u> will always <u>take precedence over</u> her <u>career.</u> (One must ask, why shouldn't it take precedence over a man's as well?)

It has <u>also</u> been argued that promotion policies don't favor women because <u>companies</u> prefer long tenure for those elevated to executive positions, and they <u>believe</u> that <u>turnover rates are greater for women.</u> <u>But</u>, not only do government figures show that <u>professional women</u> have working <u>careers comparable in length to those of men</u>, it is also clear that <u>promotions generally accrue to men regardless of age and experience.</u> Over 20% of all male engineers are in management, as opposed to an estimated 3% of female engineers.

Admittedly, because the number of women in the profession is small, the above figure is open to sampling error. Indeed, as many as 40% of the women surveyed in 1972 by the Society of Women Engineers stated that they supervised groups which ranged in size from teams to major organizations. It must be noted, however, that members of SWE (and engineering societies in general) are probably among the more qualified and professionally active engineers.

ATTITUDES VARY

A questionnaire on discrimination was included in the <u>1972</u> SWE survey. In a classic case of "which-came-first-the-chicken-or-the-egg?" the results showed that those <u>women</u> who were <u>very successful</u> in terms of salary, responsibility, and years of experience <u>felt they had not encountered any discrimination.</u> <u>Those</u> women who were <u>moderately successful</u> <u>indicated</u> that there was <u>no discrimination</u> encountered <u>from</u> their <u>immediate superiors.</u> They felt, <u>however</u>, that people in the <u>upper</u> levels of <u>manage-</u>

Margin notes:

Include factual interpretation and continuation of above finding.

Delete rhetorical question.

Include continuation of finding.

Include significant finding.

Delete statistics of questionable accuracy, along with the related explanation.

Include significant date.

Include significant finding.

ment hierarchy did discriminate and that there was
some evidence of discrimination by coworkers.

Those women on the low side of the average in
terms of salary and responsibility indicated that they
had encountered discrimination at all levels. It can
be argued that these women have less ability than
their male cohorts, and use "discrimination" as an
excuse for their lack of advancement.

SALARIES

All women encounter discrimination, perhaps not
intentional or even conscious, from their male colleagues. This contention is borne out by the results
of the SWE salary survey, compared with the results of the survey of Engineers Joint Council for the
profession as a whole. For engineers with 11 years'
experience (the median for women), the median
salary for female engineers is $14,200 per year, while
that for all engineers with 11 years' experience is
$16,700, according to the EJC. Both surveys were
completed in 1972. The disparity may be even
greater because, again, SWE members are more
professionally active than all engineers taken as a
group.

Of course, the engineering profession is not alone
in this disparity in salaries. In the federal civil service, men average $14,328 per year, and women only
$8,578. This is not because there are separate pay
scales for women, but rather because women employees are heavily concentrated in lower-grade jobs.

All is not bleak, however. In 1973, the average
starting salary offered to women engineering graduates at the bachelor's degree level was $936 per
month — $15 a month more than the average for
men, according to the College Placement Council.
This represents a closing of the gap when compared
with 1971, when women were offered $8 a month
less than men. Engineering — the profession offering
the highest starting pay for those with bachelor degrees, remains the only profession where salary offers
are higher for women than for men.

If one considers salary offers from private industry only, the salary gap between male and female
engineers was even greater than the averages indicate, and favored women. But the federal govern-

Include continuation
of finding.

Delete obvious
explanation.

Include factual
interpretation.

Delete background
information.

Include significant
statistics and date.

Delete author's
conjecture.

Delete author's
digression.

Include significant
finding, supporting
statistics, and date.

Include significant
conclusion.

ment, which offered significantly lower salaries to
entry-level female engineers than to males, dragged
the overall averages closer together.

Delete explanation.

THE FUTURE?

The current <u>energy crisis and materials shortage</u>
<u>indicate</u> that this country is fast moving from a state
of have to have not. The <u>only way to maintain</u> our
current <u>standard of living is through technology</u>,
which means that <u>engineers will continue to be in</u>
<u>great demand.</u> It also means that the <u>image of</u>
<u>engineering will continue to change</u> as attention
is focused <u>on sociological-technological problems.</u>
<u>Consequently</u>, we can <u>expect women to enter the</u>
engineering <u>profession in greater numbers.</u>[2]

Include significant
conclusion and
restatement of thesis.

With the reading, rereading and underlining, and editing completed, we can
move on to step 4: rewriting. Here is how the first rewrite of the underlined
material might read; ideas are simply listed in order, without concern for length
or subordination:

FIRST REWRITE

The all-male image has deterred women from engineering careers. This
image of a hard-hat worker is giving way to that of a thoughtful individual
working on today's engineering and social problems. Women comprise only
1% of the engineering population, but their ranks are growing. Female engineering students have increased in number while males have decreased. The
new female engineer easily finds work but is not rapidly promoted. Because
of high visibility, she may be promoted faster than a man if her performance
is outstanding. If performance is average or below, she may be judged in
terms of several myths: that people don't like to work for a woman; that a
woman in top management harms a company's public image; that a woman
won't travel on business; that women won't accept responsibility; that her
family takes precedence over her career; and that turnover rates are higher
for women. But careers of professional women are as long as those of men.
Men usually receive the promotions, regardless of age or experience.

In 1972, highly successful women engineers reported no discrimination.
Moderately successful women sensed no discrimination from immediate
superiors, but felt that higher management and coworkers did discriminate.

[2] Naomi J. McAfee, "Brighter Prospects for Women in Engineering," *Engineering Education*, vol. 64, no. 7 (April 1974), pp. 502–504. Reprinted with permission from *Engineering
Education* © 1974 The American Society for Engineering Education.

Those with minimal success felt discrimination at all levels. All women do encounter salary discrimination. In 1972, the median salary for female engineers with 11 years' experience was $14,200 yearly, as opposed to $16,700 for all engineers with equal experience. However, in 1973, the average starting salary for women engineers with bachelor degrees was $936 per month — $15 more than for men. This figure contrasts with 1971 figures when women were offered $8 a month less than men. Engineering is the only profession where salary offers are higher for women than for men.

We now have a shortage of energy and materials. We can only maintain our living standard through technology. Demand for engineers will continue to grow. Their image will continue to change with new emphasis on sociological-technological problems. Thus, women are expected to enter the engineering field in greater numbers.

Notice that this version simply includes all significant information, without particular regard for coherence. In the final draft, transitional terms and meaningful punctuation will be added, and related ideas will be combined within longer sentences to tighten the whole structure. Also, the length (roughly 330 words or 25 percent of the 1400-word original) will be further reduced in the final draft. Word length, however, is less important than accurate emphasis and faithful representation of the essential message. This version preserves the original emphasis by recording the brighter prospects as well as the continuing problem areas. Factual statements are faithfully represented because they are *fully* expressed. Imagine the factual distortion if, to save space, the statement, "The new female engineer easily finds work but is not rapidly promoted," were only partially expressed as, "The new female engineer easily finds work."

Here is the final draft of the summary, with steps 5, 6, 7, and 8 completed. All transitional terms and connecting devices, including appropriate punctuation signals, are underlined:

SUMMARY OF "BRIGHTER PROSPECTS FOR WOMEN IN ENGINEERING"

The all-male, hard-hat image, which has deterred women from engineering, is changing to that of a thoughtful individual working on today's engineering and social problems. Although women comprise only 1% of engineers, their growing ranks are evidenced by an increase in female engineering students contrasted with a decrease in male students. The graduating female easily finds work but no rapid promotion unless her performance is outstanding. An average or below-average performance may be judged in terms of several myths: that people dislike working for women; that a woman in top management harms a company's image; that she won't travel or accept responsibility; that her family takes precedence over her career; and that female turnover rates are higher. In fact, women's professional careers are as long as men's, <u>but</u> men usually receive the promotions.

In 1972, highly successful women engineers reported no discrimination. Moderately successful women sensed none from immediate superiors, <u>but</u> felt that higher management and coworkers did discriminate. Marginally successful women claimed discrimination at all levels. Women <u>do encounter</u> salary discrimination<u>:</u> the 1972 median salary for female engineers with 11 years' experience was $14,200 yearly, <u>as opposed to</u> $16,700 for all equally experienced engineers. <u>However</u>, the 1973 average starting salary for women graduates was $936 monthly — $15 more than for men. <u>By contrast</u>, in 1971, women received $8 less than men. <u>Thus</u>, only in engineering are women receiving higher offers.

Current energy and materials shortages increase our reliance on technology to maintain living standards<u>; consequently</u>, the demand for engineers with a sociological-technological commitment should attract more women.

This version is trimmed, edited, and tightened: word count has been reduced to roughly 20 percent of the original; sentences have been combined; appropriate transitional terms and punctuation signals (see Appendix A) have been added to illustrate the logical connection between related ideas; and nothing has been added to the original. A summary of this length will serve well in many situations, but in other situations you might want a substantially briefer and more compressed summary — say one that runs no more than 125 to 150 words or about 10 percent of the original:

The all-male image of engineering is changing, and although women comprise only 1% of engineers, their ranks are growing. Female students are increasing while males decrease. Although female graduates easily find work, only the outstanding are rapidly promoted, with average or lower performance often judged according to conventional myths about women in "male" professions.

In 1972 no discrimination was reported by the highly successful women engineers; selective discrimination, by the moderately successful; and general discrimination, by the marginal. Women *do* encounter salary discrimination: the 1972 median salary for experienced females was $14,200, compared with $16,700 for all equally experienced engineers. However, in 1973 women graduates commanded starting salaries of $15 more monthly than men, whereas in 1971 they had received $8 less. Only in engineering are women receiving higher offers.

As resource shortages increase reliance on technology to maintain living standards, the demand for "sociological-technological" engineers should attract more women.

Notice that the essential message is still intact; related ideas have been combined through subordination and fewer supporting details have been included. Clearly, length is adjustable according to your audience and purpose.

WRITING THE ABSTRACT

A summary reflects *what the original contains,* whereas an abstract reflects *what the original is about.* The difference between an abstract (sometimes called "descriptive abstract") and a summary (sometimes called "informative abstract") might best be clarified with a familiar analogy. Imagine that you are describing your recent summer travels to a friend; you have two options: (1) You might simply mention the places you visited in chronological order. This catalogue of major areas would convey the basic nature of your trip. (2) In addition to describing your itinerary, you might describe the significant experiences you had in each area you visited. Option 1 is like a roadmap, an overview of the areas covered in your journey. This option is analogous to an abstract. Option 2, on the other hand, is expanded to include the significant points within each area. This second, more detailed, option, is analogous to a summary.

An abstract, then, presents a table of contents (a list of major topics) in related-sentence form. Whereas the summary contains the meat of the original, the abstract contains only its skeletal structure; in effect, an abstract is "a summary of a summary," as shown in the following sample:

ABSTRACT OF "BRIGHTER PROSPECTS FOR WOMEN IN ENGINEERING"

As the all-male image of engineering changes, the number of women engineers increases. Although persisting sexist myths affect women's chances for promotion, women's salaries are increasing. Growing demands for sociologically oriented engineers promise to attract more women to the field.

Because an abstract simply discusses the focus of the original, it is always brief — usually no longer than a short paragraph. Abstracts one or two sentences long often accompany article titles in journal and magazine tables of contents; they give readers a bird's-eye view of the range of coverage of an article or report.

PLACING SUMMARIES AND ABSTRACTS IN YOUR REPORT

If your reader asks for an abstract of your report, place it in front, on a separate page, right after your table of contents. It is usually single-spaced. With an abstract in front, your summary will go in the conclusion section of your report. Sometimes you will be asked to place your summary in front, instead of writing an abstract. In this case, judgments about the quality of your whole report may depend on the clarity, organization, and conciseness of your summary. A reader who sees a garbled and confusing summary probably won't read on. In fact, the reader may well conclude that your data are useless and you, incompetent. On the other hand, a well-written summary illustrates your understanding of the subject and your competence in communicating.

With practice, you will find that much of your communicating can be done through summaries. They are a good way to save time and to achieve control of your writing.

CHAPTER SUMMARY

A summary (like this one) is an economical way of communicating because it compresses a longer message into its barest essentials. In school and on the job you will need to write summaries frequently and effectively. An effective summary extracts *only* the major points from the original and (usually) presents them in a nontechnical style that almost any reader can understand. The summary stands independently as a meaningful message and adds nothing to the original. Like most good pieces of writing, it follows an introduction-body-conclusion structure. The key word in summary writing is *conciseness;* that is, the summary must be brief but also clear, complete, and meaningful; it is better to make it a bit long than to omit some key point and distort the original. You can summarize your own work only after you have fully written the original version.

Follow these steps in writing your summary:

1. Read the entire original.
2. Reread and underline (or copy) the major points.
3. Edit the underlined or copied data to cut out needless words.
4. Rewrite the material in your own words.
5. Edit your version by crossing out needless words and prefaces, using digits for numbers, and combining related ideas through subordination.
6. Check your version against the original for accuracy.
7. Rewrite your version in an introduction-body-conclusion structure with all needed transitions.
8. Document your source if you have summarized another's work.

Analyze your audience and purpose carefully in order to adjust the length of your summary to the demands of the situation.

Whereas a summary reflects what the original contains, an abstract reflects what the original is about (a kind of summary of a summary). Abstracts are usually very short and simply give a bird's-eye view.

An abstract always belongs in front of a report, but the summary may be in the conclusion section or in front, as your reader wishes.

REVISION CHECKLIST

Use this checklist as a guide to refining your work.

1. Does your summary contain only the essential message (controlling ideas; major findings and interpretations; important names, dates, statistics, measurements; major conclusions and recommendations)?
2. Is it written in a style that is accessible to a wide range of readers?
3. Does it make sense as an independent piece?
4. Does it hang together as a logical unit?
5. Will readers understand what the original contains after they read your summary?
6. Are there enough transitions between related ideas?
7. Is the summary accurate (checked against the original)?
8. Is it free from personal comments or other additions to the original?
9. Is it free from wordiness and needless details?
10. Does it follow an introduction-body-conclusion structure?
11. Does it follow the order of the original?
12. Is it short enough to be economical and long enough to be clear, complete, and meaningful?
13. Is it written in correct English (spelling, mechanics, and usage, as discussed in Appendix A)?
14. Have you documented your source?
15. Is your abstract an effective "summary of a summary" in that it clearly expresses what the original is about?
16. Have you placed your summary or abstract at the proper location in your report?

Now list those aspects of your summary or abstract that need improvement.

EXERCISES

1. In a unified and coherent paragraph, describe the differences between a summary and an abstract in enough detail to provide the general reader with a clear understanding of the distinction.
2. *In class:* Organize into groups of four or five and choose a topic for group discussion: a social problem, a political issue, a campus problem, plans for an event, suggestions for individual energy conservation, etc. Dis-

cuss the topic for one full class period, taking careful notes of significant points. Afterward, organize and edit your notes in line with the directions for "Writing the Summary." Next, write a unified and coherent individual summary of the group discussion in no more than 200 words. Finally, as a group, compare your individual summaries for accuracy, emphasis, conciseness, and clarity.

3. In one or two paragraphs, discuss the specific kinds and frequency of summary-writing assignments you expect to encounter in your occupation. Will your reading audience be mainly colleagues, superiors, or customers, clients, or other general readers?

4. Read each of the following student-written paragraphs carefully and make lists of the significant ideas comprising the essential message in each. Next, write a unified and coherent summary of each paragraph.

In recent years, ski-binding manufacturers, in line with consumer demand, have redesigned their bindings several times in an effort to achieve a noncompromising synthesis between performance and safety. Such a synthesis depends on what appear to be divergent goals: Performance, in essence, is a function of the binding's ability to hold the boot firmly to the ski, thus enabling the skier to change rapidly the position of his skis without being hampered by a loose or wobbling connection. Safety, on the other hand, is a function of the binding's ability both to release the boot when the skier falls, and to retain the boot when subjected to the normal shocks of skiing. If achieved, this synthesis of performance and safety will greatly increase skiing pleasure while decreasing accidents.

Contrary to public belief, sewage-treatment plants do not fully purify sewage. The product that leaves the plant to be dumped into the leaching (sievelike drainage) fields is secondary sewage containing toxic contaminants such as phosphates, nitrates, chloride, and heavy metals. As the secondary sewage filters into the ground, this conglomeration is carried along. Under the leaching area develops a contaminated mound through which ground water flows, spreading the waste products over great distances. If this leachate reaches the outer limits of a well's drawing radius, the water supply becomes polluted. Furthermore, because all water essentially flows toward the sea, more pollution is added to the coastal regions by this secondary sewage.

5. In 500 words or less, discuss your reasons for applying for a certain job or to a certain school.

6. Attend a campus lecture on a topic of interest to you and take notes of the significant points. Write a clear and organized summary of the lecture's essential message.

7. Use your own modified technique of the steps in "Writing the Summary" as a study aid in preparing for an examination in one of your courses. After taking the exam, write one or two paragraphs evaluating this technique for putting yourself in control of a large and diverse body of information.

8. Find three examples of abstracts or summaries from journals and magazines in your school library and bring them to class. As a group, analyze selected examples on an overhead projector for clarity and meaning.

9. Find an article in the library pertaining to your major field or area of interest and write both an abstract and a summary of the article.

10. Select a long paper that you have written for one of your courses; write an abstract and a summary of the paper.

11. Read the following article and write both an abstract and a summary of it, using the steps under "Writing the Summary" as a guide. Bring your summary to class and exchange with another student for proofreading according to the criteria discussed in "Elements of an Effective Summary." When your proofread copy is returned, revise as necessary before submitting it to your instructor.

YOSEMITE VALLEY:
CAN IT BE SALVAGED?

That inviting sign at the entrance to the visitor center at Yosemite National Park is full of enticing words like "excitement," "serenity" and "relationships to the natural world." But some of the current real life scenes in Yosemite's Valley look a little less enticing:

— note the empty wine bottles scattered outside the supermarket;
— awaken to park police sirens blaring in the night;
— read the official memo accounting for two attempted rapes;
— meet the spaced-out man at the bus stop: "I'm waiting for my friend who's never come. It's 10:30? I've been here for hours." (He remains in place as the bus departs.)
— encounter the woman panhandling at the visitor center toilet facility;
— read the *Yosemite Guide* front-page article: "Unfortunately the 'car clout' season in Yosemite is approaching. A car clouter (auto burglar) can ruin your vacation."

These vignettes don't depict the great granite landscape nor do they refer to the vast numbers of visitors who come to Yosemite to appreciate "the natural world." They do, however, point to some of the problems of visitor use (and misuse) that are converting the valley's environment into an urbanized recreation area, something of a contradiction to the ideas incorporated in the visitor center's welcoming sign.

Talk to a ranger who refers to his job in the valley as an urban assignment: "You have to accept the idea of things as they are — urbanized. For instance, we attract people here on motor bikes; they may be noisy but that's the way things are. The emphasis now seems to be on trying to preserve the back country."

Superintendent Leslie J. Arnberger speaks of the valley as an area of "extremely concentrated public usage," a tradition that's persisted over the years. He also considers the valley as "the park's great scenic climax."

James L. Sleznick, the park's information officer, points out that on a given summer night the valley's shifting population may number 10,000 "and for many of these people the usual social restraints have been left at home." Sleznick defines the thinking of this group: "The people next door are not my neighbors, particularly if I'm here for just one or two nights. I'm doing my thing. I don't have to account to my neighbor." As Sleznick notes, the Park Service has no capacity to screen visitors at the entrance gate.

Thomas Doyle, Yosemite's administrative officer, says, "Personally, if I wanted to get away from it all, I certainly wouldn't come to Yosemite." He suggests designating the valley as a National Recreation Area. He and several other members of the Park Service think it's realistic to retain only the high country as Yosemite National Park.

Yosemite tops all other units in the National Park System in terms of gross annual revenue. The concessioner for many years had been the Yosemite Park and Curry Company, whose financial records showed a "marginal return" on investment. In August 1973 that company was acquired by Music Corporation of America, whose varied holdings include a number of popular TV ("Emergency") and movie ("Jaws") productions.

MCA's early promotional efforts featuring Yosemite as a convention center met with considerable complaint from the public. A Park Service official counters these complaints by stating that "conventions are the lifeblood of the hotel industry, so in the off-season it behooves us to allow group meetings." But a Government Accounting Office report issued in 1975 indicated that it wasn't simply an off-season matter: "About 50 percent of the 10,000 room nights used for conventions [in 1974] were during the peak season of May through September." The report added that the concessioner "offered to cancel all 1975 summer conventions but the park superintendent said such action was not necessary since these groups should not arbitrarily be denied accommodations."

As of December, 1975, Park Service officials stated that the concessioner would be allowed to schedule conventions between Labor Day and Memorial Day only. As one spokesman admitted, however, the word "convention" lacks a clear-cut definition.

There have also been numerous complaints from Yosemite visitors about prices being charged by MCA. The concessioner's rates must be approved by the Park Service, whose Yosemite officials maintain that prices within the park's gate are comparable to those in other "urban recreation areas; in some instances we compare the park's pricing policies with San Francisco or South Lake Tahoe." In its review of the subject, the Government Accounting Office stated flatly that "the Park Service had not adequately monitored concessioner prices. . . ."

Letters of complaint from visitors concerning the concessioner's maintenance and housekeeping operations have been received at Park Service offices at a rate of three or four a day during spring, summer and fall seasons; however, staffing to deal with the problems raised has been inadequate in the past.

Can the valley be salvaged — from misuse by a minority of its visitors and from urbanization? Can the Park Service adequately represent the public "owners" of a national park in dealing with a corporation whose primary obligations are to its stockholders?

Solutions to at least some of the valley's difficulties are in the works. A lawyer with previous experience in negotiating with concessioners has recently been added to the staff. Two long-standing problems — automobile congestion and automotive exhausts — are being partially controlled, as energy-efficient buses and trams replace traffic jams. Moreover, the extensive efforts of Park Service personnel to meet members of the counter culture on new terms have reduced the possibility that a 1970 Stoneman's Meadow confrontation between rangers and "non-traditionals" will recur. "Stoneman's Meadow was a boil that festered and erupted. It's gone now," says Jim Sleznick. In addition to providing traditional campfire programs, hikes and nature walks, the park's interpretive staff has experimented with programs to appeal to "non-traditional" visitors: yoga classes, meditation walks and Saturday night sessions where natural foods have been made available free of charge. Leonard W. McKenzie, chief park naturalist, says frankly: "We've aimed at reaching youths through their stomachs."

The Youth Natural High Program, run with the assistance of members of the 3HO (Healthy, Happy and Holy) Foundation of Albany, California, has promoted the idea of "getting high on Yosemite." During the summer of 1976 the Park Service anticipates expanding the organization's meditation activities among campers and also with its own interpretive staff "to strengthen their perception of Yosemite's values and to raise their level of esthetic consciousness and sensory awareness."

Len McKenzie sees the interpretive program as a substantial management tool but realizes that it doesn't reach hard-core individuals — "and it's ludicrous to think we do." He suggests that a reservation system for campsites "might somewhat inhibit those people who come here for a party; they'd have to plan ahead and organize their efforts to get to the park, so there would be fewer groups that would just pick up, take off for the park and party here. People can't be programmed, but on the other hand, national parks can't be all things to all people," says McKenzie.

In noting that the crime rate in Yosemite rivals that of a number of small cities, McKenzie wonders if "we'll have to start tightening the drawstrings, defining restraints on visitors in order to retain the values that caused national parks to be created in the first place."

Probably the most hopeful development in finding answers to Yosemite's multifaceted problems is the burst of public concern expressed in the past year about the park's master plan and its accompanying environmental impact statement. Previously the public had made known its negative reactions to master plans produced in 1971 and 1974. In turn, the Park Service rejected both of those plans and in 1975 inaugurated a series of 48 public workshops, holding 41 in California and seven in cities across the U.S. There was an astonishing response in the form of more than 5,600 people who appeared in person to consider Yosemite's future. Questions and opinions about every conceivable aspect of the park were voiced, and a wide range of philosophies about the basic purpose of a national park was expressed. The entire continuum from strict preservationists, who would remove all facilities from Yosemite and require that its visitors arrive and travel only on foot, to persons advocating greater recreational development and more extensive commercial facilities were represented. "The emotional commitment shown by the public about a master plan was unusual," says Ann Bowman, public involvement coordinator for the park planning team.

Since the workshops were completed, the planning team has received thousands of letters from citizens who took the time to write lengthy comments about Yosemite. One correspondent began his letter in a "let's develop the park" frame-of-mind; after ten pages he switched his opinions, having written himself into a "let's protect the park" corner.

Last November the planning team mailed 32,500 copies of its workbook, with four worksheets attached, to interested citizens throughout the nation. The huge worksheets with four planning options covering ten different sections of the park littered many a dining table or group conference table before completed answer sheets were returned to San Francisco this past January. The public's opinions on park transportation, accommodations, campgrounds, recreational activities, conventions, interpretive programs, wilderness, visitor use levels, insect and disease control, use of the Tioga Road, the future of the Hetch Hetchy reservoir, helicopter access and attitudes toward dogs, cats and bears have been expressed.

It remains for the planning team to digest this wealth of citizen input, prepare a new environmental impact statement, hold public hearings and come up with a new master plan. The resulting document cannot possibly please every Yosemite aficionado in every detail. But, hopefully, it will be an improvement over previous efforts as a result of the contributions of a concerned citizenry.

And the valley may yet be salvaged.[3]

[3] From Dorothy Boyle Huyck, "Yosemite Valley: Can It Be Salvaged?" *American Forests,* June 1976, pp. 43–44. Reprinted by permission of American Forestry Association.

4

Defining
Your Terms

CHAPTER GOALS

DEFINITION

PURPOSE OF DEFINITIONS

USING DEFINITIONS SELECTIVELY

ELEMENTS OF AN EFFECTIVE
    DEFINITION
  Plain English
  Basic Properties
  Objectivity

CHOOSING THE BEST TYPE OF
    DEFINITION
  Parenthetical Definition
  Sentence Definition
    Classifying the Term
    Differentiating the Term
  Expanded Definition

EXPANDING YOUR DEFINITION
  Etymology
  History and Background
  Example
  Graphic Illustration
  Analysis of Parts
  Comparison and Contrast
  Basic Operating Principle
  Specific Materials or Conditions
    Required

APPLYING THE STEPS

PLACING DEFINITIONS IN YOUR
    REPORT
  Parenthetical Definitions
  Sentence Definitions
  Expanded Definitions

CHAPTER SUMMARY

REVISION CHECKLIST

EXERCISES

CHAPTER GOALS

Upon completing this chapter you will know:

• The meaning and purpose of definitions.
• When to use definitions and how to analyze the writing situation according to the subject and your reader's needs.
• How to evaluate any definition for effectiveness.
• The differences between parenthetical, sentence, and expanded definitions.
• How to select the best type of definition for your purpose.
• How to expand a definition.
• Where to place various types of definitions in your report.
• How to proofread and revise your definitions for greatest effectiveness.

DEFINITION

To define a term is to give its precise meaning. As we have said earlier, *clarity* is the most important element in your writing. Clear writing begins with clear thinking; clear thinking begins with a clear understanding of what all the terms mean. Therefore, clear writing begins with careful definition which both reader and writer understand. Always define your terms before discussing them.

PURPOSE OF DEFINITIONS

Virtually every specialty has its own "language," its technical terms. For example, engineers, architects, and builders may talk about "prestressed concrete," "tolerances," or "trusses"; psychologists, social workers, counselors, and police officers may use terms like "manic-depressive psychosis," "sociopathic behavior," or "repression"; lawyers, real-estate brokers, and investment counselors may discuss "easements," "liens," "amortization," or "escrow accounts" — and so on. Any of these terms is likely to be unfamiliar to readers who are not specialists in the field from which it comes. In your own writing, keep your reader's needs in mind as you identify the terms that need definition.

When communicating with colleagues you rarely need to define specialized terms used in your field (unless the term is new). But reports are often written for the layperson — the manager, potential client, or other general reader. When you write for this kind of person, think about his or her needs. Don't compromise the clarity of your message by forcing your reader to consult a dictionary or encyclopedia every two minutes, just to make sense of your message. Information that seems perfectly clear to you can easily be meaningless to someone else. You must always assume that your reader knows less than you do — a general reader, much less! Make your meaning clear with good definitions.

Most of the specialized terms mentioned at the beginning of this section are concrete and specific. Once a term like "truss" has been defined in enough detail to suit the reader's purposes, its meaning will not be appreciably different in another context. And when a term is highly technical it is easy enough to figure out that it should be defined for certain readers. Anyone who isn't a specialist knows that he doesn't have any idea what "prestressed concrete," or "diffraction," or similar technical terms mean. However, your reader is considerably less likely to be aware that more familiar terms like "disability," "guarantee," "tenant," "lease," or "mortgage," acquire very specialized meanings in specialized contexts. This is where definition (by all parties) becomes crucial to a full understanding of what is being talked about. What "guarantee" means in one situation is not necessarily what it will mean in another. That is why a legal contract, in effect, is a detailed definition of the subject of the contract.

Assume that you're shopping for a disability insurance policy to provide a steady income in case injury or illness should leave you unable to work. Besides comparing the prices of various policies, you will want each company to provide a clear definition of "physical disability." Although Company A offers the least expensive policy, it might not define physical disability as your inability to work at your specific job — unless you are unable to work at any job whatsoever. Therefore, should a neurological problem prevent you from continuing your work as a designer of delicate, transistorized electronic devices, without disabling you for work as a salesperson or clerk, you might not qualify as "disabled," according to Company A's definition. In contrast, Company B's policy, which is more expensive, might define physical disability as your inability to work at your specific job. Thus, although all companies use the term "physical disability," they may not mean the same thing by it.

You will encounter similar problems in definition with the purchase of some expensive items. Should you plan to purchase a condominium, you will need to obtain the developer's full definition of "condominium." Otherwise, your failure to read the "fine print" might be disastrous. The same is true for the terms of "warranty" on a new automobile. Because you are legally responsible for all documents carrying your signature, you need to understand the importance and technique of clear definition.

Finally, on a global scale, our survival could depend on the clear definition of terms like "détente" or "nuclear proliferation pact" by the countries who are parties to these agreements. In short, definition is more than an exercise in busy work.

USING DEFINITIONS SELECTIVELY

The growth of technology and specialization will continue to make definitions an important part of communication. However, use definitions only when they are required by the subject and the audience. The point is to know for whom you're writing, and why. For instance, reports in *Psychology Today* (with a general readership) define many terms that would not be defined in reports to psychologists. It stands to reason that the expert or informed reader will need fewer definitions. If you can't pinpoint your audience, assume a general readership and define generously.

Depending on your subject, purpose, and audience, individual definitions can vary greatly in length. As a rule, make your definition long enough to be understood by a general reader. Often you will need only a *parenthetical definition* — a few words or a synonym placed in parentheses after the term. Sometimes your definition will require one or more complete sentences. Some terms may even require a definition that extends to hundreds of words — an *expanded definition*. (Each type will be discussed in detail.)

Your choice of parenthetical, sentence, or expanded definition depends on the amount of information your readers need, and that, in turn, depends on why they need it. For instance, "carburetor" could be defined in a single sentence (as shown on page 62) telling the reader what it is and how, in general, it works. However, this definition should be greatly expanded for the student mechanic who needs to know where the word *carburetor* comes from, how the device was developed and perfected, what it looks like, how it is used, how its parts work together, and so on.

In most cases, the meanings of abstract and general terms ("loan," "easy-credit plan," etc.) will need to be explained in detail.

ELEMENTS OF AN EFFECTIVE DEFINITION

For all definitions, regardless of length, use these three guidelines:

Plain English

Remember that your purpose is to clarify meaning, not muddy it. Use simple language.

> *Incorrect*
> A tumor is a neoplasm.
>
> A solenoid is an inductance coil that serves as a tractive electromagnet. (*This definition might be appropriate for an electrical engineering manual, but is too specialized for the general reader.*)
>
> *Correct*
> A tumor is a growth of cells that occurs in the body, grows independently of surrounding tissue, and serves no useful function.
>
> A solenoid is an electrically energized coil that converts electrical energy to magnetic energy capable of performing various mechanical functions.

Basic Properties

Any item, process, or concept has characteristics that make it different from all others. Its definition should express clearly these basic properties. Thus, a thermometer can be defined in terms of its singular function: it measures temperature; this is the primary information that your reader would need. All other data about a thermometer, such as types, special uses, materials used in construction, and cost are secondary. On the other hand, a book cannot primarily be defined in terms of its function, because books can have several functions. A book can be used to write in or to display pictures (if the pages are blank), to record financial transactions, to read (if the pages are printed or written), and so on. Also, other items — individual sheets of paper, posters, newspapers, picture frames, etc. — serve the same functions. The basic property of a book is physical: it is a bound volume of pages. This is the feature an item must possess in order to be called a book; it is what your reader would have to know *first* in order to understand what a book is. Comments about types of books, uses, sizes, contents, etc. provide only secondary information.

Objectivity

Make your definitions objective. Tell your reader what the item is, not what you think of it. Personal comments and interpretations should come only *after* your data and only at the specific request of your reader. For instance, "bomb" may be defined properly as "an explosive weapon that is detonated by impact, proximity to an object, a timing mechanism, or other predetermined means." If instead you define a bomb as "a weapon devised and perfected by hawkish idiots to eventually destroy themselves and the world," you are editorializing; furthermore, you are not presenting a bomb's basic property. Though your readers may learn about your attitude toward bombs, they still won't know what a bomb is! Remember that your purpose is to share factual information, not to recruit philosophical allies.

Likewise, in defining something like "diesel engine," simply tell your reader what it is and how it works. You might think that diesels are too noisy and sluggish for use in passenger vehicles, but you should reserve these judgments until *after* your definition — that is, if your reader has asked for such comments (as in a comparative study of small buses for your town's public transportation system). Otherwise, let the data speak for themselves.

CHOOSING THE BEST TYPE OF DEFINITION

After deciding to define a term in your report, choose the most appropriate type of definition: parenthetical, sentence, or expanded.

Parenthetical Definition

A parenthetical definition is the simplest type of definition, briefly explaining the term in a word or phrase. It often consists of a synonym in parentheses immediately following the term it defines:

> The effervescent (bubbling) mixture was quickly discarded.

> The leaching field (sievelike drainage area) needs fifteen inches of crushed stone.

Another option is to express your definition as a clarifying phrase:

> The trees on the site are mostly deciduous; that is, they shed their foliage at season's end.

Use parenthetical definitions to give your readers a general understanding of specialized terms so they can easily follow the discussion where these terms are used. For example, a parenthetical definition of "leaching field" might be adequate in a progress report to a client whose house you are building. But such a brief definition is not adequate in a report whose main topic is leaching fields. Here, you would need to write an expanded definition.

Sentence Definition

Often, a clear definition requires more than just a word or phrase in parentheses. A sentence definition (which may be stated in more than one sentence) follows a fixed structure: (1) the name of the item to be defined; (2) the class (specific group) to which the item belongs; and (3) the features that differentiate the item from all other items in its class.

Term	Class	Distinguishing Features
polygraph	a measuring instrument	that simultaneously records changes in pulse, blood pressure, and respiration, and is often used in lie detection
carburetor	a mixing device	in gasoline engines which blends air and fuel into a vaporized mixture for combustion within the cylinders
transit	a surveying instrument	that measures horizontal and vertical angles
diabetes	a metabolic disease	caused by a disorder of the pituitary gland or pancreas, and characterized by excessive urination, persistent thirst, and, often, an inability to metabolize sugar
liberalism	a political concept	based on belief in progress, the essential goodness of man, the autonomy of the individual, and standing for the protection of political and civil liberties
brief	a legal document	containing all the facts and points of law pertinent to a specific case, and filed by an attorney before arguing the case in court
stress	an applied force	that tends to strain or deform a body

In their presentation, these elements are combined into one or more complete sentences.

> Diabetes is a metabolic disease caused by a disorder of the pituitary gland or pancreas. This disease is often characterized by excessive urination, persistent thirst, and often an inability to metabolize sugar.

Sentence definition is especially useful if you need to stipulate the precise working definition of a term that has several possible meanings. For example, in a construction, banking, or real-estate report, a term like "qualified buyer" could have different meanings for different readers. The same is true for "compact car" in a report comparing various brands of cars for use in the company fleet.

State your working definitions at the beginning of your report, as follows:

> Throughout this report, the term "disadvantaged student" is taken to mean . . .

Classifying the Term

Be precise in your classification. The item's class will reflect its similarities to all other items with common attributes (as discussed in Chapter 5). The narrower your class, the more specific your meaning. For example, "transit" is correctly classified as a "surveying instrument," not as a "thing" or simply as an "instrument." Likewise, "stress" is correctly classified as "an applied force"; to say that stress "is what . . ." or "takes place when . . ." or "is something that . . ." is incorrect; these formulas are not words of classification. Also, select the most accurate terms of classification: "Diabetes" is accurately classified as "a metabolic disease," not as "a medical term."

Differentiating the Term

Differentiate your term by separating the item it names from every other item in its class. If the distinguishing features can be applied to more than one item, your definition is imprecise. Make these features narrow enough to pinpoint the item's unique identity and meaning, yet broad enough to be inclusive. For example, a definition of "brief" as "a legal document introduced in a courtroom" is not narrow enough because the definition doesn't differentiate "brief" from all other legal documents. Conversely, a differentiation of "carburetor" as "a mixing device used in automobile engines" is too narrow because it fails to indicate the carburetor's use in all other gasoline engines.

Also, avoid circular definitions (repeating, as part of the distinguishing features, the word you are defining). Thus, "stress" should not be defined as "an applied force which places stress on a body." In short, the class and distinguishing features must express the item's basic property.

Expanded Definition

The sentence definition of "solenoid" on page 60 would be good for a general reader who simply needs to know what a solenoid is. However, an instruction manual for mechanics or mechanical engineers would define this item in great detail (as on pages 68–70); these readers need to know what a solenoid is, how it works, and how it can be used. So the choice of length and detail in a definition of a concrete and specific term depends on the purpose of the definition and the needs of the audience.

However, the problem with defining an abstract and general word, like "condominium" or "bodily injury," is different. "Condominium," for example, is a vaguer term than "solenoid" (solenoid A is pretty much like solenoid B) because the former refers to a wide range of ownership agreements; therefore, its meaning is much more variable and needs to be spelled out.

The point is that concrete, specific terms like "diabetes," "transit," and "solenoid" often can be defined by a sentence, and will require an expanded definition only according to particular audience needs. However, terms like "disability" and "condominium" will almost always require expanded definition. The more general and abstract the term, the more likely the need for an expanded definition.

An expanded definition may be as short as one paragraph (as in defining a simple tool) or may extend to many pages (as in defining a new aerospace navigational device); sometimes the definition itself will comprise the whole report. Subject, purpose, and reader's needs govern the amount of details and the level of technicality.

The following excerpt from an automobile insurance policy defines the coverage for "bodily injury to others." Its style and detail make this definition clear to the general reader. Instead of the fine-print "legalese" seen in many policies, this definition is written in plain English.

PART 1. BODILY INJURY TO OTHERS

Under this Part, we will pay damages to people injured or killed by your auto in Massachusetts accidents. Damages are the amounts an injured person is legally entitled to collect for bodily injury through a court judgment or settlement. We will pay only if you or someone else using your auto with your consent is legally responsible for the accident. The most we will pay for injuries to any one person as a result of any one accident is $5,000. The most we will pay for injuries to two or more people as a result of any one accident is a total of $10,000. This is the most we will pay as the result of a single accident no matter how many autos or premiums are shown on the Coverage Selections page.

We will *not* pay:

1. For injuries to guest occupants of your auto.

2. For accidents outside of Massachusetts or in places in Massachusetts where the public has no right of access.

3. For injuries to any employees of the legally responsible person if they are entitled to Massachusetts workers' compensation benefits.

The law provides a special protection for anyone entitled to damages under this Part. We must pay their claims even if false statements were made when applying for this policy or your auto registration. We must also pay even if you or the legally responsible person fails to cooperate with us after the accident. We will, however, be entitled to reimbursement from the person who did not cooperate or who made any false statements.

If a claim is covered by us and also by another company authorized to sell auto insurance in Massachusetts, we will pay only our proportional share. If someone covered under this Part is using an auto he or she does not own at the time of the accident, the owner's auto insurance pays up to its limits before we pay. Then, we will pay up to the limits shown on your Coverage Selections page for any damages not covered by that insurance.

> Any payments we make to anyone or for anyone under Bodily Injury Caused By An Uninsured Auto (Part 3) or Bodily Injury Caused By An Underinsured Auto (Part 7) will reduce the amount of damages that person is entitled to recover from anyone covered under this Part.

This is the kind of writing that delivers the message, and the kind of writing you should always be doing.

EXPANDING YOUR DEFINITION

The following guidelines will help you expand your own definitions. Each of these expansion methods should be amplified by detailed description and by the use of synonyms or analogies whenever possible. Always begin an expanded definition with a formal sentence definition. In developing your expanded definition use only the expansion methods that best serve your reader's needs.

Etymology

Often, the history of a word (origin, development, and changes in meaning) sheds light on the basic properties of the item it names. For example, arbitration is the legal process of settling a dispute by obtaining the binding (obligatory) judgment of a third party. This term is derived from the Latin *arbitrari,* meaning "to examine, give judgment." The word was first used in an informal sense in 1634: "To mediate in a friendly manner in a way of arbitration." And more explicitly in 1716: "To put their differences to the Arbitration of some of their Brethren." [1] Standard college dictionaries contain some of this information, but *The Oxford English Dictionary* and various encyclopedic dictionaries of science, technology, business, etc. are your best etymological sources.

Modern technical terms are often derived from two or more traditional terms. Thus, "transceiver" is derived from "transmitter" and "receiver," and defined as "a module composed of a radio receiver and transmitter."

History and Background

The definition of highly specialized terms like "radar," "bacteriophage," "laser," or "X ray" can often be clarified through a background discussion: discovery of the item, subsequent development, method of manufacture, changing applications, and possibilities for use in exploration, medicine, etc. Specialized encyclopedias are a good source of background information.

[1] From *The Oxford English Dictionary* (New York, Oxford University Press, 1971). Used by permission.

Example

A definition containing familiar examples is very helpful. Be sure to tailor your example to your reader's level of specialized knowledge. Thus, a definition of "economic inflation," written for the general reader, could effectively use rising fuel prices as an example of higher costs per unit volume. Likewise, a definition of "clothing fashion" could be clarified by the example of changes in skirt lengths. For a more specialized reader, a definition of the mineral "borax," written for a student of ecology or chemistry, should mention its use as a cleaning agent and as a softener in detergents.

Graphic Illustration

A well-labeled diagram is also useful for clarifying a definition. The figure should be introduced by an identifying sentence: "Figure 4-1 illustrates the construction of a spark plug." If your illustration is borrowed, credit your source at the bottom-left corner of the frame. Further explanation of the figure, if needed, should *follow* the illustration. Unless an illustration occupies one full page, or more, don't place it on a separate page. Include it within the body of your definition.

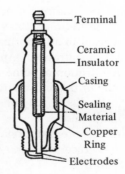

From *The McGraw-Hill Dictionary of Technical and Scientific Terms* (New York: The McGraw-Hill Book Company, 1974), p. 1388. Reprinted by permission.

FIGURE 4-1   A Spark Plug in Cross-Section

Analysis of Parts

Many items or processes consist of several parts and are best defined through detailed explanation of each part.

> The standard frame of a pitched-roof wooden dwelling is composed of floor joists, wall studs, roof rafters, and collar ties.

Psychoanalysis is an analytic and therapeutic technique consisting of four major parts: (1) free association; (2) dream interpretation; (3) analysis of repression and resistance; and (4) analysis of transference.

In discussing each part, of course, you would further define specialized terms like "floor joists," and "repression."

Comparison and Contrast

To compare is to identify similarities or likenesses; to contrast is to emphasize differences or dissimilarities. Whenever possible, compare the item with a more familiar one, or contrast it to various other models, sizes, etc.

Comparison
A cog railway, like a roller coaster, relies on a center cogwheel and a cogged center rail for transporting its cars up steep inclines.

Contrast
The X-55 fiberglass ski provides more edge control in icy conditions than its lighter but more durable aluminum counterpart, Model A-32.

Comparison and Contrast
Mediation, like arbitration, is a form of settling disputes; however, it differs from arbitration in that the decision of the mediator is not binding to the parties in the dispute.

Basic Operating Principle

Any mechanical item works according to a basic operating principle whose explanation should be part of your definition:

The Model A-23 automobile jack operates on the principle of a simple lever. The lever is a machine consisting of a rigid bar pivoted on a fixed fulcrum and used for raising heavy objects.

A clinical thermometer works on the principle of heat expansion: as the temperature of the bulb increases, the mercury inside expands and a thread rises into the hollow stem.

Even abstract items or processes can be explained this way:

Economic inflation functions according to the principle of supply and demand: if an item or service is in short supply, its price increases in proportion to its demand; this principle is evidenced by the effect of the recent United States grain sales to the Soviet Union.

Special Materials or Conditions Required

Some items and processes are highly sensitive or volatile. These may require special materials, conditions, or handling. A detailed definition should include this important information.

> Fermentation is the chemical reaction that splits complex compounds into simpler substances (as when yeast converts sugar to carbon dioxide and alcohol). This process has several special requirements: (1) a causative agent such as yeast; (2) a controlled PH (acid-base balance); (3) air-tight and sterilized containers; and (4) a narrow temperature range.

In order to obtain quality beer, the prospective home brewer needs to know all of these requirements. More abstract subjects may also be defined in terms of their special conditions.

> To be held guilty of libel, a person must have defamed the character of another through written or pictorial statements.

APPLYING THE STEPS

Each of the following expanded definitions, aimed at the general reader, uses several methods of amplification. Study them carefully. As a study aid, the specific expansion methods are identified in the right margin. Notice that each definition, like a good essay, is unified and coherent: each paragraph is developed around a central idea and logically connected to other paragraphs. The discussions are readable and easy to follow, with graphic illustrations incorporated into the text. Transitional words and phrases underscore the logical connection between related ideas.

EXPANDED DEFINITION
OF "SOLENOID"

A solenoid is an electrically energized coil that forms an electromagnet capable of performing various mechanical functions. The term, "solenoid," is derived from the word, "sole," which in reference to electrical equipment means "a part of," or "contained inside, or with, other electrical equipment." The Greek word *solenoides,* means "channel," or "shaped like a pipe."

Formal sentence definition

Etymology

A simple, plunger-type solenoid consists of a coil of wire attached to an electrical source, and an iron rod that passes in and out of the coil at right angles to the spiral. A spring holds the bar outside the coil when the current is deenergized, as shown in Figure 1.

Description and analysis of parts

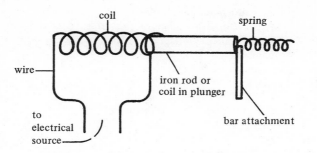

FIGURE 1   Lateral Diagram of a Plunger-Type Solenoid

When the coil receives electrical current, it becomes
a magnet and thus draws the iron bar inside, along
the length of its cylindrical center. With a lever attached to its end, the bar can transform electrical
energy into mechanical force. The amount of mechanical force produced is determined by the product of the number of turns in the coil, the strength
of the exciting current, and the magnetic conductiv-
ity of the iron rod.

    The plunger-type solenoid, shown in Figure 1,
is commonly used in the starter motor of an automobile engine. It is 4½ inches long and 2 inches in
diameter, with a steel casing attached to the casing
of the starter motor. A linkage (pivoting lever) is
attached at one end to the iron rod of the solenoid,
and at the other end to the drive gear of the starter,
as shown in Figure 2. When the ignition key is
turned, current from the battery is supplied to the
solenoid coil and the iron rod is drawn inside the

Graphic illustration

Special conditions
and principle of
operation

Example and analysis
of parts

Explanation of
illustration

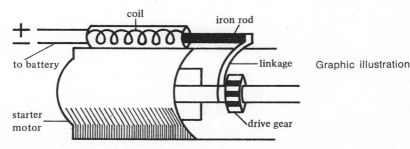

FIGURE 2   Lateral Diagram of Solenoid and Starter-
Motor Assembly

Graphic illustration

coil, thereby shifting the attached linkage. The linkage, in turn, engages the drive gear, activated by the starter motor, with the flywheel (the main rotating gear of the engine).

Because of the many uses of the solenoid, its size varies according to the amount of work it must do. Therefore, a small solenoid will have a small wire coil, hence a weak magnetic field. The larger the coil, the stronger the magnetic field; in this case, the rod in the solenoid is capable of doing harder work. It is easy to understand that an electronic lock for a standard door would require a much smaller solenoid than one for a large bank vault.

Comparison of sizes and applications

THE INTRAUTERINE DEVICE: AN EXPANDED DEFINITION

The intrauterine device, or IUD, is a small plastic (occasionally metal) device that is placed semi-permanently inside the uterus by a trained person to prevent conception. The term is derived from the Latin *intra*, meaning "inside or within," and the Latin and French *uterus*, meaning "womb."

Formal sentence definition

Etymology

A primitive type of IUD has been used in camels for centuries. In the Middle East, camel herders prepared for crossing the desert by inserting smooth pebbles, the size of olive pits, into the uteri of their camels to prevent inopportune pregnancies.

History and background

Manufactured IUDs have been used in women for about one century. The first devices were metal prongs placed inside the uterus, with a stem and button-like disk outside the cervix. Heavy bleeding and infection were common side effects; therefore, the use of this device was soon discontinued.

In 1925 Dr. Ernst Graefenburg of Berlin theorized that the portion of the IUD outside of the cervix provided a ladder for bacteria, so he developed a device contained entirely within the uterus. Graefenburg Rings, made of silkworm gut and silver wire, were about the size of a nickel. But even with the IUD contained entirely within the uterus, complications (primarily infection) developed. As a result, the IUD was largely condemned by the medical world.

In 1958 the first open-ended IUD was designed at Mt. Sinai hospital in New York. This type had two major advantages: (1) The open-ended device

Contrast

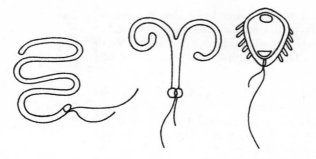

Graphic illustration

FIGURE 1   From Left to Right: Lippes' Loop, Saf-T-
Coil, and Dalkon Shield in Side View

could be stretched into a straight line and loaded
into a soda straw-like inducer for insertion; this
process caused less pain because the cervix required
little dilation. After insertion, the device regained its
original spiral form. (2) Polyethylene (fabricated
plastic), of which the device was made, was less inflammatory than metal.

The type of IUD most commonly used today is
called Lippes' Loop. It follows the construction of
the open-ended device. Other IUDs, the Saf-T-Coil
and the Dalkon Shield, are also used. All three are
shown in Figure 1. Lippes' Loop has the lowest ex-
pulsion rate of the three devices.   Comparison

The IUD is second to the birth-control pill in
effectiveness, being about 95 to 97 percent dependable in preventing conception. Women who have not   Contrast
had children are more likely to experience pain and
difficulties with retaining the device; women who
have given birth have fewer problems because of the
size and elasticity of the uterus.

No one is yet sure exactly how the IUD works to   Principle of
prevent pregnancy. There are three current theories: operation

1. The IUD touching the uterine wall at several
points irritates the lining and keeps it from developing properly. Thus, the fertilized egg cannot find a
good place to implant.

2. The IUD speeds up the muscular contractions   Contrast
that move the egg down the fallopian tube to the
uterus. The egg's normal journey of four to five days
allows the uterine lining to develop; however, if the
egg reaches the uterus too soon, the lining will not
be ready for implantation.

3. The most recent theory holds that the uterine wall responds to the foreign body by sending out macrophages (huge white blood cells) which try to destroy the IUD; failing that, they devour the egg or sperm or both.

Contrast

This form of birth control has advantages and disadvantages. Its primary advantage is convenience. Once the IUD has been inserted it only requires a periodic check of the length of the string protruding from the cervix. Checking the string allows the woman to determine if the IUD is still in the correct position. Also, there is no pill to remember to take every day and no fussing with other birth control devices. Primary disadvantages are an increase in menstrual flow and more frequent cramps.

Contrast

The following conditions prevent a woman from using an IUD: endometriosis (inflamed uterine lining), venereal disease, any vaginal or uterine infection, pelvic inflammatory disease, exceedingly small uterus, and an excessively heavy menstrual flow or cramping.

Special conditions

PLACING DEFINITIONS IN YOUR REPORT

Good definitions clarify your message; however, if not carefully placed, they can interrupt the orderly flow of information. To avoid this threat to coherence, observe the following suggestions for placement.

Parenthetical Definitions

If you have only a few informal definitions, place them in parentheses immediately following the respective terms. Several of these definitions per page will be disruptive and should be placed elsewhere. You can rewrite them as formal sentence definitions and place them in a "Definitions" section of your report introduction, or place them, in alphabetical order, within a glossary (as shown in Chapter 8).

Sentence Definitions

If your formal definitions are few, place them in a "Definitions" section of your report introduction. Otherwise, place them in a glossary. Any definitions of terms in the report's title belong in your report introduction.

Expanded Definitions

Place expanded formal definitions in one of three areas:

1. If the definition is essential to the reader's understanding of the *entire content* of the report, place it within your report introduction. For instance, a report titled "The Effects of Aerosol Spray on the Earth's Ozone Shield" would require expanded definitions of "aerosol" and "ozone" early in the report.

2. When the definition clarifies a major part of your discussion, place it in the related section of your report. In a report titled "How Advertising Influences Consumer Habits," "operant conditioning" might form a major topic area of the report; this term should then be defined early in the appropriate section. Too many expanded definitions *within* a report, however, can be disruptive.

3. If the definition is an aid to understanding, but serves as a *secondary* reference, it belongs in an appendix (see Chapter 8). For example, an investigative report on fire safety measures in a local public building might include an expanded definition of "smoke detectors" in an appendix.

Definitions placed in footnotes are distracting and should be used rarely. In all cases, place your definitions so that they make the reader's task as easy as possible.

CHAPTER SUMMARY

Giving the precise meanings of your terms is an important step in achieving clarity. Every field has its own specialized language that needs to be translated for general readers. Also, many terms whose meanings seem clear — like "guarantee" or "disability" — have different meanings in different contexts. Therefore, you need to specify your meaning so that both you and your reader will understand what you are talking about. Analyze your subject, purpose, and audience carefully in deciding when to use definitions and how long to make them. Sometimes a few words in parentheses will be enough; at other times you may need a full-sentence definition or an expanded definition, which could be several pages long. Regardless of length, write your definition in plain English, and be sure that it expresses the basic properties of the term without implying any judgment on your part.

When you write a parenthetical definition (the simplest type), place a synonym or explanatory phrase, usually in parentheses, right after the word you are defining. When writing a sentence definition, indicate the term, the class in which the item it names belongs, and the features that distinguish the item from all others in its class. When writing an expanded definition, discuss your subject from as many of the following approaches as you can use to clarify its meaning:

1. Etymology, or history, of the word.
2. History and background of the item.
3. Familiar examples of the item or process.
4. Detailed diagrams with all parts labeled.
5. Detailed explanation of the various parts of the item.
6. Comparison of the item with similar ones or contrast with dissimilar ones to emphasize differences.
7. The basic principle by which the item operates.
8. Special materials or conditions required.

Place definitions where they will do the most good in your report. Depending on the length and number of your definitions and their role in your report, you might place them in parentheses after the word defined, in a special "definitions" section of your introduction, in a glossary, at appropriate points within your discussion, or in an appendix.

REVISION CHECKLIST

Use this list to check the accuracy and correctness of your definitions.

1. Have you chosen the type of definition (parenthetical, sentence, expanded) best suited to your subject, purpose, and reader's needs?
2. In defining a concrete and specific term (like "transit" or "ophthalmoscope") have you given the reader enough details?
3. In defining an abstract and general term (like "condominium" or "partnership") have you specified its meaning in the context where you are using it?
4. Is your definition written in plain English?
5. Does it clearly express the basic properties of the item it defines (the irreducible features the item must possess in order to be what it is)?
6. Is your definition objective (free of any implied judgments)?
7. For a sentence definition, have you followed the term-class-distinguishing features structure?
8. For an expanded definition, have you used all applicable expansion techniques (etymology, history and background, examples, graphic illustrations, analysis of parts, comparison and contrast, basic operating principle, specific materials or conditions required)?
9. Is your expanded definition a logical unit?
10. Are there enough transitions between related ideas?
11. Is it free of wordiness and needless details?
12. Is it written in correct English (spelling, mechanics, and usage, as discussed in Appendix A)?

13. Have you placed your definition in the best location to achieve its purpose in your report?

Now list those elements of your definition that need improvement.

EXERCISES

1. In a three-paragraph essay discuss the differences among parenthetical, sentence, and expanded definitions, citing specific examples where each would be used.

2. In complete sentences identify the basic property of each of the following items:

desk	lamp	camel
bicycle	ski	bridge
wood stove	subway	guitar string
elevator	bed	clock

3. Adequate formal sentence definitions require precise classification and detailed differentiation. Tell whether you think each of the following definitions is adequate for a general reader. Rewrite those which seem inadequate. If necessary, consult dictionaries and specialized encyclopedias. Discuss your revision in class.

   a. A bicycle is a vehicle with two wheels.
   b. A transistor is a device used in transistorized electronic equipment.
   c. Surfing is when one rides a wave to shore while standing on a board specifically designed for buoyancy and balance.
   d. Bubonic plague is caused by an organism known as *pasteurella pestis*.
   e. Mace is a chemical aerosol spray used by the police.
   f. A geiger counter measures radioactivity.
   g. A cactus is a succulent.
   h. In law, an indictment is a criminal charge against a defendant.
   i. A prune is a kind of plum.
   j. Friction is a force between two bodies.
   k. Luffing is what happens when one sails into the wind.
   l. A frame is an important part of a bicycle.
   m. Hypoglycemia is a medical term.
   n. An hourglass is a device used for measuring intervals of time.
   o. A computer is a machine that handles information with amazing speed.
   p. A Ferrari is the best car in the world.
   q. To meditate is to exercise mental faculties in thought.

4. Think of a situation from your own experience in which someone (employer, instructor, parent, friend) failed to define a term adequately (as in giving instructions or an assignment) and caused you to misunderstand the message. Describe the situation and its consequences in two or three paragraphs.

5. *In class:* Without a dictionary, write down as many different sentence definitions for "stock" as you can think of. Compare your definitions with those of other class members and with those in a standard college dictionary. List five other terms with several meanings.

6. Both standard college dictionaries and specialized encyclopedias contain definitions. Standard dictionaries, however, define a word for the general reader, whereas specialized reference books provide definitions for the specialist. Choose an item in your major field and write the meaning as found (1) in a standard dictionary and (2) in a technical reference book. For the technical definition, label each expansion method carefully on a xerox copy that you have made. Finally, rewrite the specialized definition so that it can be understood by a general reader.

7. Using reference books when necessary, write sentence definitions for the following terms or for selected terms from your major field. In order to express the basic properties of each item clearly, be sure to narrow your classification and to name its distinguishing features.

summons	economic inflation	pipette
generator	computer	calculator
dewpoint	golf club	t-square
clinical thermometer	contract	torque wrench
capitalism	hammer	wine vintage
marsh	frisbee	gourmet
economic recession	water table	editorial

8. Select an item or concept from the list in question 7, from your major field, or from an area of interest. Begin with a sentence definition of the term and then write a 300- to 500-word expanded definition for a general reading audience. Use the sample definitions in this chapter as models. Leave a three-inch margin on the left side of your page in order to list your specific methods of expansion.

9. *In class:* Study the following student-written definition of "fashion" and identify the expansion methods used. The possibilities are: etymology, history and background, example, graphic illustration, analysis of parts, comparison and contrast, basic operating principle, special materials or conditions required, description, synonym, and analogy. Revise any section that seems unclear to the general reader. Should any other methods of expansion have been used in this definition?

AN EXPANDED DEFINITION OF "FASHION"

Fashion is the prevailing custom of dress or behavior in a given time period. The term is derived from the Latin *factio,* meaning "party," "sect," or "faction" and literally meaning "persons acting together." According to the *Oxford English Dictionary,* the term was used in reference to clothing as early as 1529: "Somtyme cappe; somtyme hoode; nowe the Frenshe fasshyon, nowe the Spanyshe fasshyon." The predominant social sense of fashion arose early in the sixteenth century in relation to various types of clothing.

"Style" should not be used interchangeably with "fashion." Styles make up fashion. For example, the knee-length skirt style is in fashion, as are leather coats. The miniskirt is a style that was in fashion in the 1960s, but not today.

Fashion reflects the events, environment, and values of its time. It is influenced by wars, conquests, laws, the arts, and personalities. For example, the folds of the Grecian tunic were influenced by the fluted (having parallel grooves) columns of Greek architecture. The world-conquering Romans displayed their wealth in colorful togas.

Personalities have had a great effect on fashion ever since the days when laws differentiating nobles, peasants, and tradesmen were eliminated, thereby making it possible for all classes of society to dress more or less alike. In 1960–61 the "Jackie Kennedy look" spread so far and fast that within weeks after the election most fashion sketches in magazines and newspapers looked like the First Lady.

Laws and regulations have also had their effect on fashion. For example, Regulation L-85 during World War II placed limitations on the amount of cloth that could be used in making certain types of clothing. Early New England laws restrained women from wearing more costly clothing than their husbands could afford.

Changes in fashion occur rapidly in our own age; at the height of the popularity of one style, silhouette, or color there are often indications of another. However, no women's fashion succeeds until women are ready to accept it.

5

Dividing
in Order
to Organize

CHAPTER GOALS

DEFINITIONS

USING PARTITION AND CLASSIFICATION

GUIDELINES FOR PARTITION
  Apply Partition to a Single Item
  Make the Partition Complete and
    Exclusive
  Make Your Division Consistent with
    Your Purpose
  Subdivide as Far as Necessary
  Follow a Logical Sequence
  Make All Parts of Equal Rank Parallel
  Make Sure That Parts Do Not Overlap
  Use Precise Units of Measurement
  Choose the Clearest Format

GUIDELINES FOR CLASSIFICATION
  Apply Classification to a Group of Items
  Make Your Classification Complete,
    Exclusive, and Inclusive
  Limit Your Classification to Suit Your
    Purpose
  Choose Bases of Comparison Consistent
    with Your Purpose
  Express All Bases in Precise and
    Objective Terms
  Make All Categories of Equal Rank
    Parallel
  Make Sure That Categories Do Not
    Overlap
  Choose the Clearest Format

APPLYING THE TECHNIQUES OF
  DIVISION

CHAPTER SUMMARY

REVISION CHECKLIST

EXERCISES

CHAPTER GOALS

Upon completing this chapter you will know:

- The meaning and purpose of two logical systems of division, partition and classification.
- How to use partition to divide a single thing into its parts.
- How to use classification to divide a group of things into smaller classes.
- How to evaluate a system of partition or classification.

DEFINITIONS

Sometimes we have to divide a single thing into its parts in order to make sense out of it. At other times we have to divide an assortment of things into classes in order to sort them out. Partition and classification are the techniques we use to make these divisions. The two activities divide for different purposes: *partition* identifies the parts of a single item; *classification* creates categories for sorting similar items.

We use partition and classification almost every day. Assume, for instance, that you are shopping for a refrigerator. If you are mechanically inclined, you will probably begin by thinking about the major parts that make up a refrigerator: a storage compartment, a cooling element, a motor, insulation, and the exterior casing. With individual parts identified, you can now ask questions about them to determine the efficiency or quality of each part in different kinds of refrigerators. You have partitioned the refrigerator into its component parts.

You then shop at five different stores and come home with a list of twenty refrigerators that seem to be built from high quality parts. You now try to

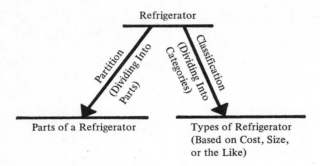

FIGURE 5-1   The Two Kinds of Division

make sense out of your list by grouping items according to certain characteristics. First, you divide your list into three classes according to size in cubic feet of capacity: small refrigerators, middle-sized refrigerators, and large refrigerators. But size is not the only concern. You want economy too. So you group the refrigerators according to cost. Or you might classify them according to color, weight, and so on, depending on your purpose.

Figure 5-1 illustrates the two kinds of division. These two kinds of division can also be used for more abstract things. You might partition a day into daytime and nighttime or into morning, afternoon, and evening. Or, for other purposes, you may want to classify days, sorting them out as good days and bad days, or profitable days and unprofitable days, and so on.

Partition is always concerned with one object. Its purpose is to systematically separate that whole object into its parts, pieces, or sections. Classification is always concerned with an assortment of objects which have some similarities. Its purpose is to group these objects in a systematic way.

USING PARTITION AND CLASSIFICATION

Whether you choose to use partition or classification in a particular situation clearly depends on the nature of your subject. If you must describe a golf club, for example, you have little choice but to begin by partitioning it into its major parts: handle, shaft, and head. But if someone has unexpectedly given you 228 record albums, which you want to arrange in some way so that you can easily locate the particular record you want, partition will not help you. You will have to classify the records by dividing the pile into smaller categories. You might want to classify them as classical, jazz, rock, and miscellaneous. Or you might classify them according to your likes and dislikes.

But whether you choose to apply partition or classification can also depend on your purpose. An architect, for example, called upon to design a library, will think almost entirely in terms of partition. Once she has defined the large enclosed area that is needed, she must identify the parts into which that space must be divided: the reference area, reading areas, storage areas, check-out facilities, and office space. In some kinds of libraries she might consider providing space for special groups of users (reading areas for children, for example). In very large libraries she might need to carry the division further into specialized kinds of space (such as highly secure areas for rare manuscripts or special collections, or areas with special acoustic provisions for listening to recorded materials). But however simple or complex her problem, she is concerned at this point only with the appropriate division of *space*. She does not have to worry about how the library will classify its books and other material.

But classification is one of the library staff's main problems. The purpose of a library is not only to store books and other forms of information, but above all to make it retrievable. To allow us to find a particular book or item, the thousands or millions of books stored in the library must be arranged in logical categories. That becomes possible only if the books are carefully classified.

The close examination of any complex problem almost inevitably requires the use of both partition and classification. If, for example, you are hired as the manager of a new supermarket, you must first partition the whole area constituting the market into its functional parts to ensure the efficiency of each part.

> display and shopping area
> receiving and storage area
> meat refrigeration and preparation area
> check-out area
> small office area

Next, you will need to sort out your inventory by dividing the thousands of items into smaller groups or classes according to their similarities, for example:

> frozen foods
> dairy products
> meat, fish, and poultry
> pet foods
> fruits and vegetables
> paper products
> canned goods
> beverages
> baked goods
> cleaning products

In turn, you will divide each of these sections even further. You might divide "meat, fish, and poultry," for instance, into three smaller groups.

> Beef
> Pork
> Lamb

Under these headings you will group the various cuts of meat in each category. And you might carry the division further for certain meat products, like types of ground beef:

> Regular
> Lean
> Extra Lean
> Diet Lean

This kind of division continues until you have enough categories or classes to sort the hundreds of crates and cartons of inventory that sit in your receiving and storage area. On the one hand, you have divided your store into its parts. On the other hand, you have divided your inventory into classes in order to sort out the items. You have used both partition and classification.

Whether you are dividing by partition or classification, you need to follow certain guidelines so that your division will make sense.

GUIDELINES FOR PARTITION

Apply Partition to a Single Item

Table 5-1 shows how a single item can be divided. Notice that the component nutrients add up to 100 percent; the total egg equals the sum of its parts.

TABLE 5-1 Approximate Composition of a Whole Goose Egg

Component	Percentage
Shell	14.0
Water	60.0
Protein	13.0
Fat	12.0
Ash	1.0

Make Your Partition Complete and Exclusive

Include *all parts* of the item. If you have omitted one or more parts for a good reason, say so in your title ("The Exterior Parts of a Typewriter"). On the other hand, be sure that each part belongs to the item. For instance, do not include "typewriter ribbon" in your partition of the exterior of a typewriter.

Make Your Division Consistent with Your Purpose

Most things can be divided in different ways for different purposes. You might divide an apple into the meat, skin, and core, but that division is useless to the nutritionist who wants to know the food value of an apple and is not interested in the fact that it has a core. You could divide a house in at least three different ways: (1) on the basis of the rooms it comprises; (2) on the basis of the materials used in construction; and (3) on the basis of the steps required to build it. The sum of the parts in each of these divisions equals 100 percent of the house. However, the basis you choose will depend on your purpose. To interest a prospective buyer you might choose option 1; to provide cost or materials specifications you would likely choose option 2; to give instructions to the do-it-yourselfer you would choose option 3. Sometimes, in fact, you might need two or more partitions of the same item.

Let your title promise what the partition will deliver: "The Jones House, Partitioned According to Materials for Construction." Under this title, you would include every item, from nails to plumbing fixtures. If your purpose is less ambitious, limit your title: "Concrete Materials," "Electrical Materials," or the like.

Subdivide as Far as Necessary

Subdivide as much as you need to show what makes up the item. This textbook, for instance, is divided into its chapters. In turn, each chapter is subdivided into major topics such as "Guidelines for Partition." Major topics are again divided into minor topics such as "Apply Partition to a Single Item," and so on.

Follow a Logical Sequence

Most items have a particular logic of organization that determines the order for listing their parts. The division of a basic house, for example, most logically follows a *spatial sequence* — the foundation, the floor, the frame, the siding, and the roof — the sequence in which the parts are arranged. A progress report (a partition of your activity during a certain time period) would best proceed in *chronological sequence* — from earliest to latest. A partition of your monthly budget might proceed on a descending scale of the *order of importance* of each expenditure. A problem can be analyzed by dividing it into its *causes and their effects.* Other specific orders of development are discussed in Chapter 6 and Appendix A.

Make All Parts of Equal Rank Parallel

All parts at any one level of division (major parts, minor parts, subparts, etc.) are considered equal in rank. Therefore, list them in equal or parallel grammatical form.

> A deed contains the following seven items:
>
> 1. The buyer and seller must be identified.
> 2. A granting clause.
> 3. Consideration, not necessarily money, must be mentioned.
> 4. An explanation of the rights being transferred
> 5. A full-length description of the property
> 6. Proper execution, signature, seals, and delivery
> 7. It must be properly recorded in the county where the property lies.

Here, items 1, 3, and 7 are not parallel to the others; they are expressed as complete sentences, whereas the others are expressed as phrases. Therefore, items 1, 3, and 7 should be revised to read as follows:

> 1. Identification of buyer and seller
> 3. Mention of consideration, not necessarily money
> 7. Proper recording in the county where the property lies

Alternatively, items 2, 4, 5, and 6 could be revised as complete sentences.

Make Sure That Parts Do Not Overlap

The logic of division requires that each item be exclusive of all others. Consider this partition of the executive branch of a corporation.

> chairman of the board
> board of directors
> president
> vice-president
> administrative officers

These parts overlap because each of the first four positions may be listed under the heading "administrative officers."

Use Precise Units of Measurement

If the parts are in percentages, pounds, feet or the like, say so, as in Table 5-2.

TABLE 5-2   The Parts of a Selected Multivitamin

Ingredient	Quantity
Vitamin A	15 International Units
Vitamin E	15 International Units
Vitamin C	60 mg.
Folic Acid	0.4 mg.
Vitamin B_1	1.5 mg.
Vitamin B_2	1.7 mg.
Niacin	20 mg.
Vitamin B_{16}	2 mg.
Vitamin B_{12}	25 micrograms
Vitamin D	400 International Units
Iron	18 mg.

Choose the Clearest Format

Select the best format for your partition: either a prose discussion, a list (as in an outline), a table, or a chart. Assume, for instance, that you need to partition the federal budget in two ways: in terms of sources of income and types of expenditure. Here is how your prose version might read:

> The federal budget dollar for fiscal year 1974 can be divided into two broad categories: sources and expenditures. Income sources are broken down as follows: Individual income tax provided $0.42 of every dollar of federal income. Social insurance taxes and contributions provided $0.29, whereas corporation income taxes provided $0.14. The smaller income sources included excise taxes ($0.06), borrowing ($0.05), and miscellaneous sources ($0.04).
>
> The greatest federal expenditure was in human resources, which consumed $0.47 of every federal dollar. Next was national defense, requiring $0.30. Smaller expenditures were for physical resources ($0.10), interest ($0.07), and miscellaneous spending ($0.06).

With an enumerative list like this, a prose discussion can be difficult to follow. Table 5-3 shows the same division in another format. Depending on the writer's purpose, any of the items in the table could be partitioned further.

TABLE 5-3   A Partition of the Federal Budget Dollar for Fiscal Year 1974

Where It Comes From	Amount
Individual income taxes	$0.42
Social insurance taxes and contributions	0.29
Corporations income taxes	0.14
Excise taxes	0.06
Borrowing	0.05
Other	ˊ0.04

Where It Will Go	Amount
Human resources	$0.47
National defense	0.30
Physical resources	0.10
Interest	0.07
Other	0.06

Notice again that all items add up to 100 percent. Figure 5-2 shows pie-chart versions of the same data. For this partition, the pie chart seems to be the most effective format because it dramatizes the vast differences in sources of income and types of expenditure. See Chapter 9 for detailed instructions on composing various types of visual aids.

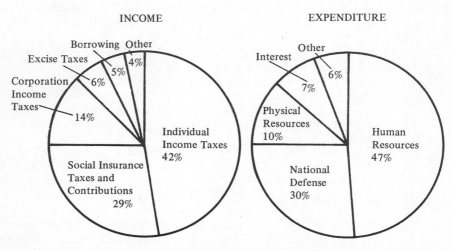

FIGURE 5-2   A Partition of the Federal Budget Dollar for Fiscal Year 1974

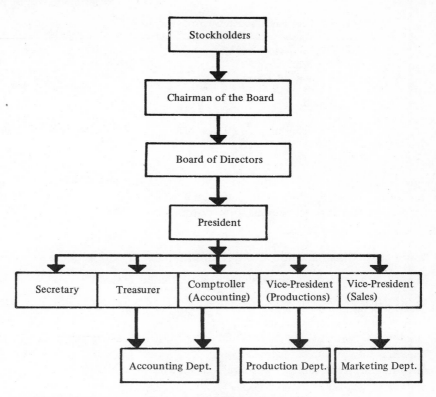

FIGURE 5-3   The Organizational Chart of a Basic Corporation

Different subjects for partition lend themselves to different formats. For instance, a subject whose parts are ranked in order of occurrence might best be partitioned as a flow-chart. A subject whose parts are ranked in order of importance might call for an organizational chart as in Figure 5-3.

GUIDELINES FOR CLASSIFICATION

Apply Classification to a Group of Items

Assume that you have studied a whole range of foods and have decided to divide the group into three classes: fat sources, starch sources, and protein sources. You might classify the foods that you have designated as protein

TABLE 5-4   Selected Protein Sources

Brewer's yeast	Sunflower (seed)
Soybean (seed)	Whole egg
Groundnut (peanut)	Coconut
Cottonseed	Cow's milk (whole)
Sesame	Potato

Source: Adapted from Johnson and Peterson, *Encyclopedia of Food Technology*, p. 722. Used by permission of AVI Publishing Company.

sources as a table (see Table 5-4). Notice that the classification is limited by the term "selected." Notice also that the whole egg partitioned in Table 5-1 is here one item in the classification system.

Make Your Classification Complete, Exclusive, and Inclusive

List *all items* that logically belong to a particular class.

> *Red Meats*
>
> Pork
> Lamb
> Beef

Also, be sure that each item belongs in that particular class.

> *Red Meats*
>
> Pork
> Lamb
> Beef
> Frozen meats

The last item, "frozen meats," does not belong to the class "red meats." It is a function of temperature, not a type of meat. This system also overlaps because all three types of meats might be included in the category "frozen."

Finally, divide the assortment into enough classes to contain every item you are sorting out. A division of red meats into pork and beef, for example, would not be inclusive because lamb products (chops, legs, ribs, etc.) would have no place in which to be grouped.

Limit Your Classification to Suit Your Purpose

Your classification becomes more specific and useful as you limit its focus. For instance, a résumé classification labeled "Work Experience" is more meaningful than one labeled "Experience." The classification "Vegetables" would require a list of every vegetable ever grown. Depending on your purpose, you might want to limit the classification to "Vegetables Sold by Our Food Co-op," "Canned Vegetables," "Green Vegetables," or another precise designation. Let your title promise what you will deliver.

Choose Bases of Comparison Consistent with Your Purpose

After limiting your classification you may need to select one or more bases by which to compare and contrast the items in your list. For example, in planning a high-protein diet, you would choose this basis: "Green Vegetables Classified on the Basis of Their Protein Content." Or you might choose several bases: protein content, caloric content, chlorophyll content, etc. A classification that includes one or more bases is called a formal classification. Table 5-5 gives the same material as Table 5-4, but presented as a formal classification. Because only one basis of comparison is used here, the items are arranged in a specific order of presentation — in this case, a descending order.

Your purpose in classifying some types of food, however, may be to achieve a healthful diet; therefore, you would arrange your items according to several bases of nutrient content — protein, fat, iron, vitamins, etc. — all in a combined table such as Table 5-6. Here the bases are listed in the left vertical column so that the table can be contained within the width of one page.

TABLE 5-5   Selected Protein Sources Classified in Descending Order of Protein Content

Source	Protein (gm/100)
Brewer's yeast	38.8
Soybean (seed)	38.0
Groundnut (peanut)	25.6
Cottonseed	20.2
Sesame	18.1
Sunflower (seed)	12.6
Whole egg	12.4
Coconut	6.6
Cow's milk (whole)	3.5
Potato	2.0

Source: Adapted from Johnson and Peterson, *Encyclopedia of Food Technology*, p. 722. Used by permission of AVI Publishing Company.

TABLE 5-6   Nutrient Content of Red Meats, Poultry, and Fish

	Chicken	Nonfatty Fish	Herring	Beef	Lamb	Pork
		Per Ounce (28.35 gm) Raw Meat				
Protein (gm)	5.9	4.5	4.5	4.2	3.7	3.4
Fat (gm)	1.9	0.1	4.0	8.0	8.8	11.4
Calories (kcal)	41	19	54	89	94	116
Calcium (mg)	3	1	28	3	3	3
Iron (mg)	0.4	0.3	0.4	1.1	0.6	0.3
Vitamin D (mg)	—	—	6.38	—	—	—
Vitamin A (mg)	—	—	13	—	—	—
Vitamin B_1 (mg)	0.01	0.02	0.01	0.02	0.04	0.28
Vitamin B_2 (mg)	0.05	0.03	0.09	0.06	0.07	0.06
Niacin (mg)	1.7	0.8	1.0	1.4	1.4	1.4
Pantothenic acid (mg)	0.19	0.06	0.28	0.11	0.14	0.17
Vitamin B_6 (mg)	0.28	0.06	0.13	0.08	0.09	0.14
Biotin (mg)	2.83	2.83	x	0.85	0.85	1.1
Folic acid (mg)	0.85	14.1	x	2.83	0.85	0.85
Vitamin B_{12} (mg)	x	0.28	2.83	0.56	0.56	0.56
Vitamin E (mg)	0.06	x	x	0.17	0.23	0.19

Source: Johnson and Peterson, *Encyclopedia of Food Technology*, p. 626. Used by permission of AVI Publishing Company.
"—" indicates nutrient not present.
"x" indicates content not yet determined.

Express All Bases in Precise and Objective Terms

The bases you use must express specific similarities and differences; vague terms of assessment are useless. Modifiers such as "long," "nice," "heavy," "good," and "strong" are not specific enough. A classification titled "Good Vegetables" is meaningless unless "good" can be defined clearly and measured — with units of nutritional value expressed in grams, milligrams, international units, or the like.

Make All Categories of Equal Rank Parallel

Consider these class headings:

Frozen Foods   *Dried Foods*   *Foods That Are Smoked*

This system is not parallel unless the last heading is revised to read "Smoked Foods."

Make Sure That Categories Do Not Overlap

Consider these headings:

Pork   *Beef*   *Ham*   *Lamb*

The headings overlap because ham is not an exclusive category; it is only a type of pork product.

Choose the Clearest Format

Select the best format for your classification: either a prose discussion, a list (as in an outline), a table, or a graph. Remember that you have two purposes in classifying: (1) to help you organize your material, and (2) to save your reader time and effort in interpreting data. Therefore, "uncomplicate" complex information by choosing the format that will be easiest to interpret. Assume, for instance, that you are classifying types of red meat, poultry, and fish on the basis of caloric content. A prose version might read:

> Red meats, poultry, and fish have widely differing caloric contents. Among red meats, pork is the highest in calories, with 116 kilocalories per ounce of raw meat. Next in caloric content are the red meats, lamb and beef, containing 94 and 89 kilocalories per ounce. Herring follows red meats with 54 kilocalories per ounce. Slightly lower is chicken, with 41 kilocalories per ounce. Finally, nonfatty fish, with 19 kilocalories per ounce, provides the least calories of all six classes.

This prose version is tedious and more difficult to interpret than a table or graph version. To express these data in a table, follow the format shown in Table 5-5. Figure 5-4 shows a bar graph of the same data.

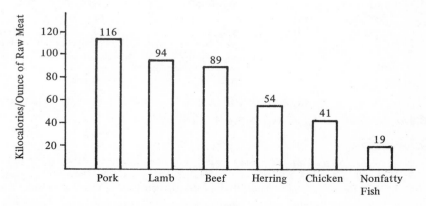

FIGURE 5-4   The Caloric Content of Red Meats, Poultry, and Fish

Sometimes, the bases in a classification cannot be expressed in simple units of measurement or by single words. Because the following classification contains detailed explanations of the various responsibilities held by dieticians, it is cast in a prose format.

DIETICIANS:
A CLASSIFICATION

A dietician is a trained professional responsible for the nutritional care of individuals and groups. This person holds a bachelor's degree from an accredited college or university, with a major in food, nutrition, or institution management. After graduation, the dietician completes an approved internship. To qualify for the title of Registered Dietician, one must meet all requirements for membership in the American Dietetics Association, pass the registration examination, and continually satisfy requirements for further education.

Dieticians work in several capacities. The three major specialties in this field are in dietetics administration, therapeutic dietetics, and consultant dietetics.

The administrative dietician is a member of the management team in an organization and is in charge of the food service systems. This person has direct authority and responsibility for the entire food service operation.

The therapeutic dietician usually works in a hospital or clinic and plans modified menus for the patients' needs as determined by the physicians. He or she cooperates and participates in research and surveys on food and nutrition in the hospital, institution, or community.

Consultant dieticians work with a health-care team to determine the nutritional requirements of patients. They provide guidance for the food service and dietetic personnel and may also evaluate their performance. In addition, they may develop budget proposals and recommend specific procedures for cost control. The consultant dietician may be shared by two or more small hospitals or clinics.

In any of these roles, the dietician applies the science and art of human nutrition to help people select the best foods in health and in disease.

Often, a visual presentation will be accompanied by a prose explanation, as shown by Table 5-7 and the text accompanying it.

Although Table 5-7 shows that some correlation exists between population level and wholesale trade among counties in our state, several inconsistencies can be noted. The most obvious inconsistency is found in comparing Medford and Latah Counties in terms of population and wholesale trade. Both have a higher-than-average ratio of population to trade for the following reasons: (1) Gotham, our state's major trade center, is located in Latah County; and (2) Medford County encompasses the Route 138 industrial belt, which creates a large population with a trade center that relies on Gotham.

Of the two smallest counties, Baker and Franklin, it appears that Franklin is better prepared to handle business-cycle fluctuations and thereby minimize deficits.

Although population level has some effect on wholesale trade in respective counties, the major determinant seems to be the location of the county.

TABLE 5-7　Counties in Our State Classified According to Population and Amount of Wholesale Trade, as of April 5, 1978

County	Population	Wholesale Trade in Dollars
Medford	1,499,386	3,841,108
Latah	821,262	5,134,250
Burns	721,814	732,816
Elrin	721,418	821,914
Worly	693,461	2,406,381
Nampa	502,016	724,572
Brighton	463,982	436,800
Stebbins	365,741	243,921
Brown	199,628	101,627
Dorin	156,524	35,996
Argot	111,428	41,824
Hollins	72,141	33,671
Baker	8,425	(−2,610)
Franklin	4,960	(−876)

Source: author.

APPLYING THE TECHNIQUES OF DIVISION

The bookkeeping form in Figure 5-5 typifies the organized records that are vital to the continued success of any business. Total monthly spending is partitioned into individual expenditures in the left column. In the right columns, expenses are sorted under eight general classes: ink, plates, films, and so on. Expenditures in each class are then totaled to provide an ongoing record of every penny spent.

CASH DISBURSEMENT JOURNAL

✓	CHECK NUMBER	CHECK ISSUED TO	DATE				CHECK AMOUNT	BANK BALANCE
		BALANCE FORWARD ⟶						6 615 30
	0001	UNITED OFFICE SUPPLIES	3/2/76	OFFICE SUP.			30 25	6 585 05
	0002	MAINE PAPER COMPANY	3/3/76	PAPER			2 615 10	3 969 95
	0003	JONES TRANSPORT COMPANY	3/3/76	FREIGHT			85 75	3 884 20
	0004	UNITED PARCEL SERVICE	3/4/76	FREIGHT			32 16	3 852 04
	0005	NEW ENGLAND TELEPHONE	3/5/76	UTILITIES			256 15	3 595 89
	0006	EASTERN GAS & ELECTRIC	3/5/76	UTILITIES			151 63	3 444 26
	0007	SMITH PRINTING COMPANY	3/7/76	PAYROLL			2 668 78	775 48
	0008	NORTHERN PRINTERS SUPPLY	3/7/76	PLATES			265 13	2 325 48 / 2 060 35
	0009	ACME SANITATION SERVICE	3/8/76	MAINTENANCE			43 50	2 016 85
	0010	JACKSON'S FILM PROCESSING	3/9/76	FILM			502 15	1 514 70
	0011	BOMARC REALTY	3/10/76	RENT			600 00	2 730 36 / 2 130 35
	0012	HAMSON OFFICE MACHINES	3/12/76	TYPEWRITER			559 75	1 570 60
	0013	HICKSVILLE WATER DEPT.	3/12/76	UTILITIES			6 23	1 564 37
	0014	SAM'S INDUSTRIAL LAUNDRY	3/14/76	MAINTENANCE			14 70	2 537 62 / 2 522 92
	0015	BLOTTO INK CORPORATION	3/14/76	INK			212 63	2 310 29
	0016	SCRUBBO CLEANING SERVICE	3/14/76	MAINTENANCE			60 00	2 250 29
	0017	DUMONT'S BOTTLED GAS	3/15/76	UTILITIES			48 00	2 209 29
	0018	ABCO INC.	3/17/76	OFFICE SUPPLIES			41 17	2 161 12
	0029	TRUE BLUE INK, INC.	3/28/76	INK			69 99	813 03
	0030	SCRUBBO CLEANING SERVICE	3/30/76	MAINTENANCE			60 00	753 03
							13 484 30	753 03

FIGURE 5-5   Bookkeeping Form

CHAPTER SUMMARY

When we divide a single thing into its parts we use partition. When we divide an assortment of things into specific categories we use classification. Partition is always applied to a single object. Its purpose is systematically to separate that whole object into its parts, pieces, or sections. Classification is always applied to an assortment of objects that have some similarities. Its purpose is to group these objects in a systematic way.

Whether you choose to apply partition or classification will depend on your subject and your purpose. In analyzing complex problems you will often have to use both techniques.

Follow these guidelines for dividing a single item into its parts:

– Apply partition to a single item (e.g., a golf club).
– Include all parts and be sure that each part belongs.

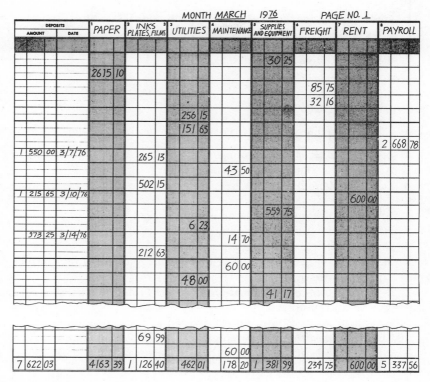

FIGURE 5-5 (*Continued*)

— Divide in a way that is consistent with your purpose.
— Subdivide as far as needed to show what makes up the item.
— Make sure your sequence of division follows the item's logic of organization (spatial, chronological, or the like).
— Make parts of equal rank parallel in grammatical form.
— Make sure that parts do not overlap.
— Choose the clearest format (prose, list, or visual aid).

Follow these guidelines for dividing an assortment of things into classes:

— Apply classification to a group of items.
— Include all items that belong to a particular class; be sure that each item belongs in that class; and divide the assortment into enough classes to contain every item you are sorting out.
— Limit your classification to a specific focus.

– Choose useful bases for comparison and contrast and express them in precise and objective terms.

– Make equal categories parallel and make sure categories do not overlap.

– Choose the clearest format.

REVISION CHECKLIST

Use this list to refine your system of partition or classification.

1. Is the title clear and limiting (promises exactly what you will deliver)?

2. Are all data sources fully documented?

3. Is the system both complete and exclusive (includes all items but no extraneous ones)?

4. Are items presented in parallel grammatical form?

5. Have you avoided overlapping?

6. Are all units of measurement given (grams, pounds, etc.)?

7. Have you chosen the clearest format for your individual purpose (table, chart, graph, prose discussion)?

8. Is the partition or classification integrated into the surrounding discussion (introduced and discussed)?

9. Are all items in a partition subdivided as far as necessary?

10. Does the partition follow a logical sequence (spatial, chronological, etc.)?

11. Are all items in a partition divided according to a basis that suits your purpose?

12. Are all items in a classification arranged according to a meaningful basis of comparison?

13. Are the bases objective and precise?

14. If a chart, graph, or table format is used, does it follow the criteria for visual aids discussed in Chapter 9?

Now list those elements of the classification or partition system that need improvement.

EXERCISES

1. In a short essay, discuss the types of partition and classification systems that you expect to use on the job. Be as specific as possible in identifying typical subjects, your intended audience, and uses to which your data will be put.

2. Is the following classification effective? Use the revision checklist as a guide for evaluation.

1975 Beer Production
in the Top Six National Breweries

Langdon Brewing Co.	14,678,400
Kastel Inc.	21,739,200
Flagstaff Brewing Co.	7,635,800
King Inc.	10,478,300
Rothberg Brewing Co.	23,547,700
Case Brewing Co.	9,658,400

3. In a unified and coherent paragraph discuss the difference between classification and partition. List three items that can be classified and three that can be partitioned.

4. Jot down each of your activities on any given day. When your list is complete, group related activities under specific headings: ("Social Activities," "Schoolwork," etc.). Next, choose a basis of comparison for arranging items within a given class in a specific order: (descending order of time spent on each activity, order of desirability, etc.). Finally, choose one class of activities — "Schoolwork," for example — and present your formal classification as a bar graph, a table, and a prose discussion. Which form of presentation seems most "readable" here?

5. Classify the following items in terms of five different bases of comparison. Be sure to limit and define your classification with an explicit title: lettuce, celery, cabbage, asparagus, broccoli, spinach.

6. Assume that you are planning a week-long camping trip into a wilderness area. Make a list of all the items you will need. Next, group related items under specific headings in order to organize your inventory. Finally, take one item from the list (e.g., "tent") and partition it into its various parts (pegs, poles, canvas, guy lines, mosquito netting, etc.).

As an alternate assignment, assume that you are planning a one-week spring vacation in Bermuda, and perform the same tasks.

7. (a) Take a deck of ordinary playing cards and partition it according to three different bases. Title each partition accordingly. In two cases, your partition will yield general classes under which related cards can be grouped through classification. (b) Classify the possible hands in a poker game in descending order of value.

8. Some items listed in the following classification systems are not logically related. Identify the specific error in each group — faulty parallelism, overlapping, inconsistent general meaning, or incompleteness — and correct it.

Classification of selected alcoholic beverages	*Classification of winter sports*
beer	hockey
wine	curling
whiskey	handball
bourbon	skiing
	figure skating
	sledding

Classification of automobiles on the basis of body type	*Classification of technical writing tasks*
sedans	proposals
family cars	sending memos
roadsters	specifications
coupes	work orders
hardtops	progress reports
station wagons	instructions
	writing letters
	reports which are formal

9. Find an example of a formal classification in a magazine, such as *Consumer Report,* or in a textbook. Is the classification effective? Using the criteria for effectiveness discussed in this chapter, formulate a one-paragraph answer. Do the same for a partition.

10. Choose an item with a singular meaning (bicycle, digital calculator, clock, retail store, stereo system, etc.). Partition the item on all possible levels as shown in the following example:

(1st level)

Major parts of a bicycle

frame
wheels
drivetrain
attachments

(2nd level)

Parts of a frame	*Major parts of a wheel*	*Major parts of a drivetrain*	*Major attachments*
	hub		
	spokes		
	rim		

(3rd level)

Etc.	*Parts of a hub*	Etc.	Etc.
	etc.		

Notice how this partition moves from division to subdivision, and so on. Hence, the partition at each level is complete. Complete the partition by filling in the required items, or construct one of your own, using a subject that you know well.

11. Keep a record of every penny you spend during one week, or review your checkbook record for the semester. Partition your spending, in chronological order, in the lefthand column of an accounting sheet like the one in Figure 5-5. Now, group your expenses under specific class headings, in terms of similarity of expense ("Rent and Household Expense," "Automobile Expense," "Food Expense," "Entertainment Expense," "School Expense," and any other categories needed to include specific expenditures). Next, add up your totals in each category, write a prose analysis of your findings, and make specific recommendations for overhauling your budget, if necessary. (Use Figure 5-5 as a model.) Present the same findings (1) in a bar graph, and (2) in a pie chart.

6

Charting
Your Course:
The Outline

CHAPTER GOALS

DEFINITION

THE PURPOSE OF OUTLINING

CHOOSING THE BEST TYPE OF
    OUTLINE
  The Informal Outline
  The Formal Topic Outline
    Roman Numeral–Letter–Arabic
      Numeral Notation
    Decimal Notation
  The Formal Sentence Outline

ELEMENTS OF AN EFFECTIVE FORMAL
    OUTLINE
  Full Coverage
  Successive Partitioning
  Logical Notation and Consistent Format
  Parallel Construction for Parallel Levels
  Clear and Explicit Headings
  Parts in Logical Sequence
    Chronological Sequence
    Spatial Sequence
    Reasons For and Against
    Problem-Causes-Solution
    Cause and Effect
    Comparison-Contrast
    Simple to Complex
    Sequence of Priorities
  Items Relevant to Purpose

CONSTRUCTING THE FORMAL OUTLINE
  Preliminary Steps

General Outline Model
Introduction
Body
Conclusion

USING YOUR OUTLINE TO ADVANTAGE

THE REPORT DESIGN WORKSHEET

CHAPTER SUMMARY

REVISION CHECKLIST

EXERCISES

CHAPTER GOALS

Upon completing this chapter you will know:

- The meaning and purpose of an outline.
- The differences among informal outlines, formal topic outlines, and formal sentence outlines.
- The differences between the two most common systems of notation: roman numeral–letter–arabic numeral and decimal notation.
- How to choose the best type of outline for your purposes.
- How to evaluate a formal outline for effectiveness.
- How to construct each type of outline.
- How to revise your outline for greatest effectiveness.

DEFINITION

An outline is a preliminary sketch or plan for anything you may write.

Throughout this book we talk about your responsibility to deliver what you promise to your reader: a message that is clear, complete, and well organized. In your outline you draw your roadmap for delivery in three ways:

1. You identify and list each major part of your subject.
2. You divide each major part into its constituent minor parts.
3. You choose the most logical framework for including each major and minor part within the framework of your report.

Does this process sound familiar? It should, for it is simply the process of partitioning a subject into its parts and classifying these parts.

Outlines come in many shapes and sizes: a few key words or phrases listed on a page is an outline; a grocery list is an outline; a daily reminder calendar is an outline. In each of these examples the list of words or phrases reminds the writer or reader of important things to be done. The size and complexity of your own outline will vary according to your specific writing task. Sometimes an informal list of words or ideas will be enough of a guide; at other times you will need a highly systematic arrangement of topics arranged in a formal numbering and lettering system. In any case, don't write your report — long or short — until you feel good about your outline.

THE PURPOSE OF OUTLINING

Why does a writing assignment seem to fall easily into place for one writer but not for another? Because *the successful writer usually spends more time planning than writing.* To write effectively you need to take several distinct steps: (1) thinking about your idea until you see it clearly; (2) developing your idea; (3) dividing it into its parts; (4) arranging the parts into a discussion that continually relates to your original thesis; and (5) expressing your message in clear, correct English. Rushing through these steps all at once is like trying to build a house before the plans have been drawn up and the materials delivered. You should begin with a list of materials ranked in order of their proper place in the completed house, or in the order in which you will use them. Otherwise, you might forget the cement blocks for the foundation or forget the door openings, or find that you have nailed your roofing shingles to the siding. No quality structure *just happens:* anything worthwhile that people create is the product of careful planning and deliberate choices.

Last-minute changes in planning and building a house are made more easily on the blueprints than by tearing down actual walls or moving a bedroom wing from one side to another. Likewise, you can modify your outline more easily than your written report. Like the blueprint, the outline is not a set of commandments but simply a tool for your convenience. For example, in planning a long and complex research report you can sketch an informal outline long before you write the actual report. This list of ideas will provide a general direction for your evidence-gathering. As your investigation proceeds you can revise and refine your outline. Before you begin to write your report you will compose a formal outline — the detailed, polished version that will guide you to your finished product. The outline will serve as a map for constant revision as you work.

Whether your project is simple or complex, an appropriate outline will help you keep control while you gather evidence, and while you write, revise, and proofread.

CHOOSING THE BEST TYPE OF OUTLINE

The Informal Outline

An informal outline is simply a list of words or phrases that serve as brief re-minders and directional markers. This list may be all that you need if you are planning a short report. First, identify your direction of approach by formu-lating a clear statement of purpose. Next, brainstorm your topic (as discussed in Appendix B) in order to generate as many related ideas as you can. After selecting the most pertinent ideas (expressed as topic phrases), arrange them in the sequence that makes the most sense. Here is a sample statement of purpose, with its outline.

> The purpose of this report is to describe the evaluation of a lakefront building site to determine the appropriate type of waste-disposal system needed.

> TOPICS
>   1. Location of the Site.
>   2. Physical Description of the Site.
>   3. Type of Water Supply.
>   4. Instructions for Constructing the Gray-Water System (sink drain).
>   5. Instructions for Constructing the Privy (Outhouse) Pit.
>   6. Instructions for Applying for a Gravel Waiver.

In formulating this sequence of topics the writer observed the principle that anything to be discussed must first be described. With this kind of list in hand, the writer can now compose the report quickly and efficiently.

If you are planning a longer, formal report, an informal outline is still a handy tool. In this case it is a tentative outline, or a working outline, because it is designed to keep you on track without excluding possibilities for additions, deletions, and other revisions as you move toward the final planning and writ-ing of your report. This casual form of outline helps solve the chicken-and-egg problem faced by writers, namely: "How can I know where I'm going if I don't have a plan yet?" or "How can I make up a plan if I don't know where I'm going yet?" The informal outline frees you from this circular dilemma by giving you a starting point.

Here is a student-written informal outline for a report titled "An Analysis of the Advisability of Converting Our Office Building from Oil to Gas Heat." The writer begins by formulating her statement of purpose.

> The purpose of this report is to inform the president of Abco Engineering Consultants, Inc. of the advisability of converting our office building from oil to gas heat.

As the writer brainstorms her subject she produces the following list of major topics for research and discussion.

> Estimation of Gas Heating Costs
> Removal of the Oil Burner and Tank
> Installation of a Gas Burner
> Description of Our Present Heating System
> Installation of a Gas Pipe from the Street to the Building

She then arranges these topics in the sequence that makes the most sense — in this case, a chronological sequence.

> 1. Description of Our Present Heating System.
> 2. Removal of the Oil Burner and Tank.
> 3. Installation of a Gas Pipe from the Street to the Building.
> 4. Installation of a Gas Burner.
> 5. Estimation of Gas Heating Costs.

Notice that the topics are arranged parallel to the sequence of steps in the actual conversion process, beginning, of course, with a description of the present system. The writer now has a general plan for gathering data. She can expand this outline and make it more specific by adding subtopics from her brainstorming list. For example, the subtopics of major topic 1 might include descriptions of the physical condition of the present system, required yearly maintenance, fuel supply problems, and cost of operation. When her data-gathering is complete, the writer develops her informal outline into a formal outline *before* writing her report.

The Formal Topic Outline

The formal topic outline is a more detailed and systematic arrangement of topics and subtopics using a formal system of notation (numbers, letters, and other symbols marking logical divisions). You may use one of two popular systems of notation: the roman numeral–letter–arabic numeral system or the decimal system.

Roman Numeral–Letter–Arabic Numeral Notation

Here are the five topics from the informal outline developed into a formal outline using roman numeral–letter–arabic numeral notation:

> II. REPORT BODY (or COLLECTED DATA)
>   A. Description of Our Present Heating System
>   1. Physical condition
>   2. Required yearly maintenance
>   3. Fuel supply problems
>   a. overworked distributor
>   b. varying local supply
>   4. Cost of operation

    B. Removal of the Oil Burner and Tank
      1. Data from the oil company
      2. Data from the salvage company
        a. procedure
        b. cost
      3. Possibility of private sale
    C. Installation of a Gas Pipe from the Street to the Building
      1. Procedure
      2. Cost of installation
      3. Cost of landscaping
    D. Installation of a Gas Burner
      1. Procedure
      2. Cost of plumber's labor and materials
    E. Estimation of Gas Heating Costs
      1. Rate determination
      2. Required yearly maintenance
      3. Cost data from neighboring facility
      4. Overall cost of operation
        a. cost of conversion
        b. cost of maintenance
        c. cost of gas supply

With the body section of her report fully mapped out, the writer adds the introduction and conclusion sections to complete the formal outline:

  I. INTRODUCTION
    A. Background
    B. Purpose of the Report
    C. Intended Audience
    D. Information Sources
    E. Limitations of the Report
    F. Scope
      1. Description of our present heating system
      2. Removal of the oil burner and tank
      3. Installation of a gas pipe from the street to the building
      4. Installation of a gas burner
      5. Estimation of gas heating costs

  II. BODY (as shown earlier)

  III. CONCLUSION
    A. Summary of Findings
    B. Comprehensive Interpretation of Findings
    C. Recommendations

Any subject needs to be introduced before it is discussed, and reviewed after it has been discussed. Therefore, the introduction and conclusion sections are essential parts of a formal outline and report. (In an informal report, these sections are still included, but are usually shortened to one or two sentences apiece.)

Decimal Notation

Here is a partial version of the same outline in decimal notation:

    2.0 Collected Data
        2.1 Description of Our Present Heating System
            2.1.1 Physical condition
            2.1.2 Required yearly maintenance
            2.1.3 Fuel supply problems
                2.1.3.1 overworked distributor
                2.1.3.2 varying local supply
            2.1.4 Cost of operation
        2.2 Removal of the Oil Burner and Tank
            2.2.1 Data from the oil company
            2.2.2 Data from the salvage company
                2.2.2.1 procedure
                2.2.2.2 cost
            2.2.3 Possibility of private sale

As you can see, the decimal outline makes it easier to refer your reader to various sections as he or she reads your report. However, both systems of notation help you to achieve the same organizing objective. Unless your reader expresses a distinct preference, use the system with which you are most comfortable.

The Formal Sentence Outline

The above outline is called a *topic outline* because each division is expressed as a topic phrase. Although this is the most popular type of outline, it may be expanded one step further before the report is actually written. This final version is called a *sentence outline* because each major and minor topic phrase is developed as a complete sentence. The time and effort required for developing a sentence outline is well spent; this detailed plan brings you much closer to your goal. Here is our earlier topic outline expanded into a sentence outline:

    I. INTRODUCTION
        A. In recent years, the cost of heating oil has risen sharply while its availability has decreased steadily.
        B. The purpose of this report is to inform the president of Abco Engineering Consultants, Inc. of the advisability of converting our office building from oil to gas heat.
        C. This report is written for a general reading audience: specifically, all interested members of our firm.
        D. The data in this report were obtained from the gas company, our oil company representative, the Tubo Plumbing Corporation, the Junko Salvage Company, and Watt Electronics, Inc.

E. Only the data for the spring 1977 gas and electric rates are part of this analysis. No rate-change forecast for gas or oil is available. Also, the projected supply of each of these fuels in our area has not been determined by either distributor.

F. The five major topics discussed in this report are: (1) description of our present heating system, (2) removal of the oil burner and tank, (3) installation of a gas pipe from the street to the building, (4) installation of a gas burner, and (5) estimation of gas heating costs.

II. COLLECTED DATA

A. Our present heating needs are supplied by circulating hot air generated by a Model A-12, electrically fired, Zippo oil burner fed by a 275-gallon fuel tank. Both are twelve years old.

  1. Both burner and tank are in good working order and physical condition, as they have been carefully maintained.

  2. The oil burner and associated components require cleaning once yearly at a service charge of $18.00. The air filter, costing $2.25, is replaced three times yearly at a total cost of $6.75.

  3. On three occasions during the past two years our system has run out of fuel for periods ranging from twelve to twenty-four hours for one of two reasons:

    a. Our town has only one fuel oil distributor who lacks the manpower and machinery to provide immediate service to all customers during the peak heating season.

    b. The supply of fuel allocated to our local distributor has fluctuated rapidly and unpredictably in recent months; at times, his oil supplies are not adequate to satisfy local demand.

  4. Our firm's oil bill for 1976 was $533.53; this figure added to the yearly maintenance charges amounts to an overall cost of $558.28.

B. Before the gas burner and fixtures could be installed, the oil burner and tank would have to be removed from the basement.

  1. The oil company has no provisions for removing these items or for repurchasing them from the owner.

  2. The Junko Salvage Company is willing to remove the oil tank and burner.

    a. The oil tank, which was placed in the cellar before the building was constructed, is too large to be removed through our single cellar entrance located inside the building; therefore, it would have to be disassembled for removal.

    b. The salvage company will remove the items at no cost to our firm provided they keep them; otherwise, their charge is $150.00.

  3. An alternative is to pay the salvage company and to sell these items on our own at an asking price of $200.00.

C. A gas pipe from the street to the building would have to be installed by the gas company.

1. A trench 3 feet deep and 2 feet wide must be dug to install the gas pipe.
2. Our building is only 60 feet from the street and the gas company provides and installs the first 100 feet of pipe free of charge.
3. Our landscaping cost for removing and replacing shrubs and resodding the lawn after pipe installation will be $85.00.

D. The gas burner would have to be installed by a plumber.
1. The plumber installs the gas burner, a pipe running to the meter (installed by the gas company), and an exhaust pipe — all of which must be inspected by the gas company before the meter is activated.
2. The plumber's charge for his labor and all materials is $570.00.

E. Overall gas heating costs are the sum of a number of individual costs.
1. Because our firm is nonindustrial, we would pay the residential gas rates of $10.00 for the first ten units per month and $0.16 for each additional unit.
2. Yearly maintenance is restricted to the air filter, costing $2.25, which is replaced three times at a total cost of $6.75.
3. Watt Electronics, whose building was built by the same contractor to the same specifications as our own, and which maintains the same 68-degree temperature during working hours, had a gas bill of $616.75 for 1976.
4. The calculation of our overall cost of operating a gas system would have to include the cost of conversion and maintenance as well as the cost of gas supply for a total estimated yearly cost of $702.25.
   a. Total conversion costs including costs of plumbing and landscaping, will be $655.00, or $65.50 per year over a ten-year period.
   b. Maintenance costs will be $6.75 yearly.
   c. Projected gas supply costs, based on Watt Electronics figures, will be roughly $615.00 yearly.

III. CONCLUSION

A. Our present heating needs are supplied by an oil burner and tank, which are in good working order and whose replacement by a gas system would entail substantial conversion expenses and higher fuel rates: the overall yearly cost of gas heating would be roughly $129.00 higher than the cost of oil heating.

B. The advantage of a constant fuel supply (assuming that local gas shortages will not occur) does not offset the expense and inconvenience of conversion.

C. I recommend that we retain our present system and explore the possibility of installing an auxiliary 500-gallon underground oil tank to ensure an adequate supply during the peak heating months.

When you have completed a sentence outline like this one, writing your actual report will be fairly easy. Each item in the outline is a complete idea and serves as a topic sentence for a full paragraph in your report. You simply need to support each topic idea with specific details (examples, statistics, diagrams, quotations, photos, etc.). With these prewriting steps completed, you are ready to write with assurance and control. The better your plan, the better your report.

ELEMENTS OF AN EFFECTIVE FORMAL OUTLINE

Full Coverage

Make your list of major topics broad enough to encompass the full range of your subject. For example, the outline for the heating conversion report would not be adequate if the topic, "Description of Our Present Heating System," were not included. Without this discussion, the reader has no basis for comparing the two forms of heating.

Besides making your outline inclusive, make it specific enough so that you can discuss each topic in detail. Thus, the sample outline partitions "Estimation of Gas Heating Costs" into five subtopics. The fifth subtopic, "overall cost of operation," is further partitioned into its three constituent sub-subtopics. This finite breakdown helps the reader understand the specific steps in the cost determination (e.g., how the conversion expense is calculated into the overall cost).

Successive Partitioning

Each division must yield at least two parts. Also, parts or subparts of equal rank must be placed in the same level:

> *Faulty*
>   C. Installation of a Gas Pipe from the Street to the Building
>   1. Procedure
>   2. Cost of installation
>   D. Cost of Landscaping

These topics are not correctly partitioned: *D* is not equal to *C*, but only a subtopic of *C*, since the lawn has to be dug up and repaired as part of the installation procedure.

Each successive level represents a partitioning of the immediately preceding level. Therefore, the subdivisions at any given level must always add up to the immediately preceding item at the next higher level. Thus, "procedure," "cost of installation," and "cost of landscaping" add up to "Installation of a Gas Pipe. . . ."

Logical Notation and Consistent Format

We have defined notation as the system of numbers, letters, and other symbols marking the logical divisions of your outline. Format, on the other hand, is the arrangement of your material on the page (the layout). Proper notation and format show the subordination of some parts of your topic to others. Because your formal outline contains both major and minor parts, be sure that all sections and subsections are ordered, capitalized, lettered, numbered, punctuated, and indented to show how each part relates to other parts, and to the overall discussion.

Here is how outline parts are properly placed with the roman numeral–letter–arabic numeral system of notation:

    I. INTRODUCTION
        A. First Major Point in Introduction
            1. First related minor point (if needed)
            2. Second related minor point (if needed)[1]
        B. Second Major Point in Introduction etc.

    II. BODY
        A. First Major Point in Body
            1. First related minor point (if needed)
            2. Second related minor point
                a. further division of second related minor point (if needed)
                b. etc.
        B. Second Major Point in Body etc.

    III. CONCLUSION
        A. First Major Point in Conclusion[2]
        B. Second Major Point in Conclusion
        C. Third Major Point in Conclusion

[1] Any division must yield at least two subparts. For example, you could not logically divide "Types of Strip Mining" into "1. Contour Mining," without other subparts. If you can't divide your major topic into at least two subtopics, change your original heading.

[2] Each of these major points may also be divided into two or more related minor points, as needed.

The general pattern of notation, then, is as follows:

    I.
       A.
           1.
           2.
       B.
           1.
           2.
               a.
               b.
                   (1)[3]
                   (2)
       C. etc.

Here is the same general pattern of notation in decimal form:

    1.0
      1.1
         1.1.1
         1.1.2
      1.2
         1.2.1
         1.2.2
             1.2.2.1
             1.2.2.2
                1.2.2.2.1
                1.2.2.2.2
      1.3 etc.

Either system of notation follows the principles of effective classification: each item is arranged in a fixed and clear relationship to all other items.

Use indentation that is consistent from category to category and from level to level. The same applies for line spacing. If, for instance, you indent your first A notation five spaces from the margin, indent all other uppercase letter notations identically. If you leave a triple space between notations I and II, be sure to triple space between II and III. Likewise, if you single space your first set of arabic numerals — 1, 2, and 3, — single space all other sets of arabic numerals at this level of division.

Express topics at particular levels in consistent letter case: all BLOCK LETTERS; First Letter of Each Word in Caps (except articles, conjunctions, and prepositions); First letter capitalized; or all lowercase letters.

Whatever form of indentation, spacing, and letter case you choose, be consistent.

---

[3] Further subdivisions can be carried as far as needed, as long as the notation for each level of division is individualized and consistent.

Parallel Construction for Parallel Levels

Make all items of equal importance parallel, or equal, in grammatical form. Then your outline will emphasize the logical connections among related ideas.

> *Faulty*
> E. Estimation of Gas Heating Costs
>   1. Rate determination
>   2. The system requires yearly maintenance
>   3. Cost data were obtained from a neighboring facility
>   4. Overall cost of operation

Each item at this level of division is presented as equal in importance to the other items that enter into the cost estimation. However, 1 and 4 are expressed as topic phrases, whereas 2 and 3 are expressed as complete sentences. These items can easily be made parallel.

> *Correct*
> E. Estimation of Gas Heating Costs
>   1. Rate determination
>   2. Required yearly maintenance
>   3. Cost data from neighboring facility
>   4. Overall cost of operation

Conversely, each item could be expressed as a complete sentence. See Appendix A for a full discussion of parallelism.

Clear and Explicit Headings

As you compose your outline by listing and arranging various topics, be sure that your headings contain *specific* information. Choose words that are highly descriptive. For example, under "Description of Our Present Heating System," a heading titled "Fuel" is not as informative as one titled "Fuel supply problems." Clear topic headings remind you of your purpose as you write various sections of your report.

Also, avoid repetitions that offer little information.

> *Faulty*
> C. Environmental Effects of Strip Mining
>   1. Effects on land
>   2. Effects on erosion
>   3. Effects on water
>   4. Effects on flooding

Correct
   C. Environmental Effects of Strip Mining
      1. Permanent land scarring
      2. Increased erosion
      3. Water pollution
      4. Increased flood hazards

In the correct version, each topic heading contains key phrases that summarize the message as it will appear in the final report. The more specific your outline, the less effort you will need later.

Parts in Logical Sequence

Which details does your reader need — and in what order? Which specific item comes first? Which comes last? Does your subject have any special traits that might determine the sequence of presentation? Answer these questions as you plan your outline. Some possible sequences for ordering the data in your body section follow.

Chronological Sequence

In a chronological sequence you follow the time sequence of your subject (for example, the sequence of steps in a set of instructions). Also, follow this sequence to explain the order in which the parts of a mechanism operate (for example, how the heart works to pump blood). Begin with the first step and end with the last.

Spatial Sequence

In a spatial sequence you follow the physical arrangement of parts (left to right, top to bottom, front to rear, etc.), as when you describe various rooms in a college building as possible sites for a radio station.

Reasons For and Against

In giving reasons for and against something, follow the sequence in which both sides of an issue are argued — first one side, then the other — as in an analysis of the value and danger of a proposed flu-vaccination program.

Problem-Causes-Solution

Follow the sequence of the problem-solving process from posing the problem, through diagnosis, to a solution. An analysis of the rising rate of business failures in your area would require this sequence.

Cause and Effect

In a cause-and-effect sequence you follow actions to their specific results. You would use this sequence in analyzing the therapeutic benefits of transcendental meditation.

Comparison-Contrast

In evaluating two items, you can discuss first their similarities and then their differences. An example would be the item-by-item comparison of two sites for locating a small business.

Simple to Complex

A complex subject is often best explained by beginning with its most familiar or simplest parts. For example, an explanation of color television transmission follows the logic of the learning process by describing what we see on our TV screens *before* discussing the complex mechanism that creates the picture.

Sequence of Priorities

Sometimes, you will want to place items in sequence according to their relative importance, as in a proposal for increasing the school budget in your town.

These sequences are illustrated in the sample reports throughout this text and in Appendix A. Many reports will involve more than one sequence. For example, the heating-conversion outline fuses the chronological sequence, the comparison-contrast sequence, and the cause-and-effect sequence.

Items Relevant to Purpose

Be sure that all items in your outline add up to your statement of purpose. Don't include topics that are not directly relevant. For example, a sixth topic, titled "Temperature Forecast for Next Winter" would be irrelevant to the stated purpose of the report outlined earlier.

CONSTRUCTING THE FORMAL OUTLINE

Preliminary Steps

Because you can't make something from nothing, complete the following steps *before* beginning work on your formal outline:

1. _Write out a full statement of purpose_. Decide specifically what you intend to accomplish in this report and write your intention out in one or two
sentences. You will then have a constant point of reference as you work.

2. _Brainstorm your subject._ Do some hard thinking about your subject to
identify all related ideas and topic divisions. The more time you spend on this
step, the more concrete details you will have to work with. Follow the suggestions in Appendix B for brainstorming.

3. _Construct your informal (or working) outline_. Organize the relevant
major topics from your brainstorming list in the most logical sequence for discussing your subject according to your stated purpose.

4. _Collect your data._ Using your rough outline as a guide, collect all the detailed information you will need for your report. Your data may suggest ideas
for additional topics or subtopics. If so, revise your working outline accordingly.

After completing these steps, you have something to work with: a clear intention, raw materials (your data), and a tentative plan (working outline). All
these can be refined into a final plan (your formal outline). When you have
answered the first essential question — What is my intention, or goal? — your
formal outline will help you answer the second essential question — How will
I achieve my goal in a way that is clearest to my reader? At this point, in addition to the major topics from your brainstorming list, you should have identified
all subtopics to be included in your formal outline.

With the preliminary steps completed, you can easily construct your formal
outline. It follows the same introduction-body-conclusion structure that governs
any good paragraph or essay.

GENERAL OUTLINE MODEL

   I. INTRODUCTION
      A. Definition, Description, and History (and significance of the subject)
      B. Statement of Purpose
      C. Target Audience (including assumptions about the reader's prior
         knowledge)
      D. Information Sources (including research methods and materials)
      E. Working Definitions
      F. Limitations of the Report
      G. Scope of Coverage (major topics from your brainstorming list in the
         sequence in which you will discuss them)

  II. BODY (the component parts of your subject, divided into their sub-
      parts, as necessary)
      A. First Major Topic
        1. First subtopic of A

        2. Second subtopic of A
          a. First subtopic of 2
          b. Second subtopic of 2
             etc. (subdivision carried as far as necessary to isolate the important points in your topic)
     B. Second Major Topic
       etc.

  III. CONCLUSION (where everything is tied together)
     A. Summary of Information in II
     B. Comprehensive Interpretation of Information in II
     C. Recommendations and Proposals Based on Information in II

When you write a formal sentence outline or the actual report, you will fill out these three sections with enough specific details to get your message across. Detailed suggestions for developing each section follow.

Introduction

Your introduction should contain the following parts:

1. *Definition, description, and history.* Define and describe your subject before you discuss it, and outline its history, as needed. In short, introduce your reader to *what* you will talk about in your body section.

2. *Statement of purpose.* In one or two sentences, state what you plan to achieve in your report. A statement of purpose is like your thesis statement in writing an essay. Why are you writing this report?

3. *Target audience.* Specifically identify the audience for whom you are writing. If you can, explain how the target reader will use your information. How much prior knowledge does your reader need to understand the report as written?

4. *Information sources.* If your report will include data from outside sources, identify them briefly here (you will identify them in detail in your footnotes). Outside sources might include interviews, questionnaires, library research, company brochures, government pamphlets, personal observation, etc. By showing your reader that you work from reliable sources you increase your report's credibility.

5. *Working definitions.* Do you need to define any technical terms, like "autoanalyzer," or general terms, like "liability," for this report? If you have a long list of technical terms to define (ten or more), you might save them for a glossary at your report's end.

6. *Limitations of the report.* State the reasons for any information that is incomplete. For instance, perhaps you were unable to locate a key book or inter-

view a key person. Or perhaps your study can only be titled "preliminary," instead of "definitive" (the final word on the subject), because facts that might throw new light on your subject have yet to be made public. Or perhaps your report discusses only *one side* of an issue, as in a study of the *negative* effects of strip mining.

7. *Scope of coverage.* In your final subsection, preview the scope of your report by listing all major topics to be discussed in section II, the body.

Not all reports will require each of these subsections in its introduction. For some subjects, sources, definitions, and limitations subsections might be optional.

Body

Your body section is the heart of your report. In it you develop major topics and subtopics logically. Whether you are describing an item or a process, giving instructions, or analyzing a subject, the facts in this section support and clarify your statement of purpose, your conclusions, and any needed recommendations. "Show me!" is the implied demand that any reader will make of your report. Your body section should satisfy that demand by giving your reader a step-by-step view of the process by which you move from your introduction to your conclusion. Any interpretations or recommendations you might later express will be only as credible as the evidence you generate to support them.

Whenever possible, give your body section an explicit title to reflect the specific purpose of your report. For example, if your report is written to present a physical description of an item, you might title your body section "Description and Function of Parts." The same section in a set of instructions might be titled "Instructions for Performance," or "Collected Data" in a report designed to analyze a problem or answer a question. The body sections in various reports throughout this textbook have explicit titles that clearly reflect their contents.

Conclusion

Whatever the subject, your conclusion contains no new findings. Instead it reinforces, interprets, or otherwise clarifies the facts in your body. The following subsections are most often used. However, except for the summary, which is always used, the subsections in your conclusion will vary with different types of reports. For example, in a report describing a mechanism, your conclusion might simply review the major parts of the mechanism discussed in the body, and briefly describe one complete operating cycle. Although a good beginning, middle, and ending are indispensable, feel free to modify, expand, or delete any subsections as you see fit.

1. *Summary of information in the body.* Always summarize your body discussion to give your reader a ready reminder of the major points you have developed.

2. *Comprehensive interpretation of information in the body.* Tie your report together by giving an overall interpretation of your data and drawing relevant conclusions based on facts.

3. *Recommendations and proposals based on information in the body.* Be sure that all needed recommendations or proposals are based directly on your overall interpretations and conclusions.

USING YOUR OUTLINE TO ADVANTAGE

As you will see in the following chapters, the general outline model shown earlier can be adapted to most formal reporting assignments. Moreover, a topic outline (like the one for the heating-conversion report) is easily converted into a table of contents for your finished report (as we will show in Chapter 8). To make your table of contents, simply indicate the page numbers corresponding to your various topic headings.

Remember that your outline is a helpful tool — not another obstacle between you and a completed assignment. Don't make the mistake of struggling through your report and then constructing an outline *afterward,* simply to please the instructor. Following this backward sequence is like building a house before you have drawn up the plans. If you give some thought to your subject, your purpose, and your reader's needs, your outline should fall into place easily.

On the other hand, your prepared outline ought not to be a trap. It is not so sacred that you must bend and warp your report to follow it. If, as you work your way through your report, you find your outline deficient, revise it.

THE REPORT DESIGN WORKSHEET

Some writers may wish to use a planning sheet in mapping out their approach to a report. The report design worksheet shown in Figure 6-1 can be used along with an outline to help you zero in on your audience and purpose. This worksheet can be used in planning almost any report or letter. Figure 6-2 shows a completed worksheet for the heating-conversion report outlined earlier.

REPORT DESIGN WORKSHEET

Preliminary Information

What is to be done? _____

Whom is it to be presented to, and when? _____

	Primary Reader(s)	Secondary Reader(s)
Audience Analysis		

Position and title:

Relationship to author
  or organization:

Technical expertise:

Personal characteristics:

Attitude toward author
  or organization:

Attitude toward subject:

Effect of report on
  readers or organization:

Reader's Purpose

Why has reader requested it?

What does reader plan to do
  with it?

What should reader know
  beforehand to understand
  it as written?

What does reader already know?

What amount and kinds of
  detail will reader find
  significant?

What should reader know and/or
  be able to do after reading
  it?

Writer's Purpose

Why am I writing it?

What effect(s) do I wish to achieve?

FIGURE 6-1   Report Design Worksheet

Design Specifications
Sources of data:

Tone:

Point of view:

Needed visuals and supplements:

Appropriate format (letter, memo, etc.):

Rhetorical mode (description, definition, classification,
                etc.--or some combination):

Basic organization (problem-causes-solution, intro-instruc-
                tions-summary, etc.):

Main points in introduction:

Main points in body:

Main points in conclusion:

Other Considerations

FIGURE 6-1   (*Continued*)

REPORT DESIGN WORKSHEET

<u>Preliminary Information</u>
A report on the feasibility of converting
What is to be done? our home office from oil to gas heat

Whom is it to be presented to, and when? Charles Jones, company
president: April 1

	Primary Reader(s)	Secondary Reader(s)
<u>Audience Analysis</u>		
Position and title:	President, Abco Engineering Consultants	Company officers, engineering staff
Relationship to author or organization:	Employer	supervisors, colleagues, junior members
Technical expertise:	nontechnical (for this subject)	nontechnical
Personal characteristics:	highly efficient; demands quality and economy	all serious-minded professionals
Attitude toward author or organization:	is considering me for promotion to assistant V.P.	friendly and respectful; officers will vote on my promotion
Attitude toward subject:	highly interested because of last winter's inconvenience	interested
Effect of report on readers or organization:	will be read closely and acted upon	will be read and discussed at our next staff meeting

<u>Reader's Purpose</u>

Why has reader requested it?	wants to make a practical decision	_____
What does reader plan to do with it?	use the data to make the best choice	confer with the president about the choice
What should reader know beforehand to understand it as written?	nothing special; history of problem is reviewed in report	some
What does reader already know?	remembers last winter's problems	some
What amount and kinds of detail will reader find significant?	brief description of conversion procedures and detailed cost analysis	some
What should reader know and/or be able to do after reading it?	make an educated decision	advise the president about his decision

<u>Writer's Purpose</u>

Why am I writing it? to communicate my research findings clearly

What effect(s) do I wish to achieve? to have my readers conclude that conversion is not economically feasible; to persuade them to accept my recommendation of an alternative to conversion.

FIGURE 6-2 Completed Report Design Worksheet

<u>Design Specifications</u>

Sources of data: *gas company, our oil company representative; Tubo Plumbing Corp., Jumbo Salvage Co., Watt Electronics, Inc.*

Tone: *formal*

Point of view: *third-person*

Needed visuals and supplements: *title page, letter of transmittal, table of contents, informative abstract, data sheet appendix reviewing the procedure for cost analysis.*

Appropriate format (letter, memo, etc.): *formal report format with full heading system.*

Rhetorical mode (description, definition, classification, etc.—or some combination): *primary mode: analysis; secondary modes: description, process narration*

Basic organization (problem-causes-solution, intro-instructions-summary, etc.): *questions - answers - conclusions and recommendations*

Main points in introduction: *Background*
Purpose
Intended Audience
Data Sources
Limitations Scope

Main points in body: *Description of Present System*
Removal of Oil Burner and Tank
Installation of Gas Pipe
Installation of Gas Burner
Estimation of Gas Heating Costs

Main points in conclusion: *Summary of Findings*
Interpretation of Findings
Recommendation

<u>Other Considerations</u> *no frills; these readers are all engineers interested in hard facts.*

FIGURE 6-2 (*Continued*)

CHAPTER SUMMARY

An outline is a plan for anything you may write. It partitions a subject into its parts and classifies these parts on the basis of their similarities. In order to stay in control, the successful writer usually spends more time in planning than in writing.

Choose the best type of outline for your purpose:

1. *An informal outline.* A simple list of words or phrases, especially useful for a short report.

2. *A formal topic outline.* A highly systematic arrangement of topics using a formal system of notation (either roman numeral–letter–arabic numeral or decimal notation).

3. *A formal sentence outline.* A further development of the topic outline. Each major and minor topic phrase is developed as a complete sentence which, in turn, serves as a topic sentence for a paragraph in the report.

Make your formal outline broad enough to encompass your subject and specific enough so you can discuss each topic in detail. Make each division yield at least two subparts and place all subparts of equal rank at the same level. Use a logical system of notation and a consistent format, expressing all divisions in parallel form. In a formal topic outline use clear and explicit headings and choose the most logical sequence for arranging the parts. Be sure that all items are relevant to your statement of purpose.

Follow these steps in constructing your formal outline:

1. Before writing the actual outline, complete all preliminary steps.
   a. Formulate your statement of purpose.
   b. Brainstorm your subject for specific ideas and topic breakdowns.
   c. Write your informal outline.
   d. Collect your data.

2. In your introduction, map out your background discussion, which begins with a definition or description of your subject and its history. Follow this discussion with a statement of your intention and a description of your target audience. Next, identify outside sources of data and explain any limitations of your report. Place working definitions in the following section, and end your introduction with a list of all major topics to be discussed in the body.

3. In your body, divide major topics and subtopics in logical sequence, presenting all relevant evidence. Give your body section an explicit title that reflects its contents.

4. In your conclusion, summarize the main points in your body, give an overall interpretation of these points, and draw conclusions based on facts.

Base any recommendations or proposals on your conclusions. Vary these sub-sections, except for the summary, according to the type of report you are writing.

Add, delete, or modify any subsections in this three-section structure as needed. Remember that your outline is a tool, not an obstacle or a trap. Write it *before* you begin your report, and revise it as necessary while you write.

REVISION CHECKLIST

Use this list to check the quality of your outline.

1. Is this the best type of outline for your purpose (informal, formal topic, formal sentence)?
2. Is your outline broad enough to encompass the full range of your topic?
3. Is it specific enough in its divisions so that all major and minor points are represented?
4. Does each division yield at least two subparts?
5. Are parts or subparts of equal rank placed at the same level?
6. Do subparts at any given level add up to the immediately preceding items at the next higher level?
7. Should some minor points be major points, or vice versa?
8. Is the system of notation logical (roman numerals for major areas; capital letters for major topics; arabic numerals for subtopics; lowercase letters for further division; "(1)" for even further division)?
9. Is your format consistent (uniform indentation, spacing, and letter case)?
10. Are items of parallel importance expressed in parallel grammatical form?
11. Are all headings clear and explicit?
12. Is the subject arranged in the most logical sequence?
13. Is every item in the best possible location?
14. Are all topics and subtopics directly relevant to the stated intention of the report?
15. Are all necessary topics and subtopics included?
16. Is the introduction-body-conclusion structure fully developed?
17. Does the total of all parts in the body add up to the statement of purpose?
18. Is the outline clear and easy to follow (does it make sense)?
19. Are all items consistently stated either as topic phrases or as complete sentences?

Now list those elements of your outline that need improvement.

EXERCISES

1. In a unified and coherent paragraph, explain the difference between an informal outline and a formal outline. What is the major function of each?

2. Locate a short article (2000-word maximum) from a journal in your field and make a topic outline or sentence outline of the article. Use the sample outlines in this chapter as models. Does the article conform to the general outlining procedures discussed in this chapter? If not, how could the original article be improved? Discuss your conclusions in class or in a written evaluation of one or two paragraphs.

3. For each of the following report topics, indicate the most appropriate sequence for organizing the subject. (For example, a proposal for playing fields at your college would best proceed in a spatial sequence.)

- A set of instructions for operating a power tool.
- A campaign report describing your progress in gaining support for your favorite political candidate.
- A report analyzing the weakest parts in a piece of industrial machinery.
- A report analyzing the desirability of a proposed nuclear power plant in your area.
- A detailed breakdown of your monthly budget to trim excess spending.
- A report investigating the reasons for student apathy on your campus.
- A report investigating the effects of the ban on DDT use in insect control.
- A report on any highly technical subject, written for a general reader.
- A report investigating the value and success of a no-grade policy at other colleges.
- A proposal for a no-grade policy at your college.

4. *In class:* Organize into groups of four or five. Choose *one* of the following topics and, *after* you have formulated a clear statement of purpose, brainstorm in order to divide it into its components. Extend your partition into as many parts and subparts as possible. Rearrange the parts in logical order and in a consistent format, as you would in developing the body section of an outline. When each group completes this outlining process, one representative can write the final draft on the board for class criticism and suggestions for revision.

- Job opportunities in your career field.
- A description of the ideal classroom.
- How to organize an effective job search.
- Can the quality of your higher educational experience be improved?
- Arguments for and against a formal grading system.

5. Use the checklist at the end of this chapter to evaluate the formal topic outline on pages 104–105. Suggest any needed revisions. Do the same in class for the outlines produced by various groups in doing exercise 4.

6. Assume that you are preparing a report titled "The Negative Effects of Strip Mining on the Cumberland Plateau Region of Kentucky." After brainstorming on your subject, you settle on the four following major topics for investigation and discussion:

- Social and economic effects of strip mining.
- Description of the strip-mining process.
- Environmental effects of strip mining.
- Description of the Cumberland Plateau.

Arrange these topics in the most effective sequence for presentation.

When your topics have been effectively arranged, assume that subsequent research and further brainstorming produces the following list of subtopics:

- method of strip mining used in the Cumberland Plateau region
- location of the region
- permanent land damage
- water pollution
- lack of educational progress
- geological formation of the region
- open-pit mining
- unemployment
- increased erosion
- auger mining
- natural resources of the region
- types of strip mining
- increased flood hazards
- depopulation
- contour mining

Arrange each of these subtopics (and perhaps some sub-subtopics) under their appropriate topic headings. Use an effective system of notation and a good format to create the body section of a formal outline.

7

Researching
Information

CHAPTER GOALS

DEFINITION

PURPOSE OF RESEARCH

IDENTIFYING INFORMATION SOURCES
 Personal Experience
 The Library
  The Card Catalog
  Periodical Indexes
  Reference Books
  The Vertical File
  The Reference Librarian
 Informative Interviews
  Identification of Purpose
  Choice of Respondent
  Preparation
  Maintaining Control
  Recording Responses
 Questionnaires
 Letters of Inquiry
 Organizational Records and Publications
 Personal Observation

TAKING EFFECTIVE NOTES
 Purpose
 Instructions

PLANNING AND WRITING THE REPORT
 Preparation
  Choice of Topic
  Focus of Topic
  Working Bibliography

  Statement of Purpose
  Background List
  Working Outline
 Information-Gathering
  Beginning with a General View
  Skimming
  Selective Note-Taking
  Planning Interviews, Questionnaires,
   or Letters of Inquiry
  Direct Observation
 Writing and Documentation
  Outline Revision
  Section-by-Section Development
  Proper Documentation
 Writing the Final Draft

CHAPTER SUMMARY

EXERCISES

CHAPTER GOALS

Upon completing this chapter you will know:

- The meaning and purpose of research.
- The difference between primary and secondary research.
- How to distinguish fact from opinion.
- How to identify and locate information sources.
- How to use the library.
- How to prepare and conduct an informative interview.
- How to prepare, distribute, and tabulate questionnaires.
- How to take selective notes.
- How to plan and write a research report with full documentation.

DEFINITION

Strictly speaking, research is defined as the effort to discover any fact or set of related facts. For instance, the cost of building the first X-ray machine or the price range of half-acre building lots in Boville in January 1979. However, almost any kind of significant research is conducted for some purpose — to answer a question, to make an evaluation, to establish a principle. We set out to discover whether Wankel engines work well and are efficient for a reason: we're thinking about buying a car equipped with one, or we're trying to decide whether to start producing them, or the like.

Depending on the information sources, research may be classified as *primary* or *secondary*. Primary research is a firsthand study of the subject; its sources are memory, observation, questionnaires, interviews, letters of inquiry, and records of business transactions or scientific and technological activities. Secondary research is based on information that other researchers — by their first-hand studies — have compiled in books, articles, reports, brochures, and other publications. Most research projects combine primary and secondary research.

Research depends on *facts*. In this chapter, you will look at ways of finding facts and reporting them for your reader's uses.

PURPOSE OF RESEARCH

The purpose of all research is to arrive at an informed opinion, to establish a conclusion that has the greatest chance of being valid.

We might have uninformed opinions about political candidates, kinds of cars, controversial subjects like abortion and capital punishment, or anything else that may touch our lives. Opinions are beliefs that are not proven but seem to us true or valid. Without a basis in fact, opinions are uncertain, disputable, subject to change in the light of new experience. But sometimes we forget that many of our opinions really don't rest on any objective data. Instead, they rest mostly on a chaotic collection of the beliefs that are reiterated around us, notions we've inherited from advertising, things we've read but never checked the validity of, and so on. Television commercials, for instance, are especially designed to manipulate the consumer's uninformed opinion about the quality of certain products. Often, an advertiser's claims have no way of being proved and may even be false. Political speeches can work the same way — claiming absolute truth for something that is subject to dispute.

Any claim is valid only insofar as it is supported by facts. A fact is a truth known by actual observation or study. Therefore, an opinion based on fact is more valuable than an uninformed opinion. In many cases we must consider a variety of facts. Consider for instance a commercial claim that Brand X toothpaste makes teeth whiter. Although this claim may be factual, a related fact may be that Brand X toothpaste contains tiny particles of ground glass, thereby harming more than helping teeth. The second fact may change your opinion about whether you want to use Brand X toothpaste. Similarly, a United States senator may claim that he is committed to reducing environmental pollution. However, he may have voted against all ecology-based legislation. Therefore, if you want to know whether to believe his claim, you need to establish the facts. You want your opinion to rest on objectively verifiable information, not merely on the basis of his claim.

Of course, some emotional, moral, or religious issues cannot be weighed on factual bases. But, on the whole, informed opinions help us to be more effective consumers, voters, and workers. Clearly, we respect some opinions more than others. For example, let us assume that you are a personnel executive interviewing candidates for a position with your firm. Which of the following responses would you find more impressive?

1. Q. What is your opinion of the condition of our national economy?
    A. I think the economy is improving.
    Q. Why?
    A. Well, I just have that feeling. . . .

2. Q. What is your opinion of the condition of our national economy?
    A. I think the economy is improving. My opinion is based on the following indicators:
    a. Our gross national product has risen steadily over the past five months for a total 6.5 percent increase.
    b. The Dow Jones has climbed slowly and steadily for the past four months, and has now exceeded the 1000-point mark.
    c. The wholesale price index has dropped an average of 1.5 percent monthly since last June.
    d. Seasonally adjusted unemployment figures have dropped from 9.1 percent to 7.6 percent in the past six months.
    e. New-home construction has doubled in the past year.
    f. Detroit reports a record-breaking year for automobile sales. Thus, the auto industry seems to have recovered from last year's slump.

    In short, inflation is decreasing, production and employment are increasing and the recession seems just about over.

When we compare the above responses, it seems clear that the second candidate can support his opinions with fact because he has done his homework. In an increasingly complex world, you need to be able to search out facts and use them constructively.

Facts also can affect the quality of your decision. For example, before buying that quiet little farm at such a reasonable price, be sure that the country road by the house is not the site for a superhighway. Before spending the weekend climbing the big mountain, investigate weather conditions, trail conditions, and temperature range at higher elevations. Before studying for a specific career, investigate job openings, salary range, and requirements; better yet, interview someone who has such a job. Conduct the same kind of background research before buying a new car, emigrating to Australia, or making most major decisions. Although the facts may contradict your original opinion, they will help you make an informed decision.

Research is a prerequisite to starting your own business. Before locating and opening a motorcycle shop, for example, you should investigate the local marketing possibilities and consumer profiles. In what age range and socio-economic level do most motorcycle buyers fall? What percentage of your local population is made up of such consumers? Are motorcycle sales increasing or decreasing nationwide? How many motorcycles are now registered in your town? Are there other motorcycle shops in the area?

If answers to these and other questions are encouraging, you now must choose the best location. First, identify the type and amount of space needed. Next, inspect all available local rentals, comparing rental costs and advantages of each. Now, choose the best location, basing your choice on rental cost, customer traffic, parking area, and types of neighboring businesses. Should you locate downtown on Main Street, in the shopping mall just outside of the center, or in a small, free-standing building two miles out of town, where motorcycle noise will bother no one?

These are just a few of the questions that a businessperson must answer accurately. And your answers are found in the facts you uncover through library materials, personal observation of possible sites, interviews and meetings with small-business advisory services, questionnaires distributed to a cross-section of the consumer public, letters of inquiry to motorcycle manufacturers, and a review of various records (registry records, census records, sales records, etc.). Finally, you will present your purpose, findings, and conclusions in a report to the local bank to justify your request for a business loan. (See the sample feasibility report in Chapter 14.)

If you join an organization instead, you may be asked to investigate and report on the feasibility of a new product, the benefits of merger with another corporation, the value of a proposed building site for a new branch, the advisability of purchasing a new piece of medical or dental equipment, and so on. Anyone in a responsible position — store owner, technician, or executive — needs to keep up with new developments. Research is by no means the exclusive activity of eccentric scientists or bleary-eyed scholars.

IDENTIFYING INFORMATION SOURCES

Personal Experience

As a logical first step, begin with what you already know about your subject. Search your memory and use the brainstorming technique discussed in Appendix B.

The Library

A library is a kind of supermarket of ideas and information, a place where food for thought is stored. It is one of the best examples of the power of the human mind for classification, for making order out of chaos through a system of categorizing knowledge. In a large library you can find information on just about anything when you understand the library's classification system.

For most research work the library should be your first stop to gain theoretical background for your work. You may even learn that your problem has been studied and solved by others before you. In this case your library visit could save you from wasting many hours covering old ground.

In school, public, or company libraries, systems of classifying information are similar. Your own library should contain one or more of these classification systems: card catalog, indexes to periodicals, reference works, and a vertical file.

The Card Catalog

The card catalog is the backbone of the library. In many libraries, every book, film, filmstrip, phonograph album, and tape is indexed in the card catalog under three separate designations: author, title, and subject. Thus you have three possible ways of locating the item.

Your library may place author, title, and subject cards in a single catalog in their respective alphabetical listings or may provide individual groups of drawers labeled "author," "title," and "subject." In either arrangement, author cards are filed alphabetically by the author's last name. When looking for books by a particular writer, begin here.

Locating the Card.   Assume that you are looking for a book on food technology written by Norman W. Desrosier. If your library has a divided catalog, locate the D cards in the author section. If not, locate the D cards in the combined catalog. Flip through the cards in the drawer until you locate those listed under "Desrosier, Norman W." Figure 7-1 shows a typical author catalog card. Each major item is labeled and explained.

As entry F on the author card indicates, you can find the same book listed alphabetically under its title, as shown in Figure 7-2. All other information on the title card is identical to that on the author card.

If you know neither the authors nor titles of books in a subject area, turn to the subject listing. Figure 7-3 shows the card for the same book found under the subject heading "Food — Preservation." Here again, all other items on the card remain the same.

Locating the Book on the Shelf.   If your library has closed stacks, you will need to fill out a call slip with book title, author, and call number. You then wait for

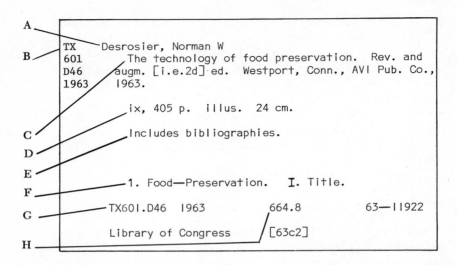

A: The author's name, listed last name first. (On some cards the author's name is followed by his date of birth — and death, if he was deceased at the time of the book's last printing.)

B: The call number: each book has a different call number under the coding system by which books are classified. Books are arranged on the shelves in the order of their respective call numbers. This number is your key for locating the book.

C: The title of one book written by this author, followed by the number of the edition, city of publication, publisher, and publication date.

D: Technical information: This book has 9 chapters, 405 pages, illustrations, and is 24 centimeters high.

E: Special information about the book: This book includes bibliographies listing related sources of information.

F: Other headings under which this book is listed in the card catalog: In the subject section, the book is listed under "Food — Preservation"; it is also listed alphabetically by title.

G: Library of Congress call number.

H: Dewey Decimal System call number.

FIGURE 7-1   A Catalog Card Classified by Author

a staff member to find your book. If the stacks are open, you will have to find the book yourself. The call number is your key for locating the book. In the card catalog area, in stairways and elevators, and on doors to individual floors, you will see posted copies of a guide like the one in Figure 7-4.

```
              The technology of food preservation.

   TX     Desrosier, Norman W
   601         The technology of food preservation.  Rev. and
   D46         augm. [i.e.2d] ed.  Westport, Conn., AVI Pub. Co.,
   1963        1963.

                 ix, 405 p.  illus.  24 cm.

                 Includes bibliographies.


              1. Food—Preservation.   I. Title.

              TX601.D46  1963              664.8            63—11922

              Library of Congress        [63c2]
```

FIGURE 7-2   A Catalog Card Classified by Title

Now simply follow the letters and numbers until you find your book. For example, the call number for Desrosier's *The Technology of Food Preservation* is


```
                 Food - Preservation

   TX     Desrosier, Norman W
   601         The technology of food preservation.  Rev. and
   D46         augm. [i.e.2d] ed.  Westport, Conn., AVI Pub. Co.,
   1963        1963.

                 ix, 405 p.  illus.  24 cm.

                 Includes bibliographies.


              1. Food—Preservation.    I. Title.

              TX601.D46  1963              664.8            63—11922

              Library of Congress        [63c2]
```

FIGURE 7-3   A Catalog Card Classified by Subject

THE LIBRARY OF CONGRESS CLASSIFICATION SYSTEM

The books in this library are arranged on the shelves according to the Library of Congress Classification System, which separates all knowledge into 21 classes, as outlined below. Each class is identified by a letter of the alphabet, subclasses by combinations of letters, and subtopics within classes and subclasses by a numerical notation.

Classes 2nd Floor

A   GENERAL WORKS (1st Floor)
(General encyclopedias, reference books, periodicals, etc.)

B   PHILOSOPHY — RELIGION

B–BJ	Philosophy, including BF, Psychology
BL–BX	Religion

C   AUXILIARY SCIENCES OF HISTORY

CB	History of civilization (General)
CC	Archaeology
CD	Archives
CJ	Numismatics
CR	Heraldry
CS	Genealogy
CT	Biography (General)

D   HISTORY: GENERAL AND OLD WORLD
(Including geography of individual countries)

D	World history, including World Wars
DA	Great Britain
DB	Austria
DC	France
DD, etc.	Other individual countries

E-F   HISTORY OF AMERICA
(Including geography of individual countries)

E 1–143	America (General)
E 151–857	United States (General)
F 1–957	United States: States and local
F 1001–1140	Canada
F 1201, etc.	Other individual countries

Classes 3rd Floor

P   LANGUAGE AND LITERATURE

P	Philology and linguistics
PA	Classical languages and literatures
PC	Romance languages
PD–PF	Germanic languages, including PE, English
PG	Slavic languages and literatures
PJ–PL	Oriental languages and literatures
PN	General and comparative literature
PQ	Romance literatures
PR	English literature
PS	American literature
PT	Germanic literatures
PZ	Fiction in English. Juvenile literature

Q   SCIENCE

QA	Mathematics
QB	Astronomy
QC	Physics
QD	Chemistry
QE	Geology
QH	Natural history
QK	Botany
QL	Zoology
QM	Human anatomy
QP	Physiology
QR	Bacteriology

R   MEDICINE

S   AGRICULTURE

G	GEOGRAPHY, ANTHROPOLOGY, FOLKLORE, ETC.
G	Geography (General)
GB	Physical geography
GC	Oceanography
GN	Anthropology
GR	Folklore
GV	Recreation
H	**SOCIAL SCIENCES**
HA	Statistics
HB–HJ	Economics
HM–HX	Sociology
J	**POLITICAL SCIENCE**
JA–JC	Political science
JF–JQ	Constitutional history and public administration
JS	Local government
JX	International law
K	**LAW**
L	**EDUCATION**
M	**MUSIC**
M	Scores
ML	Literature of music
MT	Musical instruction
N	**FINE ARTS**
NA	Architecture
NB	Sculpture
NC	Graphic arts
ND	Painting
NK	Decorative arts

SD	Forestry
SF	Animal culture
SH	Fish culture and fisheries
SK	Hunting sports
T	**TECHNOLOGY**
TA	General engineering, including general civil engineering
TC	Hydraulic engineering
TD	Sanitary and municipal engineering
TE	Highway engineering
TF	Railroad engineering
TG	Bridge engineering
TH	Building construction
TJ	Mechanical engineering
TK	Electrical engineering. Nuclear engineering
TL	Motor vehicles. Aeronautics. Astronautics
TN	Mining engineering. Mineral industries. Metallurgy
TP	Chemical technology
TR	Photography
TS	Manufactures
TT	Handicrafts. Arts and crafts
TX	Home economics
U	**MILITARY SCIENCE**
V	**NAVAL SCIENCE**
Z	**BIBLIOGRAPHY AND LIBRARY SCIENCE**

BIOGRAPHY: (*1st Floor*) Lives of individuals, illustrative of any subject, are normally classified with that subject, *e.g.* Albert Einstein is classified in QC16.E5. Otherwise, they are classified with general biography in CT.

The complete Library of Congress call number for any book may be found by consulting the card catalog.

THE LIBRARIAN WILL BE HAPPY TO ASSIST YOU IF YOU ARE UNABLE TO FIND THE BOOK YOU WANT

FIGURE 7-4 A Guide to a Library's Classification System

TX601. D46. 1976.[1] By locating T on the call-number map, you learn that your book is on the third floor of this library. More specifically, the card tells you that the book is in the TX section of the third floor.

Remember that the card catalog is only *one* source of information in a library. Don't stop here and ignore the periodical section. A periodical is a publication issued at regular intervals. *Time* magazine, for example, is a weekly periodical. Periodicals often contain information that is more up-to-date than that contained in books. Information in a book may be two or three years old by the time the book is published, whereas information in a periodical may be only a few days old.

Periodical Indexes

An index is an alphabetical guide, listing names, titles, and subjects, and telling you how to find each item. (This textbook has an index to its contents on pages 601–605.) Through various periodical indexes you can locate most recently published articles. The most popular and comprehensive index is the *Readers'*

---

[1] Instead of the Library of Congress classification system, some libraries use the Dewey Decimal System which divides all books into ten numbered categories:

000–999 General Works		500–599 Pure Science	
100–199 Philosophy		600–699 Technology	
200–299 Religion		700–799 Fine Arts	
300–399 Social Sciences		800–899 Literature	
400–499 Language		900–999 History	

Any one of these categories, in turn, forms ten smaller categories:

600–609 Technology	650–659 Business
610–619 Medical Science	660–669 Chemical Technology
620–629 Engineering	670–679 Manufactures
630–639 Agriculture	680–689 Other Manufactures
640–649 Home Economics	690–699 Building Construction

Each of these last categories can be further divided:

660– Chemical Technology	665– Oils, Fats, Waxes, Gases
661– Industrial Chemicals	666– Ceramic and Allied Industries
662– Explosives and Fuels	667– Cleaning and Dyeing
663– Beverages	668– Other Organic Production
664– Food Technology	669– Metallurgy

More specific breakdowns within each category are represented by numbers after the decimal:

664.1 Sugar Manufacturing and Refining

· · · · ·

664.8 Commercial Preservation of Food

In libraries that use this system, the Dewey Decimal classification number will be found in the upper left corner of the catalog card, replacing the Library of Congress number.

Guide to Periodical Literature, which indexes articles from over 150 popular magazines and journals. Because a new volume of the *Readers' Guide* is published every few weeks, you often can locate articles that are less than one month old. The *Readers' Guide* indexes items alphabetically by subject, author, and book or film title. Figure 7-5 shows a section from one of its pages.

Locating the Entry. Assume that you are researching a question about the physiological effects of food additives and preservatives. As you turn to a recent issue of the *Readers' Guide,* you find many entries under the general heading "Food." Scanning the entries classified under "Food additives," you spot an item that looks useful: "Food Additives and Hyperactive Kids" — item A. From this entry you gain the following information: because the author's name is not given, the article probably was written by a writer on the magazine staff; the name of the periodical is *Science Digest* (abbreviations are explained in the

FOOD. Organic
    Energy scorecard: the nutritionist vs. the health
      food freak. Mademoiselle 82:163 Ap '76
    Food your family eats. E. M. Whelan and F. J.
      Stare. il Parents Mag 51:34-5+ Jl '76
    Health-food hoax. F. J. Stare. Harp Baz 109:
      71+ My '76
    Notes from a has-been: a mother's confession
      about food and her family. E. Baldwin. il Org
      Gard & Farm 23:94+ N '76
    Organic foods: today's big rip-off. il Farm J 100:
      66 F '76
    Organic living almanac. Org Gard & Farm 23:
      90-1 My '76
    Proxmire liberates vitamins. il Bus W p36 Mr
      29 '76
    Whole earth organic food fad. T. H. Jukes.
      Parents Mag 51:46-7+ Mr '76
      See also
    Cookery—Organic food
FOOD. Raw
    International chef: Hamlin, Germany steak tar-
      tare. D. Reynolds. il Travel 147:12 Ja '77
FOOD. Wild
    Foraging for food provides rewards for a brave
      palate. L. Pringle. il Smithsonian 7:120-9 S
      '76
      See also
    Plants, Edible
FOOD additives
    Are you eating dangerously? N. Simon. Vogue
      166:112-13+ Jl '76
    Experts are divided about food additives. J.
      Mayer. il Fam Health 8:36-8 Jl '76
    Food additives and federal policy: the mirage
      of safety, by B. T. Hunter. Review
      Consumers Res Mag 59:30 Mr '76
A—— Food additives and hyperactive kids. Sci Digest
      80:13 N '76
    Food additives: how safe is safe? F. Warshof-
      sky. Read Digest 108:117-21 My '76
    Testing for seeds of destruction; research on
      food additives as causing cancer. J. Miller.
      Progressive 40:37-40 D '76
      See also
B—— **Coloring matter in cosmetics, food, etc.**
    Nitrosamines
FOOD and drug administration. See United States
    —Food and drug administration

FIGURE 7-5 A Page Section from the *Readers'*
Guide to Periodical Literature

opening pages of each *Readers' Guide*); the volume number is 80; the article is found on page 13 of the November 1976 issue. Item *B* refers to other headings under which you might find relevant articles.

Locating the Indexed Article. Each work listed in the card catalog is actually held by that library. Therefore, unless the item has been borrowed by someone else, you should locate it easily under its call-number designation. Periodicals are more of a problem, however; not all works listed in periodical indexes are likely to be held by your library. The indexes list articles from hundreds of journals, newspapers, and magazines, but your library most likely subscribes only to a cross-section. If you find an index reference to an article not held by your library, check with other libraries or ask your librarian to see if the article is available through interlibrary loan.

Scan the periodicals holdings list to determine which periodicals are held by your library. Copies are available in the area where indexes are shelved. Figure 7-6 shows a sample page from one library's list.

Earlier, you located an entry in the *Readers' Guide* titled "Food Additives and Hyperactive Kids," printed in *Science Digest*. Now, as you scan the periodicals holdings list you learn that your library subscribes to this journal (see item *A*). You also learn that all back issues to 1960 are recorded on microfilm.[2] Your article, however, is probably recent enough to be found in the actual journal (most libraries keep at least one year of back issues). For earlier articles, ask your librarian to explain the use of microfilm files and readers.

If your article is in a recent journal, scan the periodical shelves, usually arranged alphabetically by title, to find your issue. In some libraries older issues are bound together in hard-cover bindings instead of being microfilmed. In this case, each bound volume has a call number and is listed in the card catalog under "Title."

Here are some titles of other useful indexes:

> *Agricultural Index*
> *Applied Science and Technology Index*
> *Business Periodicals Index*
> *Cumulative Index to Nursing Literature*
> *Education Index*
> *Engineering Index*
> *International Nursing Index*
> *New York Times Index*

---

[2] In order to save space, many libraries subscribe to a microfilm service that photographs all back issues of major periodicals on microfilm. In this way, they can store several periodicals on one small roll of film, and you can read the original on a microfilm reader, which magnifies the reduced image.

-Q-

Quest   1973-

-R-

RN National Magazine for Nurses   Microfilm 1966-
RQ (ALA)   Microfilm 1970-
Ramparts (disc. micro. only)   Microfilm 1962-
                                         Sept. 1975
Readers Digest   Microfilm 1960-
Research in Education (ERIC)   1970-
Respiratory Care   1971-
Revista Rotaria (Spanish)   1970-
Revue d'Histoire Litteraire   1969-
    de la France
Rights   1971
Romanic Review   Microfilm 1960-
Rotarian   1974

-S-

Saturday Evening Post (micro. disc.)   Microfilm 1960-1969
                                         1971-
Saturday Review (Saturday Review World) Microfilm 1924-1972,
                                         1975
Saturday Review World (formerly: 1973-1974
    Saturday Review)
Scholastic Teacher (for microfilm   1972-
    see: Senior Scholastic)
School & Society (now: Intellect)   Microfilm 1960-1972
School Libraries (now: School Media   Microfilm 1951-1972
    Quarterly)
Science   Microfilm 1959-
Science Books   1970-1975
Science Digest   Microfilm 1960-
Science News   Microfilm 1960-
Scientific American   Microfilm 1929
Sea Change (Cape Cod Community
    College Literary Magazine)
Sea Frontiers (micro.)   Microfilm 1954-1975
Secretary   1973-
Senior Scholastic   Microfilm 1960-
Sewanee Review   Microfilm 1960-

FIGURE 7-6   A Page from a Library's Periodicals Holdings List

Psychological Abstracts
Social Sciences and Humanities Index
U.S. Government Publications (catalog issued monthly)

Besides these, your library may have many other indexes.

Reference Books

Reference books include technical encyclopedias, almanacs, handbooks, dictionaries, histories, and biographies. These are often a good place to begin your research, because they provide background information and bibliographies that can lead you to more specific information. The one drawback here is that some reference books that have not been revised recently (within five years) may be out of date. Always check the last copyright date.

Reference works held by your library will be found in a special section marked "Reference" — usually on the main floor of the building. All works will be indexed in the "Subject" card catalog, with a "Ref." designation immediately above the call number. Here is a partial list of reference works:

Cassell's Encyclopedia of World Literature
Civil Engineering Handbook
Dictionary of American Biography
Encyclopaedia Britannica
Encyclopedia of Food Technology
Encyclopedia of the Social Sciences
Fire Protection Handbook
Handbook of Chemistry and Physics
The Harper Encyclopedia of Science
Information Please Almanac
McGraw-Hill Encyclopedia of Science and Technology
The New Dictionary and Handbook of Aerospace
The New York Times Encyclopedic Almanac
Oxford English Dictionary
Paramedical Dictionary
The Times Atlas of the World

In addition, your reference librarian can direct you to any of hundreds of other reference books.

The Vertical File

Written information is not limited to books and magazines. Corporations and government and private organizations issue pamphlets, newsletters, brochures, circulars, booklets, and other unbound information. Also, your librarian will clip items and articles of interest from selected newspapers. All unbound informa-

tion is then filed under appropriate headings. As you open a vertical file drawer
— let's say a drawer labeled "A–Al" — you will see a series of manila folders
filed alphabetically according to headings like these:

ABM System	Aging
Abortion	Air Transportation
Academic Freedom	Air Pollution
Acupuncture	Agriculture
Adolescence	Alaska
Adoption	Alcoholism
Aeronautical Charts	Allergies
Africa	

Each folder will contain an assortment of information about the subject. Here,
you can often find important, up-to-date information. Don't overlook this
valuable resource.

The Reference Librarian

Your best bet for mastery of library research is the reference librarian, who is
found at the reference desk. This person can help you help yourself. His or her
function — as the title implies — is to *refer* people to information sources. So
don't be afraid to ask for assistance. Even professional researchers sometimes
need help. Your reference librarian can save you hours of wasted time by showing you how to use various indexes, or microfilm and microfiche readers; how
to locate reference books or bibliographies; or how to use duplicating machines;
moreover, he or she can order items from other libraries.

Libraries are a good secondary research source. However, you may also need
to consult firsthand, or primary, sources. One excellent primary source can be
the personal interview.

Informative Interviews

Conducting a good interview is not easy. Some of my own students who are
reporters for the campus newspaper have complained that their informative
interviews are often disappointing and embarrassing. They tell of not knowing
what questions to ask and having to suffer through long, terrible silences.
Afterward, they become confused about writing up their findings. Much of this
frustration results from one or more of the following errors:

1. The wrong choice of interviewee (respondent).
2. Inadequate preparation for the interview.
3. Failure to exercise control in conducting the interview.
4. Failure to record vital information immediately after the interview.

Each of these errors derives from the interviewer's inability to identify a clear purpose and to formulate a plan. You need to know *exactly* what you are looking for! An informative interview is not a casual bull session. When well planned and carefully directed it can be a pleasurable and rewarding experience and a solid example of your ability to engage in professional dialogue. The following suggestions should help you conduct a good interview: identify your purpose; choose the most knowledgeable interviewee; prepare well; control the interview; record your responses.

Identification of Purpose

Keep in mind the statement of purpose discussed in earlier chapters. Determine what information you hope to obtain:

> The purpose of my interview with Ms. Jones, city clerk, is to learn how licensing requirements, fees, and zoning restrictions would affect the operation of my proposed motorcycle shop. Also, I need to know how best to proceed in satisfying the legal requirements for this business.

When you are sure enough about your purpose that you can write it clearly in one or two sentences, you are ready for your next step.

Choice of Respondent

Because your purpose is to obtain detailed, factual answers to specific questions, choose your respondent carefully. Don't waste time interviewing someone who knows little about the subject. For instance, as part of your motorcycle-shop feasibility study you might select these respondents: the head of your chamber of commerce; a representative for the brand of machine you expect to sell; a member of your local retail licensing authority board; the loan officer at your local savings bank. Any of these should provide more vital information than, say, neighboring merchants. Moreover, they might give helpful leads for interviews with other key people.

One way to ensure that you will interview a knowledgeable person is to state the purpose of your interview when you call for an appointment:

> I am studying the possibility of opening a motorcycle shop in Winesburg, and I would appreciate the opportunity to meet with you, at your convenience, because I feel that you could answer some important questions about the future of such a business in our town.

If you communicate your purpose clearly, your intended respondent can immediately tell you whether he or she knows enough to make an interview worthwhile. If you both conclude that a personal meeting would be useful, try to arrange a time when your respondent may not be particularly busy. Your next step is to do your homework.

Preparation

Preparation is the step that requires imagination. You have identified your purpose and chosen your respondent. Now you need to plan questions that will get exactly the information you need. Begin by collecting all available information on your subject. In order to ask meaningful questions, you must know your subject! Complete your background investigation *before* the interview. When your homework is done, formulate your questions, *on paper.* Too many beginners set out for an interview armed only with a few blank notecards, a pencil, and a confident feeling that "the questions are all in my head." This mistake leads to embarrassing silences. Do not expect your respondent to keep the ball rolling.

Write out your questions on 3×5 notecards, one question per card, and arrange them in order. You then can jot notes about specific responses on the appropriate card.

Make your questions specific and direct. For example, when interviewing your motorcycle wholesale representative you might phrase a question in one of two ways:

> 1. Does your company have a provision for buying back unsold stock from the retailer?
> 2. What provisions, if any, does your company have for buying back unsold stock from the retailer?

Version 1 can yield a simple yes or no answer, whereas version 2 requires a detailed explanation of the yes answer. Likewise, a question from a problem-solving interview can be worded in one of two ways:

> 1. Do you think this problem can be solved?
> 2. What steps would you recommend to solve this problem?

Notice that version 2 again requires an answer based on hard information. In any case, the answer you receive will only be as good as the question you ask.

Also, be sure that your questions cover all important parts of your subject. Brainstorming can help here (as discussed in Appendix B). For instance, your questions for an interview about financing for your shop might cover these subtopics: interest rate, required down payment, other required security or collateral, credit background, other provisions (such as cosigner), application procedure, time required to process the application, prepayment penalties, length of loan period, total amount to be repaid (including yearly interest), amount of monthly payments, emergency loan provisions, and so on.

Avoid questions with simple yes or no answers and questions whose answers can be found in books, articles, newspapers, and town bylaws. Finally, phrase your questions so that you do not influence the respondent's answer:

1. Don't you think this is a good plan?
2. What do you think are the principal (faults, merits) of this plan and how should they affect my success?

Version 1 suggests that you want your respondent to agree with you, whereas version 2 encourages an expression of true opinion.

Organize your questions by following the outlining procedure in Chapter 6. Move from one logical consideration to another. When your questions are specific, comprehensive, and written out in logical order, you can face your next step with confidence.

Maintaining Control

You — not your respondent — are responsible for conducting a professional and productive interview. These suggestions should help:

1. Dress neatly and arrive for your appointment on time.
2. Begin by thanking your respondent, in advance, for giving valuable time.
3. Restate the purpose of your interview.
4. Tell your respondent why you feel he or she can be helpful.
5. Discuss your plans for using the information.
6. Ask if your respondent objects to being quoted or taped. (Although taping is the most accurate means of recording responses, it makes some people uncomfortable.)[3]
7. Avoid small talk.
8. Ask your questions clearly and directly, in the order you prepared them.
9. Be assertive but courteous. Don't be afraid to ask pointed questions, but remember that the respondent is doing you a favor by spending time with you.
10. Let your respondent do most of the talking. Remember that you are not there to instruct, but to learn. Keep your opinions to yourself.
11. Guide the interview carefully. If your respondent begins to wander from the main points, politely bring the conversation back on track (unless, of course, the additional information is useful).
12. Be a good listener. Don't stare out the window, doodle, or ogle the secretary while your respondent is speaking. No one seems ruder than a person who appears to be daydreaming while being addressed.
13. Be prepared to explore new areas of questioning, if the need arises.

[3] In an interview about your prospective business it would be inappropriate and unnecessary to tape the responses of the bank representative, sales representative, or licensing official. However, you might wish to tape an interview with a member of the Small Business Advisory Services who was giving you detailed advice about how best to proceed with your plan.

Sometimes your respondent's answers will uncover new directions for your interview.

14. Keep your note-taking to an absolute minimum. Be sure to record all numbers, statistics, dates, names, and other precise data, but don't transcribe your interviewee's responses word-for-word. This will be time-consuming and boring for the respondent, and may cause some tension. Simply record key words and phrases that will later refresh your memory.

15. If interviewing several people about the same issue, standardize your questions. Ask the same questions in the same order and phrasing to each respondent. Avoid making random comments that could affect one person's responses.

16. Don't hesitate to ask for clarification or further explanation of a response.

17. When your questions have all been answered, ask your respondent for any additional comments that might be helpful.

18. Finally, thank your respondent for his or her time and assistance and leave promptly. Don't overstay your welcome!

A final note: A successful interview is a candid and purposeful meeting between two human beings, not an encounter between computers. Although you need to prepare carefully and to execute your interview in a professional manner, you need not be a robot. Don't bury your own interesting personality beneath stilted, mechanical behavior. Be yourself!

Recording Responses

As soon as you leave the interview, find a quiet place to write out, in detail, a summary of the responses. Don't count on your memory for preserving the main points of the interview beyond this time. Get it all down on paper while the responses are still fresh in your mind. If you wait, you are bound to forget something important. Even if you have a taped record of the interview, transcribe your major points as soon as possible.

If you are seeking opinions on a highly controversial subject for a newspaper or magazine article, ask your respondents to review the final draft of your text before you quote their responses in your article.

Here is an interview text for the report titled "Survival Problems of Television Service Businesses" in Chapter 14. Notice how well-planned questions generate high-information responses.

APPENDIX A: FIRST INTERVIEW

(This interview was with Al Jones, the owner of Al's TV Shop, which grosses under $100,000 per year.)

Q. I see that you have an excellent location. Is location of a service shop important?

A. Sure. If I ever get back to selling it will be very important. Doing just service minimizes the importance since the customer will search you out if he really wants you. I suppose the same holds true if I start selling.

Q. Well, you seem to be selling car radios and stereos. Isn't that "selling"?

A. Yes. But by selling I mean TVs. Floor plans, etc.

Q. Why don't you sell now? What's a floor plan?

A. The floor plan is why I won't sell now. I used to sell with a floor plan. As you can understand quite easily, a floor plan means a TV distributor will sell me, say, $10,000 worth of TVs for only 10 percent down payment. I pay the balance as I sell the sets. The problem is that the temptation to use the distributor's money is very great. These large amounts of money in the checking account give you a false sense of security.

Q. In other words you have had a bad experience?

A. Not only me. Most TV businesses fail because they start using someone else's money. Where can a small business come up with six, eight, and even ten thousand dollars after all the stock has been sold?

Q. So you just sell car radios and stereos and parts as needed for repairs?

A. That's right. I pay for them as I use them and stay out of trouble. I realize it's better to have thirty-day charge accounts and use the distributor's money to capitalize my business, but this can also cause trouble.

Q. OK. What about advertising?

A. I use the yellow pages. That's all I can afford. Sometimes the local radio stations offer attractive deals which cost me half the usual rate. I take advantage of these. Radio is good for the stereo radio sales.

Q. Wouldn't it be a good idea for a group of you technicians to get together and do some group advertising?

A. You already know the answer to that. You helped organize the Cape Cod Chapter of the ETG [Electronic Technicians Guild]. You know what happened to that. TV technicians don't want to get together. They just don't have the time.

Q. Tell me something about your manpower situation.

A. OK. Here's something. My TV man came up to me a few days ago and told me he was giving me thirty days' notice. He wants to go into business for himself. It's always like this. You hire and train a technician for a number of years and when he gets the itch, off he goes. Better give him a copy of your report; maybe he can avoid the mistakes I made over the years.

Q. Can you think of any mistakes you made along manpower lines?

A. I don't think I'll ever hire a beginner anymore. They just aren't productive enough. From now on they must have at least formal training and the technician license.

Q. What do you mean by production?

A. I have to get so much production for every dollar I pay a technician. Unfortunately it has taken me many years to come to a good interpretation of what a reasonable return is. The minimum return I must have is $3.00 for every wage dollar.

Q. Your sign on the wall says "Minimum Labor Charge, $15.00." Does that mean you pay your technicians at least $5.00 per hour?

A. That's close enough. Sometimes technicians take longer than an hour to fix a unit. But it averages out to that.

Q. So your customers realize that they must be charged this amount so that you can cover your wages?

A. [Laughter] Customers don't realize anything. They complain no matter what we charge and no matter how long we take. I sincerely believe that customers start complaining even before their sets break.

Q. Have you ever tried discussing these notions with your customers?

A. Sometimes. I think they are beginning to learn that good shops and good technicians are getting scarcer. It pays for them to be cordial as it does for us. They are strange. They bring their TV sets in, for instance, swearing that they never watch anything on TV; there's nothing good on TV, etc. But an hour after they have dropped the set off they are on the phone inquiring about its status.

Q. Can you think of anything else you can say about customers?

A. Yes. As you know, most homes have more than one TV set. This has created an unusual problem for us. With money being tight it seems as if the customer leaves one set at home and one in the shop. I have a time getting people to pick up their merchandise. This puts a money crunch on me since I have invested labor and money in the repair.

Q. Have you thought of any solution to this problem?

A. I have tried taking substantial deposits, threatening to sell the set for the price of the repairs (which my attorney says I can't do). As you can see the place is filled with unclaimed merchandise. This is getting a little out of hand, to say the least.

Q. How about the money situation? How much did you gross last year?

A. A little over $60,000. This wasn't too good at all. I have two technicians full time with occasional part-time help. When I'm not busy doing desk work I help out with pickups, deliveries, and antenna work. At $15.00 per hour for forty hours per man that comes out just right to cover their labor, but there are many other expenses to be covered. Also my labor wasn't covered. The figure should have been closer to $90,000.

Q. How much of this was gross margin?

A. Gross margin? Let's see. That's what's left over after the cost of the parts used in the repairs or sales. Oh, about $40,000.

Q. And how much of this turned out to be net income?

A. Very little! I only paid a couple hundred dollars in taxes this year.

Q. One last question. Is it worth it? Do you think you are getting a return on your investment?

A. It beats working for someone else. I believe I have made all the mistakes there are to be made in this business. I don't intend to make them again. Don't forget to show me the completed report.

Questionnaires

An interview has some advantages over a questionnaire: first, in a face-to-face discussion, you can tell whether or not your respondent understands your questions; moreover, all your questions will be answered. Finally, you may obtain unexpected information. However, an interview sometimes creates the atmosphere of a formal interrogation. Respondents may be less than candid if they feel threatened by the questions. In this respect, a questionnaire is often a good alternative.

A questionnaire has several other advantages. First, it saves time and is an inexpensive way of surveying a large cross-section. Also, respondents can answer the questions privately and anonymously — and thus more candidly. Furthermore, respondents have plenty of time to think about their answers.

These advantages, however, can be offset by the problem of getting people to take time to fill out and return your questionnaire. Whether you mail out or otherwise distribute a questionnaire, expect no more than a 50 percent response, perhaps far less. But you can increase your chances for a healthy response by following these suggestions:

1. Introduce your questionnaire, so that your respondents will understand the importance of their answers and the purpose they will serve:

> Your answers to the following questions about your views on proposed state handgun legislation will be appreciated. Your state representative will tabulate all responses so that she may continue to speak accurately for *your* views in legislative session.

2. Keep it short. Try to limit both questions and response space to two sides of a page. Also, phrase your questions concisely. Otherwise, many people may refuse to answer.

3. Place the easiest or more interesting questions first to attract attention.

4. Make each question specific and precise. *This is a crucial step.* If your readers can interpret your question in more than one way, their responses are useless — or worse, misleading. Consider this question: "Do you favor foreign aid?" It is not specific and precise because foreign aid can mean military, economic, or humanitarian aid, or all three. Some people might support one form or another without supporting all three. Rephrase the question to allow for these differences:

> Do you favor:
> a. Our current foreign aid program of both military and humanitarian assistance to other countries?
> b. A greater emphasis on military assistance in our foreign aid program?
> c. A greater emphasis on economic and humanitarian assistance in foreign aid programs?
> d. No foreign aid program at all?

5. Avoid influencing your reader's responses with leading questions:

> Do you think foreign aid is a waste of taxpayers' money?
> Do you think foreign aid is a noble gesture by a wealthy nation toward the less fortunate?

Notice that each of these questions is phrased to elicit a definite response.

6. When possible, phrase your questions so that you can easily classify and tabulate responses: yes-or-no; multiple-choice; true-false; fill-in-the-blank.

7. Try to include a catch-all section ("additional comments") at the end of your questionnaire.

8. Enclose a stamped, self-addressed envelope along with the questionnaire.

Figure 7-7 is a student-written questionnaire designed to test listener preferences in radio news programming. The data were used in program planning for a new campus radio station. Notice that each question is clearly phrased and easy to answer. Multiple-choice questions list *all* possible choices. In many ways, such a questionnaire is more effective than an interview.

Caution: Although questionnaires can provide valuable data, be cautious in interpreting statistical results. With a political questionnaire, for example, more people with strong views (likes, dislikes) will respond than people with moderate views. Therefore, your data may not truly reflect a cross-section of attitudes. To avoid inaccurate generalizations remember that a questionnaire should be validated by other sources whenever possible.

Include the full text of the interview or questionnaire (with questions, answers, and tabulations) in an appendix (as discussed in Chapter 8). You can then refer to these data in your report discussion, as needed.

Letters of Inquiry

Letters of inquiry are a handy way to obtain specific information. These are discussed in Chapter 10.

Organizational Records and Publications

Company records are a good primary data source. Most organizations also publish pamphlets, brochures, or prospectuses for consumers, employees, prospective investors, voters, and so on. For example, your local nuclear power company may publish several pamphlets explaining the basic principles of nuclear power generating systems and listing the advantages of this energy source. If you were writing a report analyzing the safety measures employed in your local nuclear plant, you would want information representing both sides of the controversy. Along with the power company's literature you will need the

This survey is designed to record your preferences in radio news programming. Your responses will influence the planning and development of our new campus station programming. Please help us by taking a few minutes to answer these questions.

1. Do you listen to the radio daily?

2. At what hours?

3. To what stations?

4. Do you pay close attention to news reports?

5. Do you find them

   a. interesting?

   b. informative?

   c. entertaining?

6. Do you find that news programming could be

   a. more interesting?

   b. more informative?

   c. more entertaining?

7. What should be included in radio news programming?
(Please specify percentages.)

   a. national headlines? _____ percent

   b. regional and state headlines? _____ percent

FIGURE 7-7 A Student-Written Questionnaire

c. Cape Cod news? _____ percent

d. entertaining stories (trivia)? _____ percent

e. college news? _____ percent

f. other? (Please specify type and percentage.)

8. Do you feel that news receives adequate air time on local stations?

9. How much news would you prefer to hear per hour? (Please be specific: 5 minutes on the hour, etc.)

10. Which type of news should receive the most air time in your community? national local Cape entertaining college other (Circle one.)

11. Would you welcome an all-news station?

12. How often would you listen to it? often never sometimes (Circle one.)

13. Which (newspaper, television, radio) is your major source of

a. national news?   d. entertaining news?

b. state news?   e. college news?

c. Cape news?   f. other?

14. Please make any additional comments or suggestions that might help us in planning news programs.

FIGURE 7-7 (*Continued*)

publications of federal, state, and local environmental groups, to discover their assessment of these safety measures. Sometimes a pamphlet can be a good start for your research.

Personal Observation

If possible, amplify and verify your research findings with a firsthand look at your subject. For instance, conclude your motorcycle-shop feasibility study by visiting possible store locations. Measure consumer traffic by observing each spot at the same hour on typical business days.

Make observation your final step, because you now know what to look for. Observation not based on your understanding of the attendant issues, problems, and possibilities could be a waste of time. For example, a visit to the local nuclear power plant will be useful and informative if you have done your homework (if you understand how meltdown can occur or how safety systems work). Have a plan. Know exactly what to look for. Jot down any key observations immediately. Don't rely on your memory.

Sometimes a description of your observations can pinpoint a serious problem. Here is an excerpt from a report investigating poor management-employee relations at a supermarket where the writer works. In this case, the researcher's observations play a crucial role in defining the problem:

> The survey of employees did not reveal that they were aware of any of the previously mentioned barriers to communication. The 75 percent of employees who have positive work attitudes said they felt free to talk to their managers. However, the managers questioned said that only 50 percent of the employees felt free to talk to managers.
>
> The discrepancy appears to arise from the problems discussed in the section on morale: 50 percent of the employees don't know how management feels about them, and managers feel they don't hear everything that employees have to say. From questioning both sides, this writer concludes that both employees and management are assuming that messages have gotten across, instead of checking to make sure they have. For example, managers are assuming that employees know they want to hear complaints and suggestions, so they aren't asking for them. Employees, on the other hand, mention that they would like to know how they are doing. But they never ask managers about their positions.
>
> The problem involves perception and distortion from misinterpretation. Because managers don't ask for complaints, employees are afraid to make them, and because employees never ask for an evaluation, they never get one. Both sides have improper perceptions of what the other wants, and because of ineffective communications they don't know that their perceptions are wrong.

Effective research clearly requires *educated* observation.

TAKING EFFECTIVE NOTES

Purpose

Your finished report will only be as good as the notes you take. Notecards are best because they are easy to organize. I recall a college friend who thought that notecards were a waste of time and money. As a research paper became due, he diligently gathered data well in advance of the deadline date. Although his note-taking technique was unique, it was not terribly effective: he scribbled information on any available scrap of paper, keeping all scraps in a plastic folder. When his research was finished, he would begin to organize the material. First, he would take scissors and cut out, from larger sheets, slips of paper containing single ideas. This surgery was difficult because he had often written on both sides of the sheet; therefore, he had trouble isolating one fact or idea without cutting the one on the reverse side to pieces. Next, he would tape the pieces to the walls of his room so that he could sit back and browse over these items, waiting for inspiration. After countless hours of midnight oil, black coffee, and near-hysteria he would emerge with a "finished" paper. This product, as you can well imagine, was hardly a classic of coherence and organization. Yet he could never quite understand why his papers received poor grades.

Perhaps you have had similar experiences writing long papers or reports. The scene is familiar enough: After days or weeks of information-gathering, you end up with a stack of pages three inches deep. Now you need to put it all together so that your report makes sense. Too often, you might randomly stuff information into the paper just to be done with it. The result is usually a poor grade, because all of your research effort is buried beneath a rambling, incoherent product. It is then easy to conclude that research papers are just a useless form of torture devised by sadistic professors. The fact is, however, that research is one of your most valuable college activities. It helps you learn to find your own answers, to think for yourself, and to submit your opinions to the test of fact.

The point is to retain control at each step of the process. Begin by devising a system for recording your findings (an organized set of notes). For this purpose, 50 cents spent on a pack of 3×5 notecards is a good investment in professional efficiency and personal sanity. Put one idea on each card, and give each card a code number in the upper right corner. Because your cards form a kind of deck, you can shuffle them about. In this way you can organize cards into related groups and remain in control of diverse pieces of information. You can pretty well figure out the organization of your report before you actually write it by arranging the cards in logical order on a large table top.

Specific instructions for keying your cards to your outline will be discussed in the next major section, "Planning and Writing the Report."

Instructions

1. Begin by making bibliography cards, listing the books, articles and other works you plan to consult. Using a separate notecard for each source, write the complete bibliographical information for that source (as shown in Figure 7-8). This entry is identical to the bibliography entry you will include in the final draft of your report. (See Figure 7-11 for sample bibliography entries.) You can now begin recording information on your other notecards.

2. Skim the entire book, chapter, article, or pamphlet, noting the high points of information. (Review Chapter 3 for summarizing techniques.)

3. Go back over your reading and decide what to record. Use one card for each major item.

4. Decide how to record the item: as a quotation or as a paraphrase. In quoting, copy the statement word for word (as shown in Figure 7-9). Place quotation marks on your notecards around all directly quoted material, even a phrase or a word used in a special way. Otherwise, you could forget to give proper credit to the author, and thereby face a charge of plagiarism (borrowing someone else's words without giving credit, either intentionally *or* unintentionally). Sometimes you will quote only sections of a sentence or paragraph. In this case, use an ellipsis — three dots (...) indicating that words have been left out of a sentence (as discussed in Appendix A). If you leave out more than one whole sentence, use four dots (....):

> The word *technical* can be misleading. ... Factual as well as abstract subjects can best be understood from a "technical" point of view.

FIGURE 7-8 A Bibliography Card

Abell, George.   Exploration   II-A-1

P. 660

"*Our thinking in the realm of cosmology may be as rudimentary as that of the Greek Philosophers 2500 years ago, who believed that all heavenly motions must occur in perfect circles.*"

FIGURE 7-9   Sample Notecard for a Quotation

If you insert your own comments, within the quote, to clarify it, place brackets around them (as discussed in Appendix A):

> "This job [aircraft ground controller] requires undivided attention for hours on end."

Try to use direct quotes infrequently. Otherwise, your report will be simply a collection of borrowed words. Instead, synthesize and condense information by paraphrasing and summarizing.

Figure 7-10 shows a paraphrased notecard entry based on the following original. The researcher condenses the message in his own words.

> The sun is always present at some position on the celestial sphere. When the apparent rotation of the sphere carries the sun above the horizon, the brilliant sunlight scattered about by the molecules of the earth's atmosphere produces the blue sky that hides the stars that are also above the horizon. The early Greeks were aware that the stars were there during the day as well as at night.[4]

Most of your notes will be paraphrased. Some of your notecards may combine paraphrases and direct quotations. Paraphrased material needs no quotation marks, but it must be footnoted to indicate your debt to a particular source.

---

[4] This passage and those in Figures 7-9 and 7-10 (adapted) from *Exploration of the Universe*, second edition, by George Abell. Copyright © 1964, 1969 by Holt, Rinehart and Winston, Inc. Reprinted by permission of Holt, Rinehart and Winston.

Key to
Outline

Abell, George.   Exploration   II-A-3

As the earth rotates the
everpresent sun appears above the
horizon. Its light is diffused through
atmospheric molecules to produce
the blue sky which hides the
stars that are present both day
and night.

FIGURE 7-10   Sample Notecard for a Paraphrase

5. Be selective about what and how much you write in your notes. The summarizing techniques discussed in Chapter 3 should help. Unless you work from a solid understanding of your subject, your paper will be a hodgepodge of borrowed ideas simply glued together. As you read, keep your original purpose in mind. Make notes of the main points related to your purpose, along with crucial statistics, figures, and other precise data and conclusions. Follow these guidelines: (a) Preserve the original message when quoting. Don't distort it by omitting vital information. Your primary purpose is not to prove yourself correct but rather to uncover the facts. If the data disprove your theory, do not ignore them. (b) When you get an idea of your own, write it on a notecard immediately. Keep a few cards in your pocket or purse to record observations, questions, or ideas as they pop into your head.

PLANNING AND WRITING THE REPORT

So far we have discussed information sources and methods of recording your findings. Now we can review and expand our discussion with a plan for completing your assignment. This plan comprises three major steps: preparation, information-gathering, and writing and documentation.

Preparation

Choice of Topic

More than likely, your instructor will ask you to choose your own research topic. Instead of leaning on tired topics — abortion, euthanasia, life on Mars, or the Bermuda Triangle — choose a topic that concerns you or your community: job possibilities for graduates in your major, ways of improving working conditions on your part-time job, a survey of student opinions, and so on. The world is full of problems to solve and questions to answer.

Focus of Topic

Narrow your topic so that you can discuss it effectively. For example, assume that you live in a seaside resort area whose residents are becoming concerned about environmental damage that might be caused by proposed offshore oil-drilling rigs. Your broad topic would be "Offshore Oil Drilling." But this topic is much too expansive to cover in a single research paper, so you narrow it to "The Potential Environmental Effects of Offshore Oil Drilling at Georges Bank." This topic is also too broad because it includes all of the following:

> effects of oil spills on the Cape Cod shoreline
> effects on area marine life
> effects of the influx of workers on Cape Cod
> effects of the building of harbor terminals and refineries on the shoreline
> effects of other changes from a vacation area to an industrial area

A more useful approach would be to take one of these topics as a research subject: "The Potential Effects of Offshore Oil Drilling on the Marine Life of Georges Bank." You now have a topic limited enough to cover adequately in a research report.

Remember that the overall length of your report is not important, as long as you deliver what you promise in your title. In other words, make your report long enough to be comprehensive.

Working Bibliography

When you have selected and narrowed your topic, be sure that you can find sufficient resources in your library. Make your bibliography early to avoid choosing a topic and an approach only to learn later that not enough sources are available.

Conduct a quick search of the card catalog, the periodical indexes, other reference books, and the vertical file. Using a separate notecard for each work, jot down the bibliographical information, as shown earlier in this chapter.

Many of the books you locate will contain bibliographies that should lead you to additional information sources. With a current topic, such as offshore oil drilling, you might expect to find most of your information in recent magazine, journal, and newspaper articles. Your bibliography, of course, will grow as you read.

Statement of Purpose

Remember that you are doing more than collecting other people's views; you are screening and evaluating facts for a specific purpose. Identify your goal and your plan for achieving it. Then, your research will have a direction.

> The purpose of this report is to analyze data on the effects offshore oil drilling might have on Cape Cod's marine life. My study will compare characteristics of the Georges Bank ecosystem with those of existing offshore drilling sites.

Background List

Make a list of facts you already know about your topic. Some time spent brainstorming here might produce some good ideas for future investigation.

Working Outline

Now that you have identified your research goal, you need a roadmap to achieve that goal. By partitioning your topic into relevant subtopics, you emerge with a working outline:

    I. Marine Life on Georges Bank
   II. The Effects of Potential Massive Oil Spills
  III. The Effects of Chronic Low-Level Oil Spills
   IV. Physical Characteristics Affecting Oil Drilling on Georges Bank

Each of these subtopics can be further divided in accordance with instructions in Chapter 6. Your working outline is only tentative; you will change it and add subtopics as your research progresses. Depending on your findings, the major topics and the organization of your paper may shift radically by the time you make your final outline. With your working outline on paper, you can begin your second step.

Information-Gathering

Beginning with a General View

Your research will be easier to control if you move from general to specific data. Encyclopedias are often a good place to begin, because they contain general background information. Or, you might read a book or pamphlet that will give you a comprehensive view of your subject before proceeding to specialized articles in periodicals. Technical dictionaries and newspaper or magazine articles can also provide background material. Your reference librarian can help you find sources.

Skimming

Learn to skim. As you scan your bibliography cards you may find that you have a "mountain" of material to read. Don't be discouraged if you don't have time to read each source from cover to cover. With a little practice you can learn to skim pages quickly, while remaining alert for vital information. Before reading any book, look over the table of contents and scan the index. In this way you can often locate information quickly, without plodding through the entire book. In reading long articles, look for major topic headings that may help you locate specific information. Short articles and pamphlets should usually be read in their entirety.

To skim effectively you have to concentrate. If you feel yourself drifting, take a break.

Selective Note-Taking

Fight the temptation to copy or paraphrase almost every word so as not to miss anything. As you read, try to understand your subject instead of leaning too heavily on the ideas of others. Your finished report should be a combined product of your insights and the collected facts you have woven together.

Record the precise points of the message (names, dates, figures), along with the major ideas. Omit all supporting materials (examples, prefaces, background, etc.). Stay on track by following your outline.

Planning Interviews, Questionnaires, or Letters of Inquiry

Your investigation may call for primary research. If interviews, questionnaires, and letters are appropriate to your topic, and if you plan to use them, prepare for them well ahead of the time.

Direct Observation

The old proverb about a picture being worth a thousand words is especially applicable here. Now that you have read, questioned, and pondered, go and look for yourself — if direct observation is practical. Try to save this step as the conclusion of your research so that you know what to look for.

When your information is collected you should have a stack of notecards keyed to your working outline. You are now ready to write up your findings.

Writing and Documentation

Outline Revision

Throughout your investigation you have relied on your working outline. By now you probably have uncovered new ideas and categories that were not part of your original outline. Before writing your first draft, examine your outline, and make any necessary changes. Your revised outline will guide you in writing your report and your table of contents.

Section-by-Section Development

Concentrate on only one section of your report at a time. After gathering the raw material you must create a finished product. Students often find that this is the most intimidating part of their research: pulling together a large body of information and presenting it coherently in a polished report. "What do I do now with all this stuff?" you ask. Don't despair! Those long hours of work need not lead to chaos and hysteria. Don't harm the quality of your effort as you approach the finish line by randomly throwing everything on the page, simply to be done with it. Remember that your final report will be the *only* concrete evidence of the work you have done. You can communicate a sense of the quality of your work by controlling each step.

Begin by classifying your notecards in groups according to the section of your outline to which each card is keyed. Next, find yourself a flat working surface (a large table or desk). Take the notecards for your background section and arrange them in logical order. Now, lay them out, one after another, in rows on your desk, as you would lay out playing cards. Thus armed with your outline, your statement of purpose, your own expertise, and your logically ordered notecards, you are ready to write your first section.

As you move from idea to idea, provide appropriate commentary and transitions and footnote each source of data. When you have completed your introductory section, proceed to the others, weaving ideas together by following the outline. Eventually you will have a first draft, and most of the battle will be over.

Proper Documentation

Placing Numbers and Footnotes In most research projects you must rely heavily on the information and ideas of others. Use footnotes to credit each source. Footnotes satisfy three major professional requirements: ethics, efficiency, and authority.

Footnotes are a matter of *ethics* in that the originator of an idea deserves to be acknowledged whenever that idea is mentioned. This is both a moral and a legal imperative. All published material is protected by copyright laws, which, like a patent for an invention, protect the originator. Therefore, failure to acknowledge your source when quoting or paraphrasing could make you liable to a charge of plagiarism, even if your omission was unintentional.

Footnotes are also a matter of *efficiency.* They provide a continuous chain through which most of our world's printed knowledge can be readily located. For example, you may make a brief reference to an article in a professional journal. Your footnote will enable an interested reader to locate that source easily and efficiently. As you footnote, then, you add to the ongoing classification of knowledge that has made human progress possible. Without such a classification system, each new generation would have to begin near zero to rediscover things known for centuries but never passed along.

Finally, footnotes are a matter of *authority.* In making claims about situations or things ("A Mercedes-Benz is a better car than a Ford Granada") you are liable to be challenged with "Says who?" This is the time your homework will pay off. If you can produce data on road tests, frequency of repairs, resale value, workmanship, owner comments, and so on, you lend authority to your claim by showing that your statement is based on *fact* rather than sheer *opinion.* Your credibility increases in direct relation to the expert references you produce to support your claims.

Using an Effective Footnote Format   Place your footnote number immediately following and half a line above the quoted or paraphrased material, like this:[1]. Perhaps you will have a paragraph in which all the ideas are yours except for the borrowed idea in the last two lines. If so, use a hinge sentence — "Jones has shown that women are emotionally stronger than men" — to separate your own data from borrowed data. Otherwise, a footnote number at the end of the paragraph might make your reader think that the entire paragraph is borrowed.

Place the footnotes themselves at the bottom of the appropriate page or in numerical order on one page at the end of your report. The second option is easiest and most popular.

Documentation can follow several different formats. The following format is used by the Modern Language Association. However, your instructor or supervisor may request a different format, such as one of the parenthetical approaches shown later in this chapter. Whichever you choose, be sure to use *one* format consistently and to provide all necessary reference information: author; title of work; place of publication; publisher; year; exact page numbers (in most cases):

Footnote Format for Books

Single author:

[1]   John Jones, <u>How to Bore Students</u> (New York: Bogus Press, 1962), p. 151.

Two or more authors:

> [2] Harvey Keck and Roger Cayer, <u>Cave Exploration</u> (Philadelphia: Amherst Publishers, 1977), pp. 68-69.

For more than three authors, use "Harvey Keck et al."

A team of authors who are not named:

> [3] <u>The New English Dictionary</u> (Toronto, Ontario: Northwoods Press, 1950), p. 451.

An editor:

> [4] Gerald Jackson, ed., <u>Stories from the World of Wealth</u> (Boston: Leverett Publishers, 1975), p. 3.

A quote of a quote. (When the author of the book you have read has quoted from another book, begin by listing the original source.):

> [5] Thomas Ashton, <u>Tips for Driving Safety</u> (Wellfleet, Mass.: Peninsula Press, 1974), p. 431; reprinted in Leslie Foye, <u>The Car as Status Symbol</u> (New York: Tiffany Press, 1975), p. 41.

A subsequent reference to an earlier noted work. If you have cited two works by the same author, include the work's specific title in a subsequent reference:

> [6] Jones, p. 173.

Or, for the same reference used back-to-back:

> [6] Ibid., p. 42.

Footnote Format for Articles

A magazine article:

> [7] Barbara Burger, "My Life as a Playboy Bunny," <u>Atlantic</u>, 12 Dec. 1975, pp. 18-22.

If the article lists no author, list all other information.

A journal article:

> [8] John Teacher, "The Declining Literacy Rate," <u>Education Review</u>, 15, No. 4 (Fall 1969), p. 5.

A newpaper article:

> [9] Alvin Thackery, "The Nuclear Energy Compromise," <u>Boston Times</u>, 15 March 1976, p. 15, cols. 1-2.

Footnote Format for Miscellaneous Items

An interview:

      ¹⁰ John Cooper, President of Datronics, in an interview on Dec. 4, 1976.

A questionnaire:

      ¹¹ Figures for the tabulation of responses to a questionnaire administered to 150 freshmen at Idaho College, May 12, 1975.

An encyclopedia entry:

      ¹² "Hydraulics," <u>Technical Encyclopedia</u>, 1971, Vol. IX, p. 723.

If the entry is signed, begin with author's name.

    All other items (corporate or government pamphlets, reports, dissertations, or other unpublished works) should be footnoted as follows:

      ¹³ Author [if known], <u>Title of Work</u> (Organization for which the work was written, date of completion), page numbers.

In all cases, provide your reader with enough information to locate the original source. Notice that the first line of a footnote entry is indented five spaces, the footnote is single-spaced, and footnotes are separated by a double space.

Using an Effective Bibliography Format   Your bibliography is a list of all sources you have consulted, arranged alphabetically by author's last name. In some ways a bibliography repeats the information contained in your footnotes; however, it provides your reader with a quick, alphabetical reference. Moreover, it lists not only footnoted sources, but *all* sources consulted. Figure 7-11 shows a partial bibliography on a single topic, for the sample paper on pages 168–73. The entries include books, newspaper and magazine articles, research reports, and an interview. Notice that each entry is single-spaced, that the second line of the entry is indented five spaces, and that double spacing separates individual entries. When the author's name is not available, the title of the work is listed first, in the same alphabetical order. Place the bibliography page at the very end of your report.

Alternative Systems of Documentation   Here are two of several simplified systems of documentation used in technical and scientific writing:

Bibliography

Blocke, John. "Geologist Balderdashes Hopes for Offshore Drilling." The Cape Codder, 1 Aug. 1974, p. 3, cols. 2-3.

Boesch, Donald F., et al. Oil Spills and the Marine Environment. Cambridge: Ballinger Press, 1974.

"'Clean Atlantic' Vows Protection against East Coast Oil Spills." Cape Cod Times, 25 Feb. 1976, p. 1, col. 2.

Dillin, John. "Offshore Oil: America's Trillion-Dollar Decision." Christian Science Monitor, 15 Apr. 1976, p. 4., cols. 1-2.

Flanagan, Dennis. "The Energy Resources of the Earth." Scientific American, 16 Aug. 1971, pp. 19-24.

McBride, Arthur. Former Oil Geologist with Exxon. Interview regarding effects of offshore drilling. Harwich, Mass., on May 7, 1976.

Offshore Oil Task Group. The Georges Bank Petroleum Study: Impact on New England Environmental Quality of Hypothetical Regional Petroleum Development. Boston: Mass. Institute of Technology, Vol. II, Report No. MITSG 73-5, 1973.

Oil and The Environment: The Prospect. Houston, Shell Oil Co., 1972.

"Oil Drilling." The Harpers Encyclopedia of Science. New York: Harper and Row Publishers, 1963.

Raven, Peter H., and Helena Curtis. Biology of Plants. New York: Worth Publishers, 1970.

Vorse, Heaton. "Southwind." Provincetown Advocate, 16 May 1975, p. 5, col. 2.

"We Need Guarantees." Vertical File on Oil, Cape Cod Community College Library, March 18, 1975.

FIGURE 7-11   A Sample Bibliography

Parenthetical Author/Year Designations. In the author/year system, list your references alphabetically by author at the end of your report:

REFERENCES

Albey, John. *Career Choices.* San Francisco: Hamilton Publishers, 1968.
Crashaw, Harold. *Technology and Careers.* Boston: Little, Brown and Co., 1975.

When referring to a work in your text, insert the author's name and publication date in parentheses:

Seventy-five percent of dental technicians interviewed expressed an interest in further professional training. (Albey, 1968)

When quoting a passage you might include specific page numbers:

Albey (1968: 83–84) claims that medical technologists "feel challenged by their work."

When the writer's name is mentioned in the text, it is not repeated within the parentheses.

List of Parenthetical Numbers. Another technique is to number your references in the order you first refer to them in the text. If you number a reference 1, for example, use the same number (along with the page number on which the information was found) whenever you refer to that work:

Seventy-five percent of dental technicians interviewed expressed an interest in further professional training. (1:83)

Because documentation practices vary widely, check on the requirements of your school or organization before you write up your research findings.

Writing the Final Draft

When you have written and fully documented your first draft, you are ready to write your final draft. Polish your early draft by adding transitions, diagrams, examples, commentaries, and topic and area headings. Revise sentences that are awkward or unclear, or provide little information.

Figure 7-12 shows the first section (introduction) of a student-written research report. Study it carefully to see how the writer has woven multiple sources together.

THE POTENTIAL EFFECTS OF OFFSHORE OIL DRILLING

ON THE MARINE LIFE OF GEORGES BANK

INTRODUCTION

In offshore oil drilling, a well is drilled into the
suspected oil-containing sediments (bottom residue) lying
under the ocean's floor. An oil well is a steel-encased
hole that serves as a pipeline from the underground petroleum
source to the surface.[1]

The United States has potential oil reserves under its
continental shelf. The shelf surrounds the entire land mass
of North America and is an extension of, and connected with,
the adjacent coastal plain.[2] It extends from the low-water
line to the area where there is a marked increase in steep-
ness toward the deep sea floor.[3] Off the East Coast of the
United States the shelf is approximately seventy-five miles
wide.[4] Directly east of Cape Cod lies one of the potentially
richest oil reserves anywhere under the continental shelf.
This area, known as Georges Bank, has also some of the best
fishing grounds off the United States coast.

In 1973, citing our energy squeeze, President Nixon
called for immediate exploration of available energy sources,

FIGURE 7-12 A Student-Written Introduction

2

including increased drilling on the shelf.[5] By 1976, the
United States was using 30 percent of the oil produced world-
wide.[6] New England alone consumed 40 percent of the nation's
oil products.[7] The oil we are consuming today is a non-
renewable source of energy.[8] Projections of the world's
available oil show that the supply will be exhausted by the
year 2075,[9] making it imperative that we develop alternative
energy sources. The oil that can be extracted from the continental shelf will help to lengthen and stabilize our long
period of transition from fossil fuels (oil and gas) to new
energy sources. Until such a transition can take place, our
dependence on foreign oil -- more than 50 percent of United
States oil is imported[10] -- makes us vulnerable. Oil
drilling on the continental shelf could help decrease our
dependence on oil imports.

There are mixed opinions about whether a marketable
quantity of oil exists under Georges Bank. John Brown, a
geologist in Dennisport, feels that the existence of extensive reserves is possible but not probable.[11] Donald
Marshall, an oil geologist in Hyannis, is uncertain about
whether oil exists under Georges Bank.[12] On the other hand,

FIGURE 7-12   (*Continued*)

3

the Department of the Interior has reported that the Atlantic

continental shelf may contain 5.5 billion barrels of oil.[13]

If oil is indeed present, drilling on Georges Bank would

exert a positive economic influence on the area, according to

Mr. Marshall. Charter fishing should increase as a result of

increased marine life, and the fishing industry, in general,

would be revitalized. He cited the thriving fishing industry

in the North Sea as evidence:

> Once the oil-drilling activity began, the fish
> population -- which had nearly disappeared due to over-
> fishing -- began to return: especially cod, in the North
> Sea, the Java Sea, and the Persian Gulf.[14]

The legs of drilling platforms function as artificial reefs,

where marine life seems to flourish.[15]

Some critics argue that the benefits derived from

increased marine life would be wiped out in the event of a

major drilling accident. Defenders of the project, however,

argue that the waters and sands of Padre Island, the nation's

largest national seashore, remain perfectly clean; this area

forms the western end of the Gulf of Mexico, which contains

the world's most extensive offshore oil-drilling facilities.[16]

To date, offshore oil production has accounted for 2.1

percent of all oil pollution sources.[17] The oil companies

FIGURE 7-12   (*Continued*)

4

have a 99.95 percent safety record for all offshore drilling

activities. Out of approximately 18,200 producing oil wells

in the United States coastal waters, nine have caused "major"

spills.[18]

Against this general background, the purpose of this re-

port is to analyze information on the possible effects of off-

shore oil drilling on Cape Cod's marine life. It will compare

characteristics of the Georges Bank ecosystem with those of

already existing offshore oil drilling locations. The report

is intended to inform the general reader about the most recent

data on this subject.

My information sources include research reports, news-

paper and magazine articles, interviews with two local geolo-

gists, a statement by the Association for the Preservation of

Cape Cod, scientific encyclopedias, and a botany textbook. A

glossary of terms is included at the end of this report.

The major topics to be discussed include:

      I.   Marine Life on Georges Bank

     II.   The Effects of Potential Massive Oil Spills

    III.   The Effects of Chronic Low-Level Oil Spills

     IV.   Physical Characteristics Affecting Oil
            Drilling on Georges Bank

FIGURE 7-12   (*Continued*)

5

FOOTNOTES

[1] *The Why and How of Undersea Drilling* (Washington, D.C.: The American Petroleum Institute, 1970), p. 4.

[2] "Oil," *McGraw-Hill Encyclopedia of Science and Technology*, 1960, Vol. III, p. 481.

[3] "Oil Drilling," *The Harpers Encyclopedia of Science*, 1963, p. 282.

[4] *McGraw-Hill Encyclopedia*, p. 482.

[5] Andrea Stevens, "Biggest Oil Spills Caused by Tankers," *Cape Cod Standard Times*, 20 Sept. 1973, p. 5, cols. 1-2.

[6] John Brown, Geologist, in an interview on the effects of offshore oil drilling on May 7, 1976. See Appendix A for full text of interview.

[7] Charles Koeler, "Geologist: Offshore Oil Drilling 'has to happen,'" *Cape Cod Standard Times*, 28 July 1975, p. 1, cols. 3-4.

[8] Brown interview.

[9] M. King Hubbert, "The Energy Resources of the Earth," *Scientific American*, 224, No. 3 (1969), p. 69.

[10] Donald Marshall, Geologist, in an interview on the effects of offshore oil drilling on May 7, 1976. See Appendix B for full text of interview.

[11] John Blocke, "Geologist Balderdashes Hopes for Offshore Oil," *The Cape Codder*, 1 Aug. 1974, p. 3, cols. 2-3.

[12] Marshall interview.

FIGURE 7-12   (*Continued*)

6

¹³ Paul Kemprecos, "Fishing," <u>The Cape Codder</u>, 4 Apr. 1974, p. 8, cols. 1-3.

¹⁴ "We Need Guarantees," Vertical File on Oil, Cape Cod Community College Library, 18 Mar. 1975.

¹⁵ Marshall interview.

¹⁶ "Oil Rigs off Cape Cod May Aid Fishing Yields," <u>Cape Cod News</u>, 1 Aug. 1973, p. 3, cols. 3-4.

¹⁷ John Dillin, "Pollution Challenge to World Underlined," <u>Christian Science Monitor</u>, 28 June 1974, p. 2, cols. 1-4.

¹⁸ "Favors Oil Drilling," <u>Cape Cod Standard Times</u>, 24 Mar. 1975, p. 3, cols. 1-3.

FIGURE 7-12   (*Continued*)

CHAPTER SUMMARY

Research is designed to uncover facts that will increase your effectiveness as an educated person. It is not only an activity of scientists and scholars; in fact, everyone wishing to separate fact from opinion and to arrive at valid and convincing conclusions will do their homework.

There are many sources for research data: Primary sources include memory, personal observation, questionnaires, interviews, letters of inquiry and business or technological records; secondary sources include books, articles, reports, brochures, films, and other publications. Overall, the library is your most valuable secondary source. Learn early how to use the library. Ask your reference librarian for help with sticky problems.

Follow these steps in planning your report:

1. Choose a topic that is interesting and sufficiently narrow.
2. Make a working bibliography before you proceed.
3. Compose a clear statement of purpose and a working outline.
4. Move from general sources to particular ones, skimming your material to save time.
5. Take selected notes, keyed to your outline, with all sources clearly identified.
6. Plan early for interviews, questionnaires, and inquiry letters.
7. If possible, conclude by having a look for yourself.

Follow these steps in writing your report:

1. Revise your working outline.
2. Follow an introduction-body-conclusion structure.
3. Concentrate on only one section at a time.
4. Credit each data source using an acceptable documentation format.
5. Write your final draft.

EXERCISES

1. *In class:* Working in groups of four or five, decide on a subject for research. Individually, narrow this topic to a usable one and write your own detailed statement of purpose. As a group, compare your individual purpose statements for usefulness and quality of focus.

2. *In class:* As a group, choose a familiar campus or community issue. Working together, construct a set of interview questions that could be ad-

ministered to several people who are centrally involved in the issue. Also, construct a questionnaire for sampling a broad range of attitudes about this issue. Be sure to assess each question for clarity and precision.

3. Each of the sentences below states either a fact or an opinion. Rewrite all statements of opinion as statements of fact. Remember that a fact can be measured, duplicated, or defined.

    a. This book is boring.
    b. My vacation was too short.
    c. The salary for this position is $15,000 yearly.
    d. This bicycle is reasonably priced.
    e. We walked five miles last Saturday.
    f. My motorcycle gets great gas mileage.
    g. This course has been very helpful.
    h. German shepherds are larger than French poodles.
    i. This apartment is much too small for our family.
    j. Our new car is the most expensive American compact model.

4. Find three articles about the same newsworthy event. Read each article carefully, separating fact from opinion. Underline all factual statements in blue and all statements of opinion in red. Combine the articles to write a summary of the event, based exclusively on factual information. (Your instructor may provide the articles.)

5. Using the library and other sources, locate and record the required information for *ten* of the following items, and clearly document each source.

    a. The population of your home town.
    b. *The New York Times'* headline on the day you were born.
    c. The world pole-vaulting record.
    d. The operating principle of a diesel engine.
    e. The name of the first woman elected to the United States Congress.
    f. The exact value of today's American dollar in French francs.
    g. The comparative interest rates on an auto loan charged by three local savings banks.
    h. The major cause of small-business failures.
    i. The top-rated compact car in the *world* today.
    j. The origin of the word *capitalism*.
    k. The distance from Boston to Bombay.
    l. The definition of *pheochromocytoma*.
    m. An effective plant for keeping insects out of a home garden.
    n. The originator of the statement: "There's a sucker born every minute."
    o. The names and addresses of five major United States paper companies.
    p. Australian job opportunities in your major field.
    q. The titles and specific locations of five recent articles on terrorism.

6. Make a list of all periodicals in your library that relate to your major field or an area of interest. Arrange these works in their order of usefulness and save your list for future reference.

7. Choose one situation from your *personal* experience (past, present, or projected) in which research could help you solve a problem or answer an

important question. In a one- or two-paragraph memo to your instructor, describe the problem or question and the sources you would consult in order to obtain suitable answers.

8. Arrange an interview with a successful person in your major field. Make a list of general areas for questioning: current job opportunities, chances for promotion, salary range, training requirements, outlook for the next decade, working conditions, level of job satisfaction, and so on. Next, formulate an organized set of interview questions that will yield specific answers. Finally, conduct the interview and write up your results and specific conclusions in a brief, informal report to your instructor.

9. Revise the following questions in order to make them adequate for inclusion in a questionnaire:

   a. Do you feel that a woman president could do the job as well as a man?

   b. Don't you think that euthanasia is a crime?

   c. Do you oppose increased government spending?

   d. Do you feel that welfare recipients are too lazy to support themselves?

   e. Do you think that teachers are responsible for the falling literacy rate among American students?

   f. Aren't humanities studies a waste of time?

   g. Do you prefer Dipsi Cola to other leading brands?

10. *Organizing the Research and Writing Your Report:* Prepare a research report by completing the following steps. (Your instructor may establish a timetable for completion of these phases.)

Phase One: Preliminary Steps

   a. Choose a topic of *immediate* concern and interest. Avoid the old cherries and research a question that genuinely interests you.

   b. Narrow your topic and check with your instructor for approval and further advice.

   c. Make a working bibliography in order to ensure that your library contains sufficient resource materials. Don't delay this step!

   d. Write a clear statement of purpose and submit it in a proposal memo to your instructor.

   e. Make a working outline.

   f. Make a list of things you already know about your topic.

Phase Two: Collecting Data

   a. In your research, move from the general to the specific; begin with broad discussions in general reference works in order to develop a good overview.

   b. Skim your material, looking for high points. In this way, you will cover the most ground in the least time.

   c. Take selective notes. Don't write everything down! Use notecards.

   d. Plan and administer (or distribute) questionnaires, interviews, and letters of inquiry.

   e. Whenever possible, conclude your research with direct observation.

Phase Three: Organizing Your Data and Writing Your Report

   a. Revise and adjust your working outline, as needed.

   b. Follow the introduction-body-conclusion format in writing your report.

   c. Concentrate on only *one* section of your report at a time.

   d. Fully document all sources of information.

   e. Write your final draft.

   f. Proofread carefully and add all needed supplements (title page, letter of transmittal, abstract, summary, appendix, glossary).

Due Dates:

   List of possible topics due:

   Final topic due:

   Proposal memo due:

   Working bibliography and working outline due:

   Notecards due:

   Copies of questionnaires, interview questions, and inquiry letters due:

   Revised outline due:

   First draft of report due:

   Final draft of report with all supplements and full documentation due:

   Here is a list of possible research projects:

   a. Trace the history of your major department through its stages of planning, formation, staffing and growth as part of your college. Do your findings show a steady growth, periods of decline, or some other trend? What is the outlook for your department within the institution?

   b. Trace the history of your major as an academic specialty. Which institutions offered the first courses or the first major? To what needs were institutions responding in offering this major? Where are the highest-ranked programs now offered? What is the outlook for further growth in this discipline?

   c. Identify a modern discovery in your field that dramatically advanced the state of the art (as the discovery of antibiotics revolutionized medical treatment). Establish how the discovery was made and trace its beneficial effects along with any negative effects (antibiotics can cause severe allergic reactions and organic complications, and have caused resistant strains of organisms to develop).

   d. Conduct a survey of student opinions about some proposed changes in the curriculum or another controversial campus issue. If possible, compare your findings with national statistics about student attitudes on this issue.

   e. Discover how faculty and tenure decisions are made at your school. What are the primary criteria, and how are they ranked (e.g., research activity, publication, quality of teaching, service to the department and college, community service)? Trace the history of tenure decisions over the last ten years. Do any trends emerge?

   f. Find out how the quality of your local water supply measures up to national standards. Has the quality increased or decreased over the past ten years? What are the major factors affecting local water quality? What is the outlook for the next decade?

g. Trace the modern history of zoning ordinances in your town. How has residential zoning affected the character of the town? How has business zoning affected the character and economy of the town? What is the outlook for future zoning changes?

h. Find out which major department on your campus attracts the most students, and why. Has this department always been so popular? Will it continue to be? Trace its recent history.

i. Discover what qualities most employers look for in a job candidate. Have employers' expectations changed over the last ten years? If so, why?

j. Find out which geographic section of the United States is experiencing the greatest economic and population growth. What are the major reasons for this growth? Trace the recent history of this change.

8

Using an Effective Format and Supplements

CHAPTER GOALS

DEFINITIONS
  Report Complexity: Informal or Formal
  Format
  Supplements

PURPOSE OF AN EFFECTIVE FORMAT

PURPOSE OF REPORT SUPPLEMENTS

CREATING AN EFFECTIVE FORMAT
  High-Quality Paper
  Neat Typing
  Uniform Margins, Spacing, and
      Indentation
  Consistently Numbered Pages
  Introduction-Body-Conclusion Structure
    Introduction
    Body
    Conclusion
    Section Length
  Effective Headings
    Make Your Headings Informative
    Make Your Headings Comprehensive
    Make Your Headings Parallel
    Lay Out Headings by Rank

COMPOSING REPORT SUPPLEMENTS
  Cover
  Title Page
    Title
    Placement of Title-Page Items

Letter of Transmittal
    Introduction
    Body
    Conclusion
  Table of Contents
  Table of Illustrations
  Informative Abstract
  Glossary
  Footnote Page
  Bibliography Page
  Appendix

CHAPTER SUMMARY

EXERCISES

CHAPTER GOALS

Upon completing this chapter, you will know:

- The general differences between informal and formal reports.
- The meaning and purpose of report format and supplements.
- How to create a format of professional quality.
- How to select and compose supplements that follow the conventions of formal reporting and make your formal report more accessible to your reader.
- Where to place these supplements to complement your report.

DEFINITIONS

Report Complexity: Informal or Formal

Depending on your specific job and reporting responsibilities you may be writing brief (informal) reports, longer and more complicated (formal) reports, or both.

Informal reports vary in length and arrangement. Often you might write brief memos of less than a page, as well as progress reports and proposals of several pages. These are usually written for readers within your organization. From time to time you might write formal reports, which are usually at least ten pages long and contain information about projects or studies too complex to be covered in an informal report. Accordingly, formal reports contain parts not found in informal reports. Formal reports are often written for readers outside as well as inside your organization and may form part of a permanent record.

Both types follow certain format conventions that make their information more accessible and give them a professional appearance.

There is no rule for deciding whether any given data should be presented in an informal or a formal report. For instance, a short proposal to improve safety procedures in your laboratory might be written as a memo, whereas a proposal for merging with another company would most likely be written as a formal report. Likewise, a set of instructions for a colleague who will fill in as department supervisor during your absence might be informally written in a few pages, whereas instructions for operating new equipment in your inhalation therapy unit would most likely be formally written and permanently filed as a manual. In short, the specific reporting task will determine the complexity of the report. Sometimes, in fact, a certain report may not fit neatly into either the informal or formal category, but may fall somewhere in between. The point is to make your report only as detailed and as formal as it needs to be to get the job done.

Whether you write an informal or formal report, you will need to create a professional format. In a formal report you will need to include some or all of the supplements discussed in this chapter.

Format

Format is the mechanical arrangement of words on the page: indentation, margins, spacing, typeface, headings, page numbering, and division of report sections. Format determines the physical appearance of your report.

Supplements

Supplements are added elements that make the formal report more accessible or convenient for the reader. The title page, letter of transmittal, table of contents, and the abstract give the reader quick summary information of one kind or another about the content of the report. The glossary and appendixes either detail supporting data or help the reader follow certain technical sections of the report. A reader may refer to them or skip them according to his or her needs. Footnotes and bibliography identify your sources of data. All supplements are written *after* you complete your report proper. These items greatly affect your report's readability.

PURPOSE OF AN EFFECTIVE FORMAT

Your writing should be impressive in appearance and readability as well as in content. *What your report looks like* and *how it is arranged* are just as important as what it has to say. An effective format shows that you have refined your product — the product that represents *you* (your commitment to quality, attention to detail, and overall competence) to your reader. Sometimes you will write for someone you haven't yet met. Then it will be especially important not to have inadequate margins, ugly erasures, or poorly organized information. A good format helps you look good.

All readers expect material that is pleasing to the eye and easy to follow. No matter how accurate and vital your information, a ragtag presentation will surely alienate the reader. How seriously, for instance, would you take the information in a textbook that looked like Figure 8-1? How would you judge the author, publisher, and credibility of this piece? Imagine trying to follow such instructions! Figure 8-2 shows the same information after a format overhaul. The information is now pleasing to the eye, easy to follow, and generally more credible. As readers, we take good format for granted; that is, we hardly notice format *unless* it is offensive.

Your format is the wrapping on your information package. Just as there are many techniques and styles for wrapping a package, there are many effective formats. In fact, many companies have their own requirements. Here you will study one style, which you may later modify according to your needs.

PURPOSE OF REPORT SUPPLEMENTS

The central message of a formal report is in its introduction-body-conclusion sections. Supplements to the report help the reader to grasp the material by providing "a place for everything." They also increase credibility by making the report look professional. Supplements can be time savers: a busy reader may read only your letter of transmittal, table of contents, and abstract for key information. If you have ever written a college research paper you probably used the same approach — skimming prefaces, tables of contents, and introductions to many library books to locate relevant information. Typical formal reports in fact are likely to be read by many people for a wide variety of purposes. Technically qualified persons may be studying the actual body of the report and the appendixes for supporting data such as maps, graphs, or charts. The managerial staff, on the other hand, may read only the letter of transmittal and the abstract. If they read any of the report proper, they are likely to read only the recommendations. Most supplements, then, are designed to accommodate readers with various purposes.

To appreciate the importance of supplements, picture yourself using a textbook that lacks a cover, title, preface, table of contents, index, or special appendixes. Without proper binding, pages would be scattered everywhere; without a title the book would not indicate whether it was about writing, whaling, worm farming, or whatever; without a preface, the book would not show whether it is written for beginning students, laypersons, or experts. If

Giving the IM Injection

First of all, the preparation for giving the injection must be ~~taken care of~~ carried out. This includes: selecting the correct medication, preparing the needle, and drawing the medication. In selecting the medication, it must be triple cheecked to ensure that the right medication and dosage is being given. This is done by checking the order against the medication card, against the label on the drug container. Have~~ing~~ the needle ready to go ~~is important because it~~ in order to prevent fumbling with the needle and medication bottle when drawing up the medication. ~~It is important to~~ Make sure that the needle is tight to the ~~syri~~ syringe and that it is the right size. Freeing the plunger so that it will draw back and push forward easily is a good idea as it prevents fighting with it when it may be in an awkward position, like in the patient's leg. Drawing up the medication has several points that are important in avoiding contamination of the needle, ormedication, and in ensuring that the right dosage is being given.

For ease of explanation I am assuming that the medication is in liquid form in a container with a rubber seal that is supposed to be the correct dose. First, the *wipe* rubber

FIGURE 8-1   An Ineffective Format

seal of the container ~~must be wiped~~ with an alcoholswab to

clean it.To draw the medication out of the container easily,

air, matching the amount of liquidto be withdrawn, must be

injected into the container. This prevents forming a ~~vacu~~

vacuum when the medication is being drawn out and the

plunger will not have to beheld. Any air that is is in

the barrel of the syringe must be broken loose by ~~taooubg~~

tapping the sides of the barrel to cuaseair bubbles to

travel to the top near the base of the need le. This is

so
~~os~~ air can be expelled ~~in the nee~~ from the needle to

avoid giving the patient an injection containing air.

FIGURE 8-1 (*Continued*)

GIVING THE INTRAMUSCULAR INJECTION

Selecting the Correct Medication and Dosage

CAUTION: Triple-check the physician's order against the medication card and the label on the medication container, to ensure that you administer the correct medication in precise dosage.

After selecting the correct medication and dosage, prepare your needle and syringe.

Preparing Your Needle and Syringe

1. Choose a twenty-six (26)-gauge needle and affix it tightly to the neck of your syringe.

2. Free the syringe plunger so that it will draw back and push forward easily, to avoid later difficulties when the needle is in the muscle.

With your needle and syringe prepared, you are ready to draw up the medication.

Drawing up the Medication

CAUTION: Use aseptic technique to avoid contamination of the needle and/or medication; recheck the correct dosage on the container label.

FIGURE 8-2   An Effective Format

1. Wipe the rubber seal of the drug container with an alcohol swab, in order to kill all surface bacteria.

2. Slowly inject a volume of air, equal to the volume of liquid to be withdrawn, into the container. (This step prevents the formation of a vacuum in the container, thereby eliminating the need to pull the plunger as the liquid is drawn out.)

3. Hold the syringe with needle-end up and tap the syringe barrel to dislodge any air bubbles from the barrel walls. The dislodged bubbles will travel to the top of the barrel, near the base of the needle.

4. Expel the air bubbles through the needle by pushing gently on the plunger with your thumb. (With this step, you avoid injecting air into your patient.)

FIGURE 8-2   (*Continued*)

there were no table of contents or index, special areas of information would be impossible to locate unless one read the whole text; if there were no appendixes, specialized data would be buried somewhere in the text, interrupting the flow of the discussion. Clearly, these items are essential.

CREATING AN EFFECTIVE FORMAT

High-Quality Paper

Do not submit your report on perfumed stationery, onionskin, erasable bond, cut-rate typing paper, or pages torn out of a notebook. Type your final draft on 8½ × 11-inch plain, white paper, not "thesis" paper with fancy red borders. Use heavy (20 lb. or higher) bond paper with a high fiber content (25 percent minimum). Erasures with typewriter correction tape are the neatest. Use onionskin paper only for carbon copies.

Neat Typing

The quality of your typing job should match that of your paper. Keep erasures to a minimum and retype all smudged pages. Use a fresh typewriter ribbon and keep your typewriter keys clean. An old ribbon will produce uneven type as in Figure 8-1, and ink-filled typewriter keys will obliterate the spaces within your letters. For quick and easy typewriter cleaning, follow the student-written instructions in Chapter 13.

Uniform Margins, Spacing, and Indentation

Leave the following margins on each page: top margin, 1¼ inches; bottom, 1 inch; left, 1½ inches; right, 1 inch (the larger left margin leaves space for binding your report).

Make your report easy to scan by double spacing within and between paragraphs. Set off a long quote (four or more lines) by separating it from your discussion with double spaces and single spacing the quote itself. Indent the entire quotation five spaces from both right and left margins. When indenting a long quote, use no quotation marks.

Indent the first line of all paragraphs five spaces from the left margin. Be sure that no illustrations extend beyond the inside limits of your margins. As a rule, avoid hyphenating a word at the end of a line; if you must hyphenate, check your dictionary for the correct syllabic breakdown of the word.

Consistently Numbered Pages

Count your title page as page i, without numbering it, and number all pages up to and including your table of contents and abstract with small roman numerals. Use arabic numerals (1, 2, 3, etc.) for subsequent pages, numbering the first page of your report proper as page 1. Place all page numbers in the upper right corner, two spaces below the top edge of the paper and five spaces to the left of the right edge.

Introduction-Body-Conclusion Structure

Organize your report as you would organize a well-structured paragraph; simply expand the basic three-part structure into larger units of information.

Introduction

Preview the discussion in your body section by giving your reader all necessary background information for your subject. This section in your report functions like a topic sentence in a paragraph. Here, the "topic sentence," expanded many times over, promises what you will deliver in your body section. Before discussing any subject, you will need to introduce it properly by describing and defining it.

Body

The body section is the heart of your report. Here, you divide your subject into its parts and their subparts. You also deliver what you promised in your introduction by presenting your collected evidence and findings.

Conclusion

The final section contains no new information. In a conclusion you tie everything together. First, you review the evidence and findings discussed in your body section. Next, you draw conclusions based on the above material. Finally, you make specific recommendations based on your conclusions, if they are needed.

Section Length

The length of each section depends on your subject. For example, a set of instructions (as shown on pages 397–404) usually begins with a detailed introduction listing materials, equipment, cautions, and so on. The body, in turn, enumerates each step and substep. These sections are followed by a brief conclusion, because the key information has been presented earlier.

On the other hand, a problem-solving report (as shown on pages 447–53) may often have a brief introduction outlining the problem. The body, however, may be quite long, explaining the possible and probable causes of the problem. Because the conclusion contains a summary of findings, an overall interpretation of the evidence, and clearly specified recommendations, it will most likely be developed in great detail. Only when your investigation uncovers one specific answer or one definite cause will your body section be relatively short.

Examples of varying section length, according to subject, are found in the sample reports in this text.

Effective Headings

No one finds chaos pleasing. A meal of several courses, with each dish attractively prepared and tastefully served, is more palatable than a mass-produced "mess" hastily cooked in giant cauldrons and dumped on food trays in a cafeteria line. An enjoyable meal is made up of a series of appealing, discrete, easy-to-digest portions.

As we have taste in food, so we have taste in what we see as we read. Imagine your frustration on opening this textbook only to find all its information presented in one big lump, hundreds of pages long, stuffed between two covers. No matter how accurate and vital the information, you would have trouble finding what you needed when you needed it. Like textbooks, many reports are not read in a linear order, from cover to cover, as a novel would be read. Just as you often refer back to specific sections in a textbook, so readers of an article or report refresh their memories by referring to specific sections. Without headings, the information is confusing and frustrating — and often useless, because the readers can't grasp it unless they take an undue amount of time.

Headings help you as well as your readers. Like points on a roadmap they keep you on course and provide transitions from one area of discussion to another. They signal your readers that a part of your discussion has ended and another is about to begin. They make a report less intimidating by partitioning large and diverse areas of data into smaller, more readable parts. Finally, they are good attention-getting devices, helping your readers focus on the parts of your report they find most important. Some guidelines for using headings effectively follow.

Make Your Headings Informative

Phrase all headings so that they are short but informative. Provide a clear and specific preview of your topic. Compare, for instance, these versions of a heading in a set of typewriter-cleaning instructions:

Uninformative
  The Carriage

Informative
  Brushing the Dirt from Beneath the Carriage

Notice that the second version creates an explicit context for the reader, showing exactly what to expect in the upcoming section.

Express your headings as phrases ("Frequency of Lubrication") rather than as awkward pieces of sentences ("Needs Frequent Lubrication").

Make Your Headings Comprehensive

Headings must be comprehensive in two ways: Individual headings must be inclusive and enough headings must be provided to cover all categories. As a frame or fence encloses a specific visual or geographic space, your heading "encloses" or contains an information category. When framing a picture you would logically frame the entire visual area, without leaving out, say, the upper right corner. Follow the same logic of inclusiveness with headings. If your discussion is about the relationship of apples to oranges, be sure that your heading is not simply "Apples."

Also, provide enough headings to contain separately each discrete information category. If apples, oranges, and elephants are three *separate* discussion items, provide a heading for each. In other words, don't combine your discussion of oranges *and* elephants under "Oranges." Take major and minor headings from your outline, as we do in this book.

Make Your Headings Parallel

Because in any set of instructions, for example, all major steps are equally important, express all of them in the same grammatical form and phrasing to emphasize that equality of importance.

Nonparallel Headings
1. Brushing the Dirt from Beneath the Carriage
2. Brushing the Dirt from the Key Faces and Surrounding Areas
3. Clean the Carriage Cylinder with Rubbing Alcohol
4. Cleaning the Paper-Bail Rolls with Rubbing Alcohol
5. Rubbing Alcohol Is Used to Clean the Key Faces
6. Wiping the Dirt from the Typewriter Exterior
7. It Is Crucial That All Dirt Be Wiped from the Work Area

Notice that headings 1, 2, 4, and 6 are expressed as participial phrases, whereas headings 3, 5, and 7 are expressed as complete sentences. Moreover, each of these nonparallel headings is presented in a different mood: heading 3, giving a command, is expressed in the imperative mood; heading 5, making a declarative statement, is expressed in the indicative mood; heading 7, making a recommendation, is expressed in the subjunctive mood. This mood shift obscures the logical relationship between individual steps and confuses the reader. To make these steps parallel, rephrase them as follows.

> *Parallel Headings*
> 3. Cleaning the Carriage Cylinder with Rubbing Alcohol
> 5. Cleaning the Key Faces with Rubbing Alcohol
> 7. Wiping All Dirt from the Surrounding Area

Parallelism is discussed further in Appendix A.

Lay Out Headings by Rank

Within its three general areas, a report will contain major topics; often, major topics will contain subtopics; in turn, subtopics may contain sub-subtopics, depending on the amount of detail the report requires. (Use the logical divisions within your outline as a model for your heading arrangement.) The logic of your divisions will be clear to your reader if your headings reflect the rank of each step in your discussion. The headings in Figure 8-3 vary in typeface, indentation, and position, according to rank. Notice that the sentence immediately following your heading stands independent of the heading. Don't begin your sentence with a pronoun such as "this" or "it" to refer back to the heading.

In keeping with the logic of division, make sure that each section (or subsection, etc.) contains at least two headings. Show major and minor headings in the same relationship in your outline or table of contents.

COMPOSING REPORT SUPPLEMENTS

Report supplements can be classified in two groups:

1. *Supplements that precede your report.* Cover, title page, letter of transmittal, table of contents (and illustrations), and abstract.

2. *Supplements that follow your report.* Glossary, footnotes, bibliography, appendix(es).

Cover

A durable cover improves your report's appearance, provides protection, and holds the pages together. Use a sturdy, plain, light cardboard cover with good page fasteners. Avoid covers with fancy etchings, life scenes, or psychedelic

MAJOR AREA HEADING

Write major headings in full capitals, centered horizontally on the page, two spaces above your following text (and three spaces below your preceding text, for subsequent area headings). Do not underline or italicize.

Major Topic Heading

Begin each word (except for articles and prepositions) in your major topic heading with a capital letter. Make the heading abut the margin, two spaces below the preceding text and two spaces above the following text. Underline or italicize this heading.

Subtopic Heading

Begin each word in your subtopic heading with a capital letter. Indent it five spaces from your left margin and place it two spaces below the preceding text and two spaces above the following text. Underline or italicize this heading.

Sub-Subtopic Heading. Begin each word in your subsubtopic heading with a capital letter. Indent it five spaces from the left margin and place it two spaces below your preceding text and on the same line as the first sentence of your following text (separated by a period). Underline or italicize this heading.

FIGURE 8-3   A Sample Heading System

colors. Reports are serious business, not carnival entries. In general, use a cover only for longer, formal reports, not for anything only a few pages long.

Center the report title and your name four to five inches from the upper edge, as follows:

AN ANALYSIS OF THE EFFECTIVENESS OF THE FRESHMAN REMEDIAL

PROGRAM AT CALVIN COLLEGE

by

Francis Freeman

Title Page

The title page signals your reader by providing certain vital information: report title, author's name, name of person or organization to whom the report is addressed, and date of submission. A good title page lends a touch of class to your report while stimulating your reader's interest.

Title

Your title promises what your report will deliver by stating the report's purpose and content. The following title is effective because it is clear, accurate, comprehensive, specific, concise, and appropriately phrased:

An Effective Title

AN ANALYSIS OF THE EFFECTIVENESS
OF THE FRESHMAN REMEDIAL
PROGRAM AT CALVIN COLLEGE

Word choice is important; notice how slight changes can distort radically this title's intended signal.

An Unclear Title

THE FRESHMAN REMEDIAL PROGRAM
AT CALVIN COLLEGE

This version does not state clearly the purpose of the report. Its signal is confusing. Is the report *describing* the program, *proposing* the establishment of such a program, *giving instructions* for setting it up, or *discussing its history?*

An Inaccurate Title

THE EFFECTIVENESS OF THE FRESHMAN
REMEDIAL PROGRAM AT CALVIN COLLEGE

This version does not state accurately the purpose of the report. In fact, it presents a distorted signal by suggesting that the program's effectiveness is already proven, instead of being an issue in question. Insert key words in your title ("analysis," "instructions," "proposal," "feasibility," "description," "progress," "proposal," etc.) which state accurately the purpose of your report.

A Noncomprehensive Title

AN ANALYSIS OF THE EFFECTIVENESS
OF THE REMEDIAL WRITING PROGRAM
AT CALVIN COLLEGE

Here is a title that fails to name all that the report will cover: namely, an analysis of *all* remedial programs, including mathematics, reading, and writing.

A Nonspecific Title

AN ANALYSIS OF THE EFFECTIVENESS
OF FRESHMAN PROGRAMS AT CALVIN COLLEGE

This version has the reverse deficiency of the one just before it: it promises an analysis of all freshman programs, without focusing on its proper subject — the freshman remedial program. The signal is too broad and imprecise.

A Long-Winded Title

AN EXHAUSTIVE ANALYSIS
OF THE OVERALL EFFECTIVENESS
OF THE SPECIAL PROGRAM
IN REMEDIATION FOR FRESHMAN
WHICH WAS RECENTLY
IMPLEMENTED AT CALVIN COLLEGE

Words like "exhaustive," "overall," "special," "recently," and "implemented" provide no useful information; on the contrary, they obscure the intended signal. Avoid wasted words.

An Inappropriately Phrased Title

THE FRESHMAN REMEDIAL PROGRAM
AT CALVIN COLLEGE:
WINNER OR LOSER?

Phrase your title to stimulate reader interest, but not like a commercial or a sideshow gimmick. Word choice should reflect the significance of your effort.

A "catchy" title too often trivializes an otherwise serious and valuable report.

Careful wording in your title is crucial. One or two missing, excessive, or inaccurate words can throw your reader off the track. To be sure that your title promises what your report delivers, write its final version *after* completing your report.

Placement of Title-Page Items

Do not number your title page, but count it as page i of your prefatory pages. Center the title horizontally on the page, three to four inches below the upper edge, using all capital letters. If the title is longer than six to eight words, center it on two or more single-spaced lines, as in Figure 8-4. Place the items in the following spacing, order, and typescript:

1. Seven spaces below the title and horizontally centered, the word "for" in small letters.

2. One space below, your reader's name followed by his or her position, organization, and address, horizontally centered with the first letter of each word capitalized.

3. Seven spaces below, the word "by" in small letters.

4. Two spaces below, your name, position, and organization on each of three separate single-spaced lines with the first letter of all words capitalized.

5. Five spaces below, the date of report submission written out in full.

You may work out your own line-spacing system, as long as your page is balanced.

Letter of Transmittal

Your letter of transmittal, otherwise called a "cover letter," comes immediately before or after your title page. It is good practice to include a letter of transmittal with any piece of formal writing for a specific reader. Your letter adds a note of courtesy — a human element — besides giving you an ideal place for adding personal remarks or opinions.

Whereas your informative abstract (discussed later in this chapter) summarizes all major findings, conclusions, and recommendations in the report, your letter of transmittal calls attention to data that might be of special interest to a specific reader. Depending on your reporting situation, your letter might:

— Give credit or thanks to people or groups who assisted you in preparing your report.

— Refer your reader to sections of special interest: unexpected or surprising findings, key charts or diagrams, major conclusions, special recommendations, and the like.

```
              AN ANALYSIS OF THE EFFECTIVENESS
                            OF
          THE FRESHMAN REMEDIATION PROGRAM AT CALVIN COLLEGE




                            for

                  Professor John Johnson
                Technical Writing Instructor
                       Calvin College
                   Kalamazoo, Minnesota




                            by

                  Sarah Jane Robertson
                         Student




                   December 25, 1978
```

FIGURE 8-4 A Title Page for a Formal Report

– Discuss the scope and limitations of your study, along with any special problems encountered in gathering data.

– Discuss the need and possible approaches for further or follow-up investigations.

– Describe any personal observations — off-the-record comments — made while you were gathering data and writing your report.

– Briefly explain how and why your report data are useful and offer suggestions for some practical uses of this information.

In many cases the letter of transmittal can be tailored to the particular reader that the report is being sent to. Thus if a report is being sent to a number of people who are variously qualified and bear various relationships to the writer, the accompanying letters of transmittal may vary. In each letter include items from the previous list that will increase your reader's interest in your report. Like your informative abstract, your letter is a preview of your report; but it is a more personal preview. The letter itself follows an introduction-body-conclusion structure.

Introduction

Open with a polite and cordial statement referring to the date and content of the reader's original request for the report. Briefly explain your reasons for submitting your letter and report.

You should maintain a confident and positive tone throughout your letter. Indicate your pride and satisfaction in the work you have done. Avoid apologetic statements, such as "I hope this information is adequate," or "I hope that this report meets your expectations."

Body

In the body of your letter, include items from our list of possibilities (acknowledgments, special problems, limitations, unexpected findings, special conclusions, recommendations, personal observations, and suggestions for further research). Although your abstract is limited to a summary of major findings, conclusions, and recommendations, the body section of your letter provides your reader with an abbreviated overview of the *entire project,* from the moment you received the original request to the moment you submit the completed report.

Conclusion

Tie earlier parts together with a statement of your willingness to answer any questions or personally discuss your findings. End your letter on a positive note, with something like "I believe that the data in this report are accurate, that they have been analyzed rigorously and objectively, and that the recommendations presented are sound." Never close with a tentative or apologetic statement such as "I hope this report is good enough." If you doubt the quality of your work, don't expect your reader to be impressed. In fact, if you feel the need to apologize for any piece of writing, don't submit it without an extensive overhaul.

Figure 8-5 shows a sample letter of transmittal. Individual items and sections are labeled in the right margin for clear illustration. (Your own letter of course would contain no such labels in final draft.)

Table of Contents

Your table of contents serves as a roadmap for your readers and an inventory checklist for you. Because it is based on your outline, this supplement is easy to compose. Simply assign appropriate page numbers to the major area headings, topic headings, and subtopic headings contained in your outline. An effective table of contents shows your readers the logical organization and the high points of your report, while allowing them to locate or review areas of interest quickly and easily.

Here are some guidelines for composing an effective table of contents:

1. List preliminary items (cover letter, abstract) in your table of contents, numbering the pages with small roman numerals. (The title page, although not listed, is counted as page i.) Also, list glossary, appendix, notes, and bibliography sections in your table of contents; number all pages with arabic numerals, continuing the page sequence of your report proper, where page 1 is the first page of your report.

2. Include no headings in your table of contents not listed as headings or subheadings in your report proper; your reader should be able to turn to the listed page and immediately locate the area of interest. Your report proper may, however, contain certain sub- or sub-subheadings that are not listed in the table of contents.

3. Phrase the headings in your table of contents exactly as you phrase the headings in your report proper.

4. List major area headings, major topic headings, and any subtopic headings in varying typescript, capitalization, and indentation to reflect clearly their respective ranks. Write major section and area headings in capital letters; begin each word in major topic headings with a capital letter, and underline and indent three spaces from the left margin; indent subtopic headings six spaces from the left margin and do not underline. Give each part a specified place and rank, in order of its importance.

5. Use double-spaced horizontal dots (.......................) to connect the individual heading to its matching page number.

The table of contents in Figure 8-6 is adapted from the outline for "An Analysis of the Advisability of Converting Our Office Building from Oil to Gas Heat." The formal outline was shown in Chapter 6.

                                        43 Ocean Avenue
                                        West Harwich,
                                           Massachusetts 02046
                                        December 1, 1978

Professor Grand Savant
Technical Writing
   Instructor
Wishbone College
Plymouth,
   Massachusetts 03456

Dear Professor Savant:

I am enclosing the report you requested on   Introduction
October 3, 1978, analyzing the alleged advan-
tages of the Wankel rotary combustion engine
over the reciprocating, piston-driven V-8
engine. Close comparison of the two indicates that the Wankel might be the engine of
the future.

Although long-term testing will take several   Body
years to complete, the engine clearly shows   Need for
economic and manufacturing advantages, as   further tests
well as unique operational qualities.
Simplicity of design, economy of operation,   Section of
and high level of performance make the   special interest
Wankel engine an attractive alternative to
the conventional piston-driven engine, as
shown in the comparative specification chart
in Appendix A. (I am grateful to Professor   Credit
John Jones, of the Engineering Department,
for his help in constructing this chart.)
Please note that absence of available data   Limitations
prevented me from including the Diesel
engine in the above comparison.

Because it is light, easy to build, and   Body
long-lasting, the Wankel engine should find
many practical applications in automobiles,   Practical
snowmobiles, boats, lawnmowers, generators,   uses
and tractors. In fact, you might wish to

FIGURE 8-5   A Letter of Transmittal for a Formal Report

page 2, Professor Grand Savant, 12/1/78

delay your own planned purchase of a new   Personal
inboard engine until next spring, when rotary   suggestion
boat engines will be available for retail
purchase.

In conclusion, I believe that the analysis   Conclusion
described in this report objectively shows
that the Wankel engine holds a great deal of
promise for energy-efficient use. If you
have any questions after reading the enclosed
analysis, please feel free to call me at
430-356-9856.

                    Sincerely,

                    Ronald Varg

FIGURE 8-5 (*Continued*)

iii

TABLE OF CONTENTS

LETTER OF TRANSMITTAL   ii

INFORMATIVE ABSTRACT   v

INTRODUCTION   1

   Background   1

   Purpose   1

   Intended Audience   1

   Data Sources   1

   Limitations   2

   Scope   2

COLLECTED DATA   2

   Description of Our Present Heating System   2
      Physical Condition   2
      Required Yearly Maintenance   3
      Fuel Supply Problems   4
      Cost of Operation   4

   Removal of the Oil Burner and Tank   5
      Data from the Oil Company   5
      Data from the Salvage Company   5
      Possibility of Private Sale   6

FIGURE 8-6   A Table of Contents for a Formal Report

iv

TABLE OF CONTENTS (continued)

Installation of a Gas Pipe from the Street to the
Building   6
    Procedure   6
    Cost of Installation   7
    Cost of Landscaping   7

Installation of a Gas Burner   8
    Procedure   8
    Cost of Plumber's Labor and Materials   9

Estimation of Gas Heating Costs   10
    Rate Determination   10
    Required Yearly Maintenance   10
    Cost Data from Neighboring Facility   10
    Overall Cost of Operation   11

CONCLUSION   11

Summary of Findings   11

Comprehensive Interpretation of Findings   12

Recommendations   12

GLOSSARY   13

APPENDIX   14

FIGURE 8-6   (*Continued*)

Table of Illustrations

Below your table of contents will be a table of illustrations, if needed. If your report contains more than four or five illustrations, place the table of illustrations on a separate page. Figure 8-7 shows a table of illustrations taken from a report titled "The Negative Effects of Strip Mining on Kentucky's Cumberland Plateau."

Informative Abstract

To your reader, your abstract (as discussed in Chapter 3) may be the most important item in your report. Because it summarizes your work, the abstract is always written after your report proper is completed. Sometimes a busy reader will read only your abstract, expecting to find the key points of your report reviewed briefly, logically, and clearly. Provide a clear overview by distilling the essence of your report (statement of purpose, major findings, conclusions, and recommendations) into the fewest words possible.

Writing the abstract gives you the chance to measure your own understanding of the material. Because you are cutting your report's text to roughly 10 percent of its original length — or much less for an abstract of a long report — you need to establish logical connections among related items. If you can't effectively summarize your report, you probably haven't fully mastered your material. In this case, more homework and revision are probably necessary. An effective abstract, on the other hand, shows that you recognize priorities and can differentiate major from minor points.

Use the following guidelines for writing your informative abstract:

1. Use one or more well-developed paragraphs. Make your abstract unified, coherent, and able to stand alone in meaning and emphasis. From this concise piece, your reader should understand your report's purpose and central message.

2. Follow an introduction-body-conclusion structure in which you discuss, in order, purpose, findings, and conclusions and recommendations.

3. Make your abstract intelligible to the general reader. Remember that the people who read it will be widely varied in technical competence, perhaps much more so than the people who read the report itself. Therefore, translate highly technical data for nontechnical readers (managers, clients, and other laypersons).

4. Add no new information to your abstract. Simply summarize your report.

5. Follow strictly the chronology of your report. If your report discusses apples, oranges, and elephants, in this order, follow the same order in your abstract.

6. Emphasize only major points. Omit prefaces, supporting details, compu-

TABLE OF ILLUSTRATIONS

Figure 1. A Contour Map of the Appalachian Region 3

Figure 2. A Contour Map of the Cumberland Plateau 4

Figure 3. Graph of a Ten-Year Contrast of Population
           Figures in the Cumberland Plateau Region . . . 13

Figure 4. Table of a Ten-Year Comparison of Population
           Figures among the Counties of the Cumberland
           Plateau 14

Figure 5. A Map of the Range of the Tennessee Valley
           Authority 20

FIGURE 8-7   A Table of Illustrations for a Formal Report

tations, and lengthy arguments. Often, your table of contents or your report headings will provide a good master plan for composing your abstract.

7. Select a clear order of development (cause and effect, problem-solution, comparison-contrast, etc., as discussed in Appendix A). Your reader should not have to struggle and sweat over your abstract, trying to manufacture the necessary logical connections. Frequent transitional expressions ("first," "next," "finally," "however," "therefore," etc.) will also help to clarify your message.

The informative abstract in Figure 8-8 accompanies the heating conversion report outlined in Chapter 13.

Figure 8-9 shows another student-written abstract that effectively condenses the central message of a long report into a concise piece that can stand alone in meaning and emphasis.

Glossary

A glossary is an alphabetical listing of specialized terms, along with their definitions, immediately following your report proper. Most reports dealing with highly technical subjects and specialized terminology contain glossaries. A glossary is especially useful in a report to be read by both technical and non-technical readers. It allows you to make key definitions available to the nontechnical reader without interrupting the technical reader throughout the report. If fewer than five terms need to be defined, you might place them instead in the introduction section of your report, listing them as working definitions (as discussed in Chapter 4). If you use a separate glossary, inform your reader of its location in your introduction, by using a cross-reference in parentheses: "(see the glossary at the end of this report)."

Follow these guidelines in composing your glossary:

1. Define all terms that would be unfamiliar to a general reader.
2. Define all terms that may have a special meaning in your report (e.g., "In this report, a small business is defined as . . .").
3. Define all terms by giving their class and distinguishing features (as discussed in Chapter 4), unless some terms need more expanded definitions.
4. List your glossary and its first page number in your table of contents.
5. List all terms in alphabetical order. Underline each term and use a colon to separate it from its single-spaced definition.
6. Do not define terms whose meanings are commonly known. In doubtful cases, however, overdefining is better than underdefining.

Figure 8-10 shows part of a glossary that supplements a student-written comparative analysis of two major techniques of natural childbirth. The term *natural childbirth* receives a more expanded definition because it is the subject of the report.

INFORMATIVE ABSTRACT

AN ANALYSIS OF THE ADVISABILITY OF CONVERTING OUR HOME OFFICE

FROM OIL TO GAS HEAT

The rising cost and declining availability of heating oil has led our company to consider the advisability of converting our home office from oil to gas heat. Our present heating needs are supplied by circulating hot air, generated by an electrically fired Zippo oil burner, which is fed by a 275-gallon oil tank. Both burner and tank are twelve years old and in good condition. However, because of short supply and an overworked local fuel distributor, our system has run out of fuel three times during the past two years. In 1976 our total heating costs were $558.28.

Conversion to gas heat would first require removal of the oil burner and tank from the basement. Junko Salvage Company will remove these items at no cost, provided they keep both burner and tank. Next, a gas line would need to be installed from the street to the building. Although the gas company will provide free installation, our landscaping costs, after installation, would be $85.00. Added to this figure is the plumber's labor and materials charge of $570.00 for

FIGURE 8-8   An Informative Abstract

installing the gas burner. These conversion costs amount to
$65.50 yearly, figured over a ten-year period. With a pro-
jected gas-supply and maintenance cost of $621.75 yearly,
the overall yearly cost of gas heating would be roughly
$129.00 higher than that of oil heating. Because the advan-
tage of constant fuel supply does not offset the expense and
inconvenience of conversion, we should retain our present
system and consider installing an auxiliary 500-gallon underground oil tank. This tank would ensure adequate supply
during peak heating months.

FIGURE 8-8   (*Continued*)

INFORMATIVE ABSTRACT

AN ANALYSIS OF THE EFFECTS, NEEDED IMPROVEMENTS,

AND FUTURE OF THE MASSACHUSETTS PRISONER FURLOUGH PROGRAM

Since November 1972, Massachusetts has been rehabili-
tating prison inmates through the furlough program, which
permits inmates to leave a state or county institution for
periods ranging from twelve hours to seven consecutive days.
The positive effects of this program include a lowering of
the recidivism rate among ex-offenders, an increase in inmate
responsibility and incentive, a reduction in violence and
homosexuality in prisons, a strengthening of inmates' family
ties, and an increase in the communities' involvement in
rehabilitation. Negative effects include inmates' difficulties in returning from furlough and readjusting to prison
life, the discouragement felt by inmates who fail to qualify
for furloughs, and the inmates' occasional escape or commission of crimes while on furlough. However, these problems
might be corrected by such improvements as an increase in
counseling services for furloughed inmates, a greater uni-
formity of furlough policy among institutions, an improved
screening process for furlough applicants, and an increased

FIGURE 8-9   An Informative Abstract

effort to educate the public about furlough programs. Overall, the furlough program will continue to play a vital role
in inmate rehabilitation only through more effective administrative measures, stricter controls, and increased public
cooperation.

FIGURE 8-9 (*Continued*)

GLOSSARY

Analgesic: a medication given to relieve pain during the
    first stage of labor.

Anesthetic: a substance administered to cause loss of
    consciousness or insensitivity to pain in a region of
    the body.

Cervix: the neck-shaped anatomical structure which forms
    the mouth of the uterus.

Childbirth Education: the process of instruction providing
    parents with information about childbirth and preparing
    them for active participation in the delivery.

Dilation: the act of cervical expansion occurring during
    the first stage of labor.

Episiotomy: an incision of the outer vaginal tissue, made by
    the obstetrician just before the delivery, to enlarge
    the vaginal opening.

First Stage of Labor: the stage in which the cervix dilates
    and the baby remains in the uterus.

Induction: the process of stimulating labor by puncturing
    the membranes around the baby or by giving an oxytoxic
    drug (uterine contractant), or both.

Natural Childbirth: (also called Prepared Childbirth, Par-
    ticipating Childbirth, Educated Childbirth, and Coopera-
    tive Childbirth) a process of giving birth in which
    parents actively participate and which is based on an
    understanding of the body, muscular relaxation,
    breathing techniques, and emotional support. It is not
    a primitive process where modern knowledge plays no
    part, or a rigid system forbidding obstetrical inter-
    ference regardless of circumstances. Medication may or
    may not be used, according to individual need. The
    natural childbirth experience is presently defined
    by the woman's preparation and knowledge of how to
    cooperate actively in her delivery.

FIGURE 8-10 A Glossary Page for a Formal Report

Footnote Pages

The footnote pages list each of your references in the same numerical order as they are used in your report proper. See Chapter 7 for a complete discussion of footnote use and format.

Bibliography Page

The bibliography lists, in alphabetical order, each of the references you consulted in preparing your report, whether or not you quoted, paraphrased, or otherwise referred to them in your report. See Chapter 7 for a full discussion of bibliographies.

Appendix

An appendix comes at the very end of your report and contains supporting details and further information about one or more topics in your report. Information in an appendix is designed to illustrate further an item discussed in your report, without cluttering your report text. Items usually placed in an appendix include technical, quantitative, graphic, and visual information, such as the following.

- details of an experiment
- statistical or other measurements
- maps
- complex formulas
- long quotes (one or more pages)
- photographs
- texts of laws, regulations, etc.
- related correspondence (letters of inquiry, etc.)
- interview questions and responses
- sample questionnaires and tabulated responses
- sample tests and tabulated results
- some visual aids occupying more than one full page

Thus, an appendix serves as a catch-all for items that are important but difficult to integrate within the text of your report.

Although appendixes are highly convenient, do not rely too heavily on them by including needless information or by not properly integrating appropriate data into your report proper. Your reader should not have to turn to appendixes every few seconds to understand a particular point. The following guidelines should help you to use appendixes effectively:

1. Include only material that is highly relevant but difficult to fit into the text of your report.
2. Use a separate appendix for each major item.
3. Title each appendix clearly and separate it from other items or appendixes with a title page: "Appendix A: A Sample Questionnaire."
4. Do not use too many appendixes. If you have four or five appendixes in a ten-page report you have probably not taken the time to organize the report material effectively.
5. Limit your appendix to two or three pages, unless greater length is absolutely necessary.
6. Mention your appendix early in your introduction section, and refer your reader to your appendix at appropriate points in your report discussion: "(See Appendix A)."

As a rule of thumb, use an appendix for any item that is related to the purpose of your report, but that would harm the unity and coherence of your discussion if placed within the report proper. Remember, however, that your reader should be able to understand your report without having to turn to your appendix. Distill the essential facts from your appendix and place them in your report text.

Improper Reference

The swordfish population declined drastically between 1976 and 1977 (see Appendix A for details).

Proper Reference

The swordfish population declined *by 16%* from 1976 to 1977 (see Appendix A for a statistical breakdown).

Figure 8-11 shows the first page of an appendix to a report analyzing the danger to whales of modern whaling techniques.

Clearly, your attention to report format and supplements is more than busy work. Because you know where you are and where you are going at each step of the writing process, your report will embody a clear sense of direction and purpose. Furthermore, because you have taken the time to design an engaging format and helpful supplements, your report will reflect your own sense of consideration and good taste. It will also be easier to write and more pleasurable to read. This kind of "professional touch" says more about you than you could ever say about yourself.

APPENDIX A

A CLASSIFICATION OF WHALE SPECIES ACCORDING TO SIZE, DIET, RANGE,
GESTATION PERIOD, AND LEVEL OF ENDANGERMENT BY MODERN WHALING

Species	Size(ft.)	Diet	Range	Gestation Period	Level of Endangerment
Sperm	M 47 F 37 baby 14	Giant squid, cuttlefish.	Cosmopolitan. F & baby remain in warm water. M have harems. Bachelors in polar seas in summer. Travels singly or in schools.	11-16 months. One calf every three years.	Threatened.
Grey	M 43 F 46 baby 16	Unknown. Main item thought to be bottom-dwelling amphipods.	Eastern No. Pacific. Summer feeding grounds off Alaska coast. Winter breeding grounds off California. Travels singly or in pairs.	13 months. One calf every two years.	At threshold of extinction.
Minke	M 27 F 27 baby 9	Krill in southern seas. Cod, herring, whiting, mackerel in northern seas.	Cosmopolitan. Highly migratory. M in deep waters. F & young in coastal waters. Travels in schools of up to 20.	12 months. One calf every two years.	At lowest ebb in history. Bordering threatened.

FIGURE 8-11   A Sample Appendix to a Formal Report

CHAPTER SUMMARY

Whether your report is informal or formal you will need to follow certain conventions to give it a professional appearance and make its information more accessible. Format and supplements determine your report's physical appearance, the arrangement of its parts, and the accessibility of your material. Both are important elements of a professional-quality presentation. To achieve an effective format follow these guidelines:

1. Use high-quality paper.
2. Type your page neatly.
3. Use uniform margins, spacing, and indentation.
4. Number your pages consistently.
5. Use an introduction-body-conclusion structure.
6. Use headings effectively and extensively.

A formal report should be accompanied by these preceding supplements: cover, title page, letter of transmittal, table of contents, and informative abstract. Include following supplements — glossary, footnotes, bibliography, and appendixes — only when they are needed. Compose your supplements *after* your report's text is fully written.

EXERCISES

1. (a) In a unified and coherent paragraph, explain the role and importance of effective format in any written report. Why are headings especially important? (b) In a second paragraph, explain the role and importance of effective supplements.

2. *In class:* Look through your textbooks to find a chapter with an effective format. Bring the sample to class and, in small groups, compare and contrast individual choices, discussing the strong and weak points of each choice. Which of the samples discussed by the group has the most effective format? Why? Subject matter aside, what makes one sample more readable than another? Concentrate on titles, headings, and overall appearance.

3. The following titles are intended for investigative, research, or analytical reports. Each should be clear, accurate, comprehensive, specific, concise, and appropriately phrased. Revise all inadequate titles according to the criteria and examples discussed in this chapter.

"The Effectiveness of the Prison Furlough Program in Our State"
"Home Solar Heating: Boom or Bust?"

"The Effects of Nuclear Power Plants"

"Woodburning Stoves"

"An Investigation and Comparative Analysis of the Mechanical and Other Advantages of the Rotary Combustion (Wankel) Engine Over the Otherwise Popular and Conventionally Manufactured V-8 Engine"

"An Analysis of Vegetables" (for a report assessing the physiological effects of a vegetarian diet)

"Will Wood Save the Day as a Fuel Source?"

"Oral Contraceptives"

4. Using the format principles discussed in this chapter, revise something you have written for one of your earlier assignments (a summary, classification, partition, expanded formal definition, or research report). (You might exchange rough drafts with fellow students in order to share specific suggestions for format revision.) Submit your revision to your instructor.

5. Prepare a title page, a letter of transmittal, a table of contents, and an informative abstract for a report that you have written earlier in this course (perhaps a research report). If you need to revise the heading system in your report's text, follow the instructions in this chapter.

9

Visual Aids

CHAPTER GOALS

DEFINITION

PURPOSE OF VISUAL AIDS

TABLES
  Levels of Complexity
  Construction

FIGURES
  Graphs
    Bar Graphs
    Line Graphs
    Construction
  Charts
    Pie Charts
    Organizational Charts
    Flow Charts
  Diagrams
    Diagrams of Mechanical Parts
    Diagrams of Procedures
    Schematic and Wiring Diagrams
  Photographs
  Samples

CHAPTER SUMMARY

REVISION CHECKLIST

EXERCISES

CHAPTER GOALS

Upon completing this chapter you will know:

- The meaning and purpose of visual aids.
- The differences between tables and figures.
- How to select the right visual aid for your purposes.
- How to construct tables.
- How to construct figures such as graphs, charts, and diagrams.
- Where to place visual aids in your report.

DEFINITION

A visual aid is any pictorial representation you use to clarify your discussion. The most common visual aids used in report writing form two broad classes: (1) tables and (2) figures: graphs, charts, diagrams, photographs, and material samples.

PURPOSE OF VISUAL AIDS

Because they engage the reader's attention and increase understanding, visual aids are included in many articles, books, and reports. Translate written words into visual images whenever you can, *as long as the visuals make your point more clearly than the prose can.* Use visuals to clarify your discussion, not simply to decorate it. And keep them simple.

Visual aids work in several ways to improve the quality of your report:

1. They increase reader interest in the material by providing another view that is more vivid and clear than its prose equivalent. They are easier for the eye to follow and, sometimes, for the mind to grasp. In effect, a visual satisfies the reader's demand to be shown.

2. They set off and emphasize significant data. A bar graph showing that the cost of a loaf of bread is three times as great as it was a certain number of years ago is more dramatic than a simple statement. Some readers, in fact, might skim the prose parts of a report and concentrate on the tables, charts, or other visuals.

3. They are a good way to condense information. For instance, a simple table often can replace a long prose passage that might obscure some important facts, relationships, or comparisons.

4. Certain types of visual aids (such as tables, charts, and graphs) are useful for pulling together diverse data on the basis of their similarities or contrasts. Thus they increase your control over the material and are easy for the reader to interpret.

Let us suppose that you are reporting on the comparative nutritional value and cost of several kinds of sandwiches — bologna, hamburger, tuna salad, egg salad, and peanut butter. From various sources you collect the following data:

1. A bologna sandwich (3½ oz. bologna, 1 T. mustard on white bread) contains 436 calories, 17 grams of protein, 30 grams of fat, at an estimated cost of $0.41.

2. A hamburger (¼ lb. cooked beef, 1 T. catsup on bun) contains 331 calories, 25 grams of protein, 16 grams of fat, at an estimated cost of $0.32.

3. A tuna-salad sandwich (3½ oz. tuna, 1 T. mayonnaise on white bread) contains 422 calories, 33 grams of protein, 21 grams of fat, at an estimated cost of $0.38.

4. An egg-salad sandwich (1 large egg — cooked, 1 T. mayonnaise on white bread) contains 313 calories, 11 grams of protein, 19 grams of fat, at an estimated cost of $0.12.

5. A peanut-butter sandwich (1 oz. on white bread) contains 296 calories, 12 grams of protein, 16 grams of fat, at an estimated cost of $0.09.

Clearly, this prose version is somewhat difficult to interpret and repetitious. When arranged in a table, like Table 9-1, the data become much more readable. Instead of plodding through a prose version, trying to make connections, the reader can scan these data in seconds to draw specific conclusions. Used effectively, visuals can be great time-savers for the reader.

A full-scale study of visual aids would require a complete course in drafting and technical illustration. Therefore, in this chapter we will discuss only those that are the most common and most easily constructed.

TABLE 9-1   Five Popular Sandwiches Classified on the Basis of Caloric, Protein, and Fat Content, and Estimated Cost

Sandwich	Calories	Protein (in grams)	Fat (in grams)	Estimated Cost
Bologna (3½ oz., 1 T. mustard)	436	17	30	.41
Hamburger (4 oz. cooked, 1 T. catsup)[a]	331	25	16	.32
Tuna salad (3½ oz., 1 T. mayonnaise)	422	33	21	.38
Egg salad (1 large egg, 1 T. mayonnaise)	313	11	19	.12
Peanut butter (1 oz.)	296	12	16	.09

Source: Figures are based on Bureau of Labor Statistics estimates found in the *Retail Food Price Index, October 1975* (Washington, D.C.: U.S. Department of Labor).

[a] The hamburger is served on a bun. All other sandwiches are on white bread.

TABLES

Tables are displays of data which can be numerical (as in Table 9-1) or non-numerical (as in Table 5-4 on page 88). The data are arranged in vertical columns under category headings so that they may be easily compared and contrasted.

Levels of Complexity

A table can be as simple as Table 9-2, which includes only one basis of data comparison. Notice the explanatory notes which limit and qualify the meaning of the categories.

A more complex table, like Table 9-3, contains several bases of comparison. Here the bases are listed in the far left column in order to make the table fit the width of the page.

Even complex tables are easy to prepare and easy to read. Although not as visually dramatic as a graph or chart, a table is best for displaying numbers and units of measurement which must be illustrated precisely.

TABLE 9-2   1977 American Subcompacts Classified in Descending Order
on the Basis of Gas Mileage

Make of Car[a]	Miles per Gallon[b]
Midgo II	33.4
Vampira ST	32.9
Locomoto	32.5
Zoomer	32.3

[a] All models tested were two-door sedans with three-speed manual transmissions.
[b] Mileage figures are based on EPA averages for combined city and highway driving.

Construction

To make a table, follow these guidelines:

1. Number each table in order of its appearance, and give it a clear title that promises exactly what the table delivers.

2. Begin each vertical column with a heading that identifies the type of items

TABLE 9-3   Stand Characteristics of White Pine and Mixed Oak

	White Pine			Mixed Oak
	#1	#2	#3	
Total stems per acre[a] over 1 inch diameter at breast height[b]	260.0	390.0	390.0	325.0
Basal area per acre (sq. ft.)	104.0	224.9	183.9	85.3
Average diameter at breast height[b]	6.2	9.9	7.8	6.0
Average age, dominant and codominant trees (yrs.)	26.0	37.2	38.2	58.6
Average height, dominant and codominant trees (ft.)	52.1	63.5	65.4	59.7
Average crown space occupied (%)	96.1	94.2	95.1	90.9
Stem density[c]	1919.0	3855.0	3673.0	1940.0

Source: James H. Brown, Jr., and Thomas W. Hardy, Jr., *Summer Water Use by White Pine and Oak in Rhode Island* (Kingston, R.I.: University of Rhode Island, 1975), p. 3. Reprinted by permission.
[a] Acreage values projected from one-tenth acre samples.
[b] Diameter at 4.5 feet above ground.
[c] Stem density is the summation of tree diameters at breast height.

listed (e.g., "Make of Car") and specific units of measurement and comparison (e.g., "Miles per Gallon," "Grams per Ounce," "Percentage"). Use only the approved abbreviations and symbols listed in Appendix A. Give all items in the same column the same units of measurement (inches, sq. ft., etc.) and keep decimals vertically aligned.

3. Use footnotes to explain or clarify certain entries. Whereas footnote notation in your discussion is in arabic numerals (1, 2, 3), in your table it is in small letters (a, b, c).

4. Set your table off from your prose discussion by framing it, leaving adequate white space above and below. Be sure that it does not extend into the page margins.

5. Try to keep the table on a single report page. If it does take up more than one full page, write "continued" at the bottom and begin the second page with the full title and "continued." Also, place the same headings at the tops of each column as appear on the first page of the table. If you need to total your columns, begin second-page columns with subtotals from the first page.

6. If your table is so wide that you need to turn it to the vertical plane of your page, place the top against the inside binding.

7. Make the table relate to your surrounding discussion. Introduce it and discuss any special features about the data. If you leave your reader to interpret raw data, you have not done your job.

8. If the table clarifies a part of your discussion, place it in that area of your text. However, if it simply provides supporting information of interest only to some readers, place it in an appendix so that readers can refer to it as they wish. The point is to avoid cluttering up your discussion.

9. Identify your data sources below the table beginning at the left margin. If the table itself is borrowed, so indicate. And list your sources even if you make your own table from borrowed data.

FIGURES

Any visual aid that is not a table is classified as a figure and should be so titled (e.g., "Figure I: An Aerial View of the Panhandle Building Site"). The most common figures are graphs, charts, diagrams, photographs, and samples.

Graphs

A graph is made by plotting a set of points on a coordinate system. It provides a picture of the relationship between two variables and is used to show a comparison, a change over time, or a trend.

When you decide to use a graph, choose the best type for your purpose: bar graph or line graph.

Bar Graphs

A bar graph, as shown in Figure 9-1, illustrates comparisons. In this case, the visual impact of the bar graph makes it a clear choice over a prose or tabular version. Percentage figures are recorded above each bar to increase clarity. The independent variable[1] range extends only from 0 to 40 percent. This range creates enough space between vertical increments to dramatize the comparison without taking up too much of the page. Units of measurement on the vertical line are clearly identified.

The choice of scale in a bar graph (such as 10 percent per inch) is crucial. Try different scales until your graph represents all quantities clearly and in

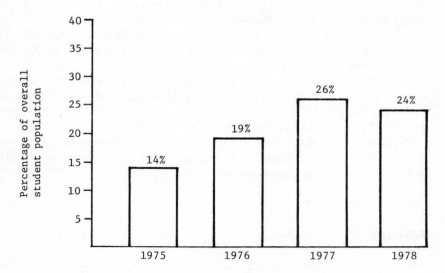

FIGURE 1. Percentage of Students Making the Dean's List at
         X College, 1975–78

FIGURE 9-1   A Bar Graph

[1] In all graphs, the horizontal line (abscissa) lists those items whose value is fixed (independent variables); the vertical line (ordinate) lists those values which change (dependent variables). The dependent variable changes according to the specific activity of the independent variable (e.g., an increase in percentage over time, as shown in Figure 9-1).

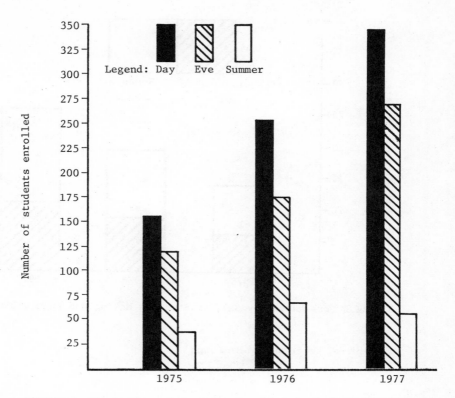

FIGURE 2. The Number of Students Enrolled in Technical Writing, 1975-77.

FIGURE 9-2   A Multiple-Bar Graph

proper proportion. For instance, if the vertical scale in Figure 9-1 were extended to 100 percent, the bars would seem dwarfed and much space would be wasted. Other distortions would occur if the vertical increments, for example, were increased to 5 percent per inch or decreased to 30 percent per inch.

A bar graph can also contain multiple bars (up to three) at each major point on the horizontal line, as in Figure 9-2. In a multiple-bar graph, include a legend to explain the meaning of the various bars.

Another common type of graph is the segmented-bar graph, which breaks down each bar into its components. Notice that the vertical scale in Figure 9-3 is large enough to show clearly relative proportions for comparison.

In some graphs, when a horizontal quantity such as distance traveled is being compared, a horizontal bar graph can be used.

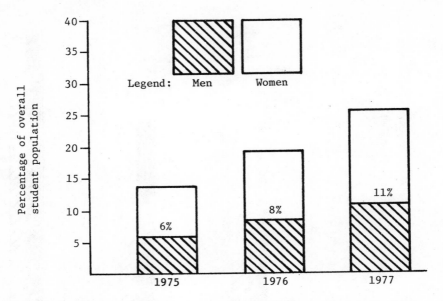

FIGURE 3. Breakdown, by Sex, of Students Making the Dean's List, 1975–77.

FIGURE 9-3   A Segmented-Bar Graph

Make all graphs on graph paper so that the lines and increments will be evenly spaced. Always begin a bar graph directly on the horizontal line. To express negative values, simply extend the vertical line below the horizontal, following the same incremental division as above it, only in negative values. Make all bars the same width so your reader will not be confused about the relative value of each.

Line Graphs

Whereas a bar graph provides units of measurement for visual comparison, a line graph, like Figure 9-4, shows change, or a trend, over a given period. Unlike a bar graph, which must begin on the horizontal line, a line graph can begin at any intersecting point on the coordinate grid. Select a readable scale and always identify the specific units of measurement (e.g., building permits issued).

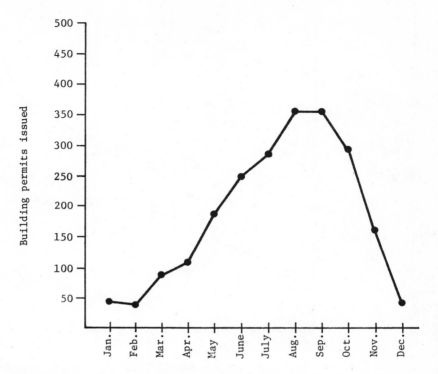

FIGURE 4. Building Permits Issued in Dade County in 1977.

FIGURE 9-4   A Line Graph

A line graph is particularly useful for illustrating a comparison of trends or changes among two or three dependent variables which are related, as in Figure 9-5. These pictorial data give an instant overview of daily shopping patterns in various locations. In this kind of multiple-line graph, your choice of scale is crucial. Imagine, for example, that the vertical scale in Figure 9-5 were condensed to $1500 per increment. The result is shown in Figure 9-6. With this reduced scale, the graph becomes almost impossible to interpret. Conversely, an overly expanded vertical scale would yield another kind of distortion. Figure 9-7 shows the same data on a graph whose scale had been increased to $250 per increment and whose vertical line begins at $1000 instead of 0 in order to save space. This distorts the quantitative relationship between lines: the high for the Midwest is $2500, and for the East, $4500 (roughly 180% higher); yet

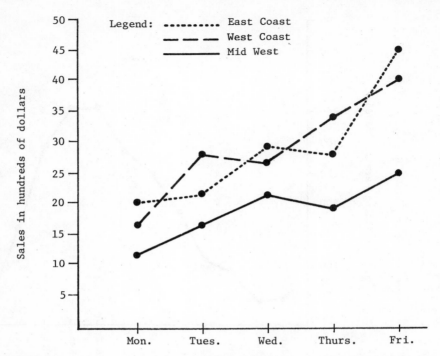

FIGURE 5. Total Sales in Our Three Major Outlets for the Week of
          June 2, 1978.

FIGURE 9-5   A Multiple-Line Graph

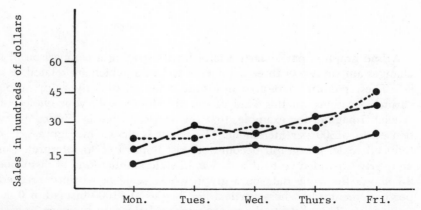

FIGURE 6. Total Sales in Our Three Major Outlets for the Week of
          June 2, 1978.

FIGURE 9-6   A Poorly Scaled Graph (Increments Condensed)

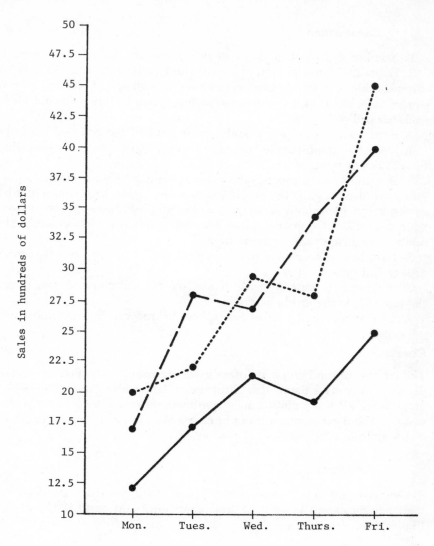

FIGURE 7. Total Sales in Our Three Major Outlets for the Week of
          June 2, 1978.

FIGURE 9-7   A Poorly Scaled Graph (Increments Expanded)

the visual relationship between these lines suggests that the sales volume for
the East is roughly 230% higher. Remember that the visual relationships should
parallel the actual numerical relationships.

Construction

1. Number the graph in order of its appearance and give it a clear title.
2. Label the items on your horizontal and vertical lines. State units of measurement along your vertical coordinate (hundreds of dollars, pounds per square inch, etc.). In a multiple-bar or line graph include a legend identifying each bar or line.
3. Experiment with various scales until you find the one that works best.
4. Keep the graph simple and easy to read. Never plot more than three different lines or types of bar.
5. Because you are using graph paper, plan carefully for integrating a graph into your discussion. If the graph is only a few inches high, you might trim the excess graph paper and paste or glue the graph in the appropriate section of your discussion. Otherwise, place the full graph page immediately after the related discussion page or in an appendix.
6. Introduce, discuss, and interpret your graph. Do not leave the reader with a page full of raw data.
7. If the graph must be presented on the vertical plane of your page, place the top against the inside binding.
8. Credit your data sources two spaces below your figure number and title.

Charts

The terms *chart* and *graph* are often used interchangeably. For our purposes we define a chart as a figure that illustrates relationships (quantitative or cause-and-effect) but is not plotted on a coordinate system. Therefore, no graph paper is used. The most common types of charts are the pie chart, the organizational chart, and the flow chart.

Pie Charts

A pie chart partitions a whole into its parts and provides a pictorial image of their relationship. The parts of a pie chart must add up to 100%, as shown in Figure 9-8.

Follow these guidelines in making your chart:

1. Number it in order of its appearance with other figures, and give it a clear and precise title. Place figure number and title two spaces below your chart.
2. Use a compass to draw a perfect circle and to locate its center. Use a protractor for precise segmentation.
3. Begin segmenting your chart by locating your first radial line at twelve o'clock. Move clockwise, in descending order, from largest to smallest segments.
4. Use at least three, but no more than seven, segments. Combine several small segments (1 percent to 5 percent each) under the heading "Other."

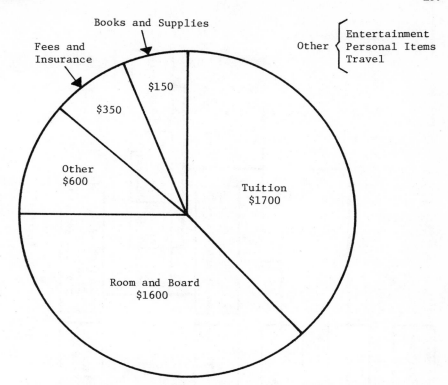

FIGURE 8. Yearly Cost Breakdown for Attending Calvin College.
(Total Cost = $4400/Year)

FIGURE 9-8   A Pie Chart

Include a parenthetical explanation of these combined items, as shown in Figure 9-8.

5. Write all section headings, quantities, and units of measurement horizontally.

6. Place your pie chart where it belongs in your discussion. Introduce it, explain it, and credit data sources.

A pie chart is not as precise as a tabular list, but it draws your reader's attention to certain dramatic elements more effectively than a list of numbers would.

Organizational Charts

An organizational chart partitions the administrative functions of an organization. It ranks each member in order of authority and responsibility as that member relates to other members and departments. Figure 9-9 shows the partial organizational chart of a typical management structure of a college.

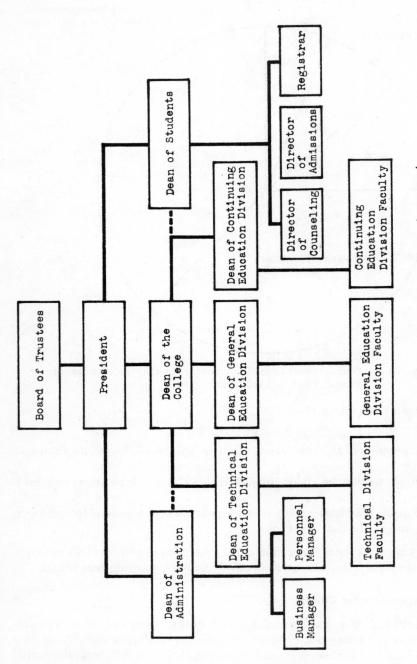

FIGURE 9-9 An Organizational Chart

FIGURE 9. An Organizational Chart of Calvin College (partial).

Flow Charts

A flow chart traces a process from beginning to end. In outlining the specific steps of a manufacturing or refining process, it moves from raw material to finished product. In illustrating how a phenomenon occurs, it moves through the specific steps which make the phenomenon possible, as shown in Figure 9-10. This chart is shown in its full textual context in the process analysis in Chapter

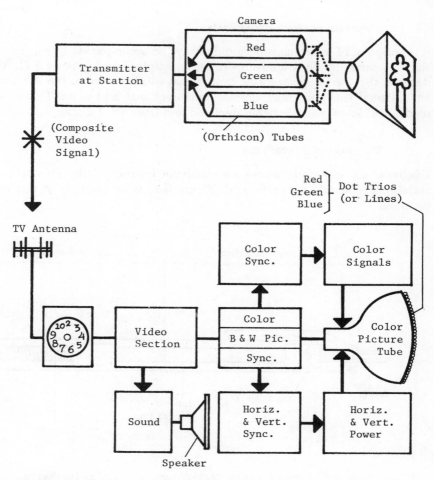

FIGURE 10. How Color Television Works.

FIGURE 9-10   A Flow Chart

13. The rules discussed earlier for placement, combination, and source credit apply for organizational and flow charts.

Diagrams

Diagrams are sketches or drawings of the parts of an item or the steps in a process. Because diagrams have a broad range of types and complexity, we will discuss only some simpler types.

Diagrams of Mechanical Parts

A description of a mechanism should always be accompanied by diagrams that show its parts and illustrate its operating principle, such as Figure 9-11. Always describe the specific perspective from which you have drawn the item: frontal view, lateral view, anterior, superior, cross-sectional, and so on. This way your reader will know what is being depicted and from what angle.

Diagrams of Procedures

Diagrams are especially useful for clarifying instructions by illustrating how certain steps should be performed. Figure 9-12 is an example of this type of diagram.

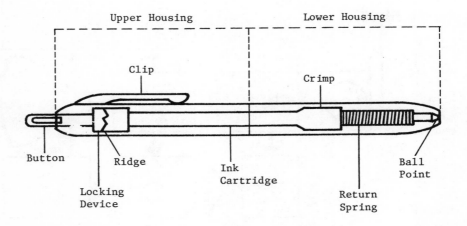

FIGURE 11. A Retractable Ball-Point Pen with Point Retracted
             (in Cross-Section).

FIGURE 9-11   A Diagram of Mechanical Parts (A Cross-Section)

FIGURE 12. Frontal View of a Camera Held Correctly.

FIGURE 9-12   A Diagram of a Procedure

Schematic and Wiring Diagrams

Science and engineering majors will find ample illustrations of electrical diagrams in physics textbooks.

Photographs

Photographs are useful for giving a realistic and accurate view of your subject. However, a photograph can sometimes be too "busy." By showing all details as more or less equal, a photograph sometimes fails to emphasize the important areas within the visual field.

When you use photographs, keep them distinct, well-focused, and uncluttered. For a complex mechanism, you probably should rely on diagrams instead, unless you intend simply to show an overall view. It is helpful to lend a sense of scale by including a person or a familiar object (such as a hand) in your photo.

Samples

If your report discusses certain materials, such as clothing fabrics, types of paper, or paint colors, you might include actual samples. The same is true when you are discussing business forms or contracts. For things like fabrics and paints, glue or paste a small sample — titled and numbered — to your report page.

CHAPTER SUMMARY

A visual aid is any pictorial device that clarifies your discussion. In report writing, the most common visual aids are tables and figures. Tables display data in vertical columns under category headings. They are best used to display precise numbers and units of measurement.

In making a table, follow these guidelines:

1. Number it chronologically and give it a clear title.
2. Begin each column with a clear heading and list all items in that column according to the same unit of measurement.
3. Use footnotes to explain complex data.
4. Leave plenty of white space between the table and your text.
5. Try to keep the table on a single page.
6. Introduce, discuss, and interpret the table.
7. Place the table appropriately in your report — in the text or in an appendix.
8. Place the top of an excessively wide table on the vertical plane against the binding.
9. Identify any data sources.

Figures include such items as graphs, charts, diagrams, photographs, and samples. Any visual aid that is not a table is a figure.

In a graph, numbers are plotted as a set of points on a coordinate system to give a picture of the relationship between data. You might choose a bar graph to show comparisons or a line graph to show change over time.

In making a graph, follow the general guidelines used for tables, with these additions:

1. In a multiple-bar or line graph, include a legend to identify various bars or lines.
2. Experiment with various scales until you find the clearest and most accurate.
3. Never plot more than three variables on one graph.
4. Use graph paper; trim away the excess; paste or glue the figure on your discussion page.

Charts also illustrate relationships, but they are not plotted on a coordinate system. Pie charts, organizational charts, and flow charts are the most common. Each of these partitions a whole item or process into its parts in order to represent the relationship of part to part and of part to whole.

Diagrams are sketches or drawings of the item or process and are usually better than photographs for emphasizing certain parts. However, photographs work well in presenting overall views.

In discussing certain materials, you might include actual samples.

REVISION CHECKLIST

1. Does the visual aid serve a real purpose; that is, does it clarify, not simply decorate, your report?

2. Have you chosen the best form of visual aid for your purposes?

3. Is the visual aid titled and numbered appropriately?

4. Can it stand alone in meaning, if necessary?

5. Does each vertical column in the table begin with a clear heading?

6. Are all units of measurement in the same tabular column identical (inches, grams, etc.)?

7. Are all decimal points in each tabular column vertically aligned?

8. Are explanatory notes added as needed (in lowercase letter notation)?

9. Are the margins clear?

10. Is the visual aid set off from the text by adequate white space?

11. Does the top of an excessively wide visual aid abut the inside binding?

12. Is the visual aid introduced, discussed, and interpreted as needed?

13. Is it in the best location for its purpose in your report (within the text if it clarifies the discussion; in an appendix if it merely supports it)?

14. Are all sources of data identified?

15. In a graph, are the independent variables plotted along the horizontal line and the dependent along the vertical?

16. Does a multiple-bar or line graph have a legend to identify each bar or line?

17. Does the graph have a clear and accurate scale?

18. Is the graph restricted to three or fewer lines or types of bars?

19. Does the segmentation in the pie chart begin at twelve o'clock?

20. Does the pie chart have at least three, but no more than seven, segments?

21. Do the segments add up to 100 percent?

22. Are any small segments in the pie chart (1 percent to 5 percent each) integrated under the heading "Other"?

Now list those elements of your visual aids that need improvement.

EXERCISES

1. The following statistics are based on data gathered from three competing colleges located in a large western city. They give the number of applicants to each college over the last six years.

   – In 1972, X College received 2341 applications for admission; Y College received 3116, and Z College received 1807.

   – In 1973, X College received 2410 applications for admission; Y College received 3224, and Z College received 1784.

   – In 1974, X College received 2689 applications for admission; Y College received 2976, and Z College received 1929.

   – In 1975, X College received 2714 applications for admission; Y College received 2840, and Z College received 1992.

   – In 1976, X College received 2872 applications for admission; Y College received 2615, and Z College received 2112.

   – In 1977, X College received 2868 applications; Y College received 2421, and Z College received 2267.

Illustrate this information in a line graph, a bar graph, and a formal table. Which form seems most effective here? Include a brief prose interpretation with the most effective illustration.

   2. Devise a flow chart for a process in your career field or in an area of interest. Include a full title and a brief prose discussion of your illustrated data.

   3. Devise an organizational chart showing the lines of responsibility and authority in an organization where you hold a part-time or summer job.

   4. Devise a pie chart to illustrate the partition of one of your typical weekdays. Include a full title and a brief prose discussion of your data.

   5. Call or visit your town or city hall and ask the town accountant for a breakdown of town income and expenditures (where each part of the revenue dollar comes from; how each part of the revenue dollar is spent). Compose the most appropriate visual aids to illustrate these partitions. Include full title, labels, and prose explanations.

   6. Obtain the enrollment figures for the past five years at your college on the basis of sex, age, race, or any other pertinent category. Construct a segmented bar graph to illustrate one of these relationships over the five-year period.

   7. Keep track of your pulse and respiration rates taken at thirty-minute intervals over a four-hour period of changing activities. Record your findings in a line graph, noting both times and specific activities below your horizontal coordinate. Write a brief prose interpretation of your graph and give it a full title.

   8. In your textbooks, locate each of the following visual aids: a table, a multiple bar graph, a multiple line graph, a diagram, and a photograph. Bring the samples to class and discuss the effectiveness of each illustration. Is it clear, readable, meaningful? Is it introduced and discussed? Is it properly titled, numbered, and labeled? Is it necessary? Choose the most effective illustration and write a prose evaluation, discussing each of its strong points.

   9. We have discussed the importance of choosing an appropriate scale for your graph and choosing the most effective form for presenting your data visually. Study the following presentation carefully:

Strong evidence now indicates that not only the nicotine and tar in cigarette smoke can be lethal. Experts have learned that a high percentage of cigarette smoke is composed largely of carbon monoxide, and the public is unaware of the danger. The bar graph in Figure 1 lists the ten leading U.S. cigarette brands according to the carbon monoxide given off per pack of inhaled cigarettes.

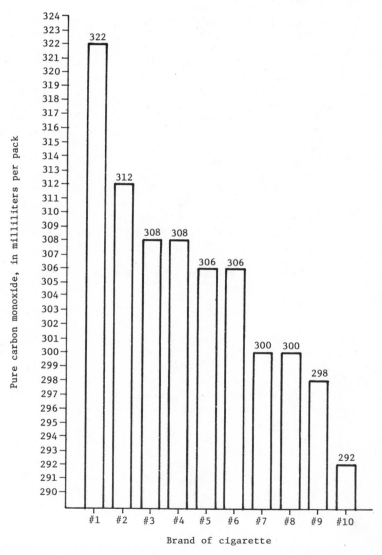

FIGURE 1   Ten Leading U.S. Cigarette Brands in Order of CO Content

Is the scale effective? If not, why not? Can these data best be presented in a bar graph? What other form of visual aid would be more effective? Present the same data in the form that seems most effective. In a short but detailed paragraph evaluate what you have learned from this assignment.

10. Choose the most appropriate visual aid for illustrating each of the following general data areas. Justify each choice in a short paragraph.

a. A comparison of three top brands of Fiberglas ski, according to cost, weight, durability, and edge control.

b. A breakdown of your monthly budget.

c. An illustration of the changing cost of an average cup of coffee, as opposed to that of an average cup of tea, over the past two years.

d. An illustration of the percentage of college graduates finding desirable jobs within three months after graduation, over the last ten years.

e. An illustration of the percentage of college graduates finding desirable jobs within three months after graduation, over the last ten years — on the basis of sex.

f. An illustration of automobile damage for an insurance claim.

g. A breakdown of the process of radio-wave transmission.

h. A comparison of five breakfast cereals on the basis of cost and nutritional content.

i. A comparison of the average age of students enrolled at your college, in summer, day, and evening programs, over the last five years.

j. A comparison of monthly sales for three models of an item produced by your company.

SPECIFIC
APPLICATIONS

10

Writing Effective Letters

CHAPTER GOALS

DEFINITION

PURPOSE OF LETTERS

ELEMENTS OF AN EFFECTIVE LETTER
Introduction-Body-Conclusion Structure
Required Major Parts
Heading
Inside Address
Salutation
Letter Text
Complimentary Closing
Signature
Specialized Parts
Typist's Initials
Enclosure Notation
Distribution Notation
Postscript
Appropriate Format
Accepted Letter Form
Plain English
"You" Perspective
Clear Purpose

WRITING VARIOUS TYPES OF LETTERS
Letter of Inquiry
Introduction
Body
Conclusion
Revision and Final Touches

Letter of Complaint
Introduction
Body
Conclusion
Letter of Instruction
Introduction
Body
Conclusion

WRITING THE RÉSUMÉ AND JOB
APPLICATION LETTER
Job Prospecting: The Preliminary Step
Being Selective
Launching Your Search
Being Realistic
The Résumé
Name and Address
*Age, Marital Status, and Physical
Characteristics*
Career Objectives
Educational Background
Work Experience
*Personal Interests, Activities, Awards,
and Special Skills*
References
Composing the Résumé
The Job Application Letter
Your Image
Targets
The Solicited Letter
The Unsolicited Letter
The Prototype

SUPPORTING YOUR APPLICATION
  Your Dossier
  Interviews
  The Follow-up Letter
  The Letter of Acceptance
  The Letter of Refusal

CHAPTER SUMMARY

REVISION CHECKLIST

EXERCISES

CHAPTER GOALS

Upon completing this chapter, you will know:

- The meaning and purpose of various types of letters.
- The elements of an effective letter.
- How to write a letter of inquiry.
- How to write a letter of complaint.
- How to write a letter of instruction.
- How to go about job prospecting.
- How to compose a résumé.
- How to write a job application letter, either solicited or unsolicited.
- How to compile and distribute a dossier.
- How to prepare for job interviews.
- How to write a follow-up letter, a letter of acceptance, and a letter of refusal.

DEFINITION

Whereas a report may be compiled by a team of writers and read by many readers, a letter usually is written by one writer for one or more definite readers. A letter is more personal than a report. Therefore, your attitude, as expressed in the tone of your letter, is a major ingredient of your message. Because most letters are written to elicit a definite response, you want the reader to be on your side. Also, because your signature certifies the statements in your letter (which may be used later as a legal document), the need for precision in letter writing is crucial.

PURPOSE OF LETTERS

Some people who use this book will be technicians; others will be managers; still others, professionals or executives. Whether you work for yourself or for a company, in any nonmenial job you will need to write letters from time to time.

Here are some of the common types of letters you will write on the job. The broad purpose of each type is to inform and persuade the reader.

— Sales letters designed to stimulate customer interest in a product or service.
— Letters of instruction outlining a procedure to be carried out by a customer or colleague.
— Letters of recommendation for friends, fellow workers, or past employees.
— Letters of transmittal (cover letters) to accompany reports and other documents that you mail out.
— General business letters describing progress on a project, requesting assistance, ordering parts or tools, confirming meeting times, and so on.
— Letters of inquiry, asking about the cost or availability of a product, requesting advice for solving a problem, soliciting comments about a job applicant, and so on.
— Claim letters written to complain about disappointing service or faulty products and to request adjustment.

From time to time you may also need to write letters of response to general business letters, letters of inquiry, or claim letters received by your company.

Most people write letters well before beginning their careers. For instance, as a student, you may write to ask for data for college research projects or to learn about certain schools or jobs. Also, you might write letters to apply to colleges, to compete for scholarships or foreign study programs, or to join a campus organization. The application letter is considered important for good reasons: this writing sample provides evidence of your verbal sophistication, your talent for clear self-expression, your level of confidence, your sensitivity to your audience, your attention to detail, your level of maturity, your ability to recognize important points, your mastery of logical reasoning, and your level of personality development. From time to time, as a consumer, you might have complaints about defective items or disappointing service. Your complaint letter will be designed to express your dissatisfaction and to secure a fair adjustment. Finally, as a job applicant, you will write letters that may well be a key to your success.

A full discussion of letter writing would more than fill a textbook. In this chapter, therefore, we will discuss only the four common types of letters you will write in college: the letter of inquiry, the letter of complaint, the letter of instruction, and the letter of application, along with its accompanying résumé.

Other useful types — the letter of transmittal and letter reports — are discussed in Chapters 8 and 11. However, regardless of type, all letters have certain elements in common.

ELEMENTS OF AN EFFECTIVE LETTER

Remember this rule of thumb: *never send a letter until you genuinely feel good about signing your name to it.* Your signature certifies that you approve of the contents and take pride in your presentation. Use the guidelines below for judging the adequacy of your letters before you sign them.

Introduction-Body-Conclusion Structure

Structure all letters to include (1) a brief *introduction* paragraph in which you attract your reader's attention by identifying yourself and stating your purpose; (2) one or more *body* paragraphs containing the specific details of your inquiry, application, complaint, or instructions; (3) a *conclusion* paragraph in which you tie your message together, offer to provide more details or appear for an interview, and courteously encourage your reader to act. For readability, type your letters if at all possible and keep your paragraphs short (usually less than eight lines). If your body section is highly detailed, divide it into shorter paragraphs, as shown in Figure 10-1. Notice that this body section is broken down into four specific questions for easy answering. Figure 10-2 shows the response to the preceding letter.

Required Major Parts

All letters should have certain parts. These, in order from top to bottom, appear as follows: headings, inside address, salutation, the letter text (with introduction, body, and conclusion), complimentary closing, and signature.

Heading

If your stationery has a company letterhead, simply include the date, two spaces below the letterhead, as shown in Figure 10-2. On plain stationery, include your own heading, as shown in Figure 10-1 and here:

```
    Street Address                          154 Seaweed Lane
    City, State  Zip Code                   East Harwich,
    Month Day, Year                           Massachusetts 02163
                                            December 24, 1976
```

154 Seaweed Lane
East Harwich,
  Massachusetts 02163
July 15, 1978

Land Use Manager
Eastern Paper Company
Waldoboro, Maine 04967

Dear Sir or Madam:

Mr. Melvin Blotter, your sales representative,   Introduction
has told me that Eastern Paper Company makes
available certain parcels of its lakefront
property in northern Maine for leasing to the
general public. Because I am very interested
in the possibility of such a leasing arrangement, please answer the following questions
for me.

1. Does your company have any lakefront   Body
    parcels in highly remote areas?

2. What is the average size of a leased
    parcel?

3. How long does a lease remain in effect?

4. What is the yearly leasing fee?

I will greatly appreciate your answers to   Conclusion
these questions, along with any other details
you might send along.

        Yours truly,

        John M. Lannon

P.S. I am planning a trip to Maine the week
of August 5–11 and would be happy to stop by
your office any time you are free.

FIGURE 10-1 A Letter of Inquiry

**Eastern Paper Company
Waldoboro, Maine 04967**

July 25, 1978

Mr. John M. Lannon
154 Seaweed Lane
East Harwich, Massachusetts 01263

Dear Mr. Lannon:

    This is in answer to your recent inquiry about leasing lakeside lots in Maine.

    We have no lands for lease in what you would classify as "highly remote areas." The most remote area is on the northern shore of Deerfoot lake where presently you would have to reach the camp lot by boat. Leases on these 30,000 square foot parcels are renewable on a yearly basis each June. The leasing fee is approximately $250.00 per year. We have a limited number of leases available, but you would have to visit our office to get meaningful information about exact locations. If you are in the area, you may drop by any weekday morning before 11 o'clock.

    The Land Use Regulation Commission in Augusta, Maine, regulates campsite leasing and you would need to apply to this body for a building permit including soil tests, etc., before you would be allowed to build.

    Thank you for your inquiry.

                Yours truly,

                EASTERN PAPER COMPANY

                A. B. Coolidge
                Townsite Manager

ABC/de

cc: Mr. Blotter

FIGURE 10-2 A Letter of Response to an Inquiry

Write out in full all items in the heading. Avoid abbreviations throughout your letter. Depending on the length of the letter, place your heading eight to ten spaces below the top of your page and far enough toward the center so that the longest line abuts your right margin.

Inside Address

Four to six spaces below your heading, and abutting your left margin, is your letter's inside address.

```
Name and Title of Reader (and position)    Dr. Marsha Mello, Dean
Company Name                               Western University
Street Address (if applicable)             Muncie, Indiana 13461
City, State  Zip Code
```

Whenever possible, address your letter to a specifically named reader, using that reader's appropriate title (Attorney, Major, etc.). However, don't be redundant by writing "Dr. Marsha A. Mello, Ph.D."; use Dr. or Ph.D., Dr. or M.D. Abbreviate only titles that are routinely abbreviated (Mr., Ms., Dr., etc.). Titles such as Captain are written out in full.

Salutation

Your salutation, placed two spaces below the inside address and abutting your left margin, is a direct greeting to your reader. Begin your salutation with *Dear* and end it with a colon. Include your addressee's full title.

Dear Ms. Jones:
Dear Professor Smith:
Dear Dr. Brown:
Dear Senator Smiley:

If you don't know your addressee's name or sex, use "Dear Sir or Madam"; when addressing several people at once, use "Gentlemen" or "Ladies" or "Ladies and Gentlemen."

Letter Text

Begin your letter text two spaces below your salutation; use single spacing within paragraphs and double spacing between them.

Complimentary Closing

Place your complimentary closing two spaces below the concluding paragraph of your letter text and aligned with your heading. Any conventional closing that is polite and not overly intimate or "gushy" will do. Select your closing on the basis of your relationship to the addressee. The following possibilities are ranked in decreasing order of formality.

> Respectfully,
> Yours truly,
> Sincerely yours,
> Sincerely,
> Best wishes,
> Warmest regards,
> Cordially,

The complimentary closing is always followed by a comma.

Signature

Type your full name and your title four spaces below and aligned on the left with your complimentary closing. Sign your name in the space between the two.

> Sincerely yours,
>
> *Martha S. Jones*
>
> Martha S. Jones
> Personnel Manager

Your signature is your personal stamp, indicating your full approval of and responsibility for the contents of the letter (even if it has been typed by a secretary). If you are writing as a representative of a company or group that bears legal responsibility for your letter, type the company's name in full caps two spaces below your complimentary closing; place your typed name and title four spaces below the company name, and sign in the space between.

> Yours truly,
>
> LEVEL BROTHERS COMPANY
>
> *Leslie L. Foye*
>
> Leslie L. Foye
> Collection Officer

Specialized Parts

Each letter should contain the six major parts. In addition, some will require one or more of the following specialized parts. Examples of these parts can be seen in the sample letters throughout the chapter.

Typist's Initials

If your letter is typed by another person, your initials and your typist's should be indicated two spaces below your typed signature and abutting the left margin.

```
        JJ/pl (typist's initials)
(your
 initials)
```

Enclosure Notation

When other documents accompany your letter, add an enclosure notation one space below the typist's initials and abutting the left margin.

```
    Enclosure (or Enclosures 2, etc.)
```

Distribution Notation

If carbon copies of your letter are to be distributed to other readers, so indicate one space below the enclosure notation.

```
    cc:  Office file
         Mr. Blotter
```

Postscript

A postscript is designed to draw your reader's attention to a point you wish to emphasize. Place your postscript two spaces below any other notations, and against your left margin.

```
    P.S.  This product has outstanding potential for capturing the
    adolescent market.
```

Use the postscript sparingly.

Appropriate Format

Apply the format instructions in Chapter 8 to each letter you write. Here is a brief summary of those instructions: (1) Use high quality 20-lb. bond, 8½ x 11 plain white stationery with a minimum fiber content of 25 percent. (2) Type neatly, avoiding erasures, retyping a smudged page, and using clean typewriter keys and a fresh ribbon. (3) Use uniform margins, spacing, and indentation: frame your letter with a 1½-inch top margin and side and bottom margins of 1 to 1¼ inches; unless your letter is very brief (three or four lines) single space within paragraphs and double space between them; avoid hyphenating at the end of a line.

If your letter should extend to more than one page, begin your second page five spaces from the top and abutting your left margin, as follows:

```
P. 2, Walter James (addressee), June 25, 1976
```

Begin the text of your second page two spaces below this notation. Place at least two lines of your paragraph at the bottom of page one, and at least two lines of your final text on page two.

Your 9½ x 4⅛-inch envelope should be of the same high quality as your stationery. Center your reader's address horizontally and vertically, and single-space if it occupies three lines or more. Again, use only accepted abbreviations. Place your own single-spaced address in the upper left corner, as shown in Figure 10-3.

```
Marvin Glick
154 Seaweed Lane
East Harwich,
   Massachusetts 02163




                      Dr. Marsha Mello, Dean
                      Western University
                      Muncie, Indiana  13461
```

FIGURE 10-3   A Sample Envelope

Accepted Letter Form

Although several acceptable letter forms exist, and your own company may have its own requirements, we will discuss the two most common forms: the semiblock form, with no indentations (Figure 10-4), and the modified block form, with the first sentence of each paragraph indented five spaces (Figure 10-5). The letters of inquiry and response earlier in this chapter are examples of semiblock and modified block forms, respectively. Either form should serve all of your letter writing needs.

Plain English

First, we should distinguish between the *conventions* of letter writing and *clichés* or *catchy phrases*. The conventions of letter writing concern format, form, letter parts, and general structure — the mechanical elements that govern the appearance of your letter and the parts that express your message. Letter writing conventions exist because, over the years, people have agreed on a set of rules for acceptable practice in composing neat, attractive, and informative letters. For example, one convention requires that you type your name (and position) under your signature. This item became part of accepted and required practice as soon as people realized that it was a handy way of clarifying your identity as a letter writer, especially if you wrote like a chicken. Likewise, other conventions came into being because they were useful and convenient.

Clichés and catchy phrases, on the other hand, are time-worn, pompous, and overblown phrases that some writers think they need in order to make their letters seem important and formal. Here is a typically overwritten closing sentence:

```
Humbly thanking you in anticipation of your kind cooperation, I
remain

                                      Faithfully yours,



                                      Marvin Glick
```

Although no one speaks like this, many writers lean on such pretentious prose in their letters instead of simply writing, "We will appreciate your cooperation." Not only is the earlier example tired and overworked; it is so clearly full of exaggeration that it sounds insincere. Unfortunately, statements like this and the others listed below are popular because they are easy to use. Like TV dinners they are effortless but not very impressive. Although you might

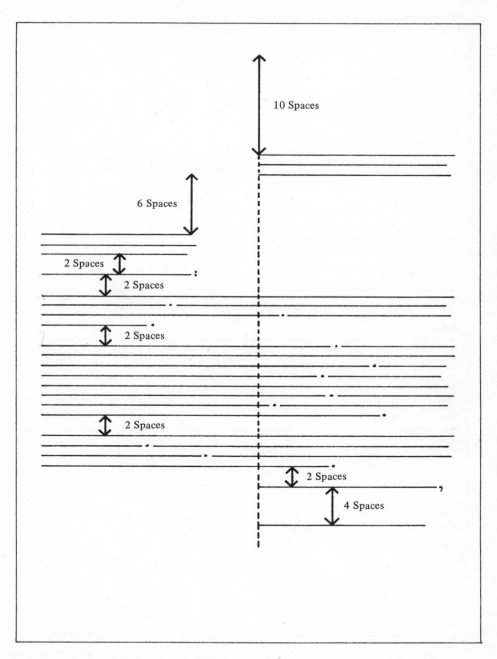

FIGURE 10-4   Diagram of a Semiblock-Form Letter

FIGURE 10-5   Diagram of a Modified Block–Form Letter

save yourself a few grey hairs by throwing such predigested stuff into your letter, your reader might well conclude that you're predigested too. Don't borrow instant phrases.

Here are a few of the many old standards that make letters seem unimaginative and boring:

Letterese	*Translation into Plain English*
As per your request	As you requested
Having received your letter, we . . .	We received your letter.
Enclosed please find my résumé.	My résumé is enclosed.
I regret to advise you that I must delay payment.	I must delay payment.
It is imperative that you write at once.	Please write at once.
I am cognizant of the fact that my payment is overdue.	I know that my payment is overdue.
At the earliest possible date	Early
I beg to differ with your estimate.	I disagree with your estimate.
Please be advised that my new address is . . .	My new address is . . .
This writer	I
At the present time	Now
I humbly request that you consider my application.	Please consider my application.
I beg to acknowledge receipt of your check.	I received your check.
In the immediate future	Soon
We are in hopes that you succeed.	Good luck.
In accordance with your request	As you requested
Our situation is such that we cannot immediately pay our complete bill.	We cannot immediately pay our complete bill.
Due to the fact that	Because
Herein enclosed	Enclosed
Please be kind enough to grant me an interview.	May I have an interview?
I wish to express my gratitude.	Thank you.
At this point in time	Now

Be natural: write as you would speak. Avoid the temptation to copy a textbook example word for word. Use the samples in this book as models only. Anyone who reads letters regularly can easily spot a borrowed letter.

Figure 10-6 shows a sample request letter that draws heavily on clichés and borrowed phrases. As you can see, the reader will find it difficult to extract the message buried beneath the redundancies and trite expressions. Because a request letter is intended to elicit a response, it should read as if written by a normal speaker of English, not by a master of purple prose.

Figure 10-7 shows the same message written in plain English. It seems more sincere. The message remains unchanged, but the writer withholds the starch. Now the letter should achieve its purpose through its clarity, conversational tone, and its "you" perspective.

"You" Perspective

In speaking face-to-face with someone, you unconsciously modify your statements and manner of expression as you read signals from the listener: a smile, a frown, a raised eyebrow, a nod, etc. Even in a telephone conversation your listener provides cues that signal approval, dismay, anger, confusion, and so on. Writing a letter, however, has one major disadvantage: because you face a blank page, it is easy to write only to please yourself, forgetting that a flesh-and-blood person will be taking the time to read your letter.

The "you" perspective concerns your tone; by your careful word choice you show respect for your reader's feelings and attitudes. Put yourself in your readers' shoes; ask yourself how they will respond to the statements you have just written. By being courteous and diplomatic you will make your reader feel important — as an individual addressed by another individual, instead of as a machine simply expected to record your message. A letter creates a relationship between you and your reader, and the words on the page are the only basis for that relationship. If you bury your readers in "letterese" and clichés, they are bound to conclude that you have a low regard for your writing task and for them — so low that you haven't taken the time to express yourself with care. As illustration, Figure 10-7 is written from a "you" perspective whereas Figure 10-6 is not.

Remember that many words have multiple meanings and implications, so choose them carefully. For example, in a letter complaining about your new camera, you have the choice of saying "the shutter mechanism of my new KL 50 is defective," or "the shutter mechanism ... is lousy." Clearly, "lousy" would be a poor choice here because of its implied insult to the manufacturer. Put yourself in the reader's place in the following example: Imagine that you manage the complaint department for a large mail-order company. Which of

234 Idle Way
Hoboken, New Jersey 34567
September 10, 1978

Marvin Mooney
Registrar
Calvin College
Plains, Georgia 38475

Dear Mr. Mooney:

Pursuant to your notice of September 6, I regret to advise
you that my tuition payment will be delayed until January 21,
when I receive my scholarship check.

I humbly request you to be cognizant of the fact that this
writer's tuition for all five prior semesters has been paid
on time. At the present time, my first, and hopefully last,
late payment is due to the fact that a computer breakdown in
the NDEA offices has occasioned a delay in the processing of
all scholarship renewal applications for two weeks. Enclosed
please find a copy of a recent NDEA notice to this effect.

I am in hopes that you will be kind enough to grant me an
extension of my tuition-due date for this brief period of
time. Thanking you in anticipation of your cooperation, I
remain

                                    Gratefully yours,

                                    Charles Jones
                                    Student

Enclosure

FIGURE 10-6   An Example of "Letterese"

234 Idle Way
Hoboken, New Jersey 34567
September 10, 1978

Marvin Mooney
Registrar
Calvin College
Plains, Georgia   38475

Dear Mr. Mooney:

I received your tuition-due notice of September 6 and regret
that my payment will be delayed until January 21, when I
receive my scholarship check.

Your payment records should show that my tuition bills for
all five prior semesters have been paid on time. This first,
and I hope last, late payment is the result of a computer
breakdown in the NDEA offices which has delayed the processing of all scholarship renewals for two weeks, as
explained in the enclosed copy of the NDEA notice.

May I have this brief extension of my tuition-due date, without causing you or the college great inconvenience, Mr.
Mooney? Your patience and consideration in this difficult
time would be a great help.

                                        Respectfully,

                                        Charles Jones

Enclosure

FIGURE 10-7   An Effectively Phrased Letter

these versions requesting repair, replacement, or refund for a faulty item would you tend to honor quickly and efficiently?

>   1. I demand that you bums immediately send me a replacement for this faulty desk calculator, and I only hope that it won't be as big a piece of junk as the first! (the belligerent attitude)
>   2. This new desk calculator does not seem to work and I wonder if you might kindly consider the possibility of sending me a replacement, if that is all right with you. Please accept my humble thanks in advance. (the pardon-me-for-living attitude)
>   3. I beg to advise you that I am appalled by the patent paucity of workmanship in this calculator and find it imperative that you refund the full purchase price at the earliest possible date. (the pompous-indignation attitude)
>   4. After I laid out all my bread on this bogus calculator it blew a fuse and blew my mind. If you are hep to my displeasure, put your money where your mouth is and send me a refund. (the pass-me-the-joint attitude)
>   5. Since this new calculator is not working and is under full guarantee, I'm sure you will send me a replacement as soon as you can. (the courteous, confident, and direct attitude)

I think you will agree that statement 5 would most likely achieve results. This statement is neither antagonistic nor apologetic. Instead, it is courteous, expresses confidence in the reader's integrity, and makes a direct request phrased in plain English. The earlier versions express only the writer's need to sound off (except 2 where the "you" perspective is carried to a ridiculous extreme), but version 5 creates a sense of respect, trust, and understanding. Even one or two carelessly chosen words can be like a slap in the face. Choose your words carefully. For further study, each sample letter in this chapter embodies the "you" perspective.

Clear Purpose

Like all pieces of effective writing, good letters do not just "happen." Each is the product of step-by-step composition. In fact, most effective letters are *rewritten;* words rarely tumble out on your page to form a perfect message on your first try. As you plan, write, and revise your letter, answer these questions about purpose and content:

1. *What purpose do I wish to achieve?* (get a job, file a complaint, ask for advice or information, answer an inquiry, give instructions, ask a favor, share good news, share bad news, etc.)

2. *What facts does my reader need?* (measurements, dates, costs, model numbers, enclosures, other details)

3. *To whom am I writing?* (Do I know my reader's name? Write to a person, not a position: "Dear Ms. Robinson," not "Dear Madam.")

4. *What is my relationship to my reader?* (Is my reader a potential employer, an employee, a person doing me a favor, a person whose service or products are disappointing, an acquaintance, a business associate, a stranger?)

Answer those four questions *before* drafting the letter. Then, after you have written a draft, think about the answers to the next three questions, which pertain most directly to the *effect* of your letter on your readers. Will they be encouraged to respond favorably?

1. *How will my reader react to my statements as phrased?* (with anger, hostility, pleasure, confusion, fear, guilt, warmth, satisfaction, etc.)

2. *What impression of me will my reader get from this letter?* (intelligent, courteous, friendly, articulate, obnoxious, pretentious, illiterate, confident, unctuous, servile)

3. *Am I ready to sign my letter with confidence?* (This bears some thought!)

Don't mail your letter until you have answered each question to your full satisfaction. Revise as often as needed to achieve your purpose.

WRITING VARIOUS TYPES OF LETTERS

This section covers three of the most common types of letters: the letter of inquiry, the letter of complaint, and the letter of instruction. The résumé and job-application letter are discussed in a separate section.

Letter of Inquiry

Letters of inquiry may be solicited or unsolicited. You often write the first as a consumer requesting detailed information about an advertised product. You can expect such a letter to be welcomed by your addressee. After all, he or she stands to benefit from your interest. In this case, you can afford to be brief and to the point. When your letter text is very brief, as in Figure 10-8, you may wish to double space.

Many of your inquiries will be unsolicited, that is, not in response to an ad, but simply requesting information for a report or a class project. Here, you are asking a favor of your addressee, who must take the time to read your letter, consider your request, collect the information, and write a response. Therefore, you need to apologize for any imposition, to express your appreciation of your reader's generosity, and to state a reasonable request clearly. Begin your letter with something a bit more cordial and less abrupt than "I need some information." This statement is clear but its tone is too demanding.

154 Seaweed Avenue
East Harwich,
  Massachusetts 02134
January 5, 1978

Western Cedar Log Homes
14 Valley Road
Rumford, New Hampshire 13101

Gentlemen or Ladies:

    Please send me your brochure describing your models of

log homes, as recently advertised in <u>Country Magazine</u>. How

far in advance must an order for a specific model be placed

in order to ensure a June 1 delivery date?

                      Yours truly,

                      John M. Lannon

FIGURE 10-8   A Solicited Letter of Inquiry

Before you can ask specific questions you need to do your homework. Don't expect your respondent to read your mind. A general question ("Please send me all your data on . . .") is likely to be ignored. Only when you know your subject can you refine your questions.

Don't wait until the last minute to write your letter. Write at least three weeks before your report is due, politely indicating the due date in your letter.

Here is a typical inquiry situation: Imagine that you are preparing an analytical report on the feasibility of harnessing solar energy for home heating in northern climates. During your investigation you learn that a private, non-profit research group in your state has been experimenting in ecologically efficient energy systems. After deciding to write for details, you plan and compose your inquiry, basing it on the questions in the previous section.

Introduction

Begin by introducing yourself and stating your purpose. Your reader should know who wants the information, and why. Maintain the "you" perspective by opening with a statement that will spark your reader's interest and good will (as shown in Figure 10-9).

Body

In the heart of your letter compose specific and clearly worded questions that can be understood easily and answered readily. Number each question and separate it from the others, perhaps leaving space for responses right on the page. If you have more than five or six questions you might place them in an attached questionnaire.

Conclusion

Conclude by telling your reader how you plan to use the information and, if possible, how he or she might benefit. Offer to send a copy of your finished report. Close with a statement of appreciation; it will encourage your reader to respond.

Revision and Final Touches

Revise your letter until its tone and content measure up to the quality of a letter you would like to receive. (See the checklist for revision at the end of this chapter.) When you feel good about your letter, sign it. Because you are asking a favor, include a stamped, self-addressed envelope for your reader's convenience. All letters need at least one revision. The job-application letter, discussed later, may need several.

When completed, your letter might look like Figure 10-9. An inquiry com-

234 Western Road
North Arlington
Massachusetts 02165
March 10, 1978

Director of Energy Systems
The Earth Research Institute
Peterborough, Massachusetts 01635

Dear Sir or Madam:

While gathering data on home solar heating, I encountered
several references (in <u>Scientific American</u> and elsewhere) to
your group's pioneering work in this field. Would you
please allow me to benefit from some of your experience? As
a science and technical writing student at Evergreen College
I am preparing an analytical report on the feasibility of
harnessing solar energy as a large-scale source of home
heating in northern climates within the next decade. Your
answers to the following questions would help me complete my
research project. I have an April 15 deadline date.

1. Have you found the active or the passive form of solar
    heating to be more practical at this stage of develop-
    ment?

2. Do you expect to surpass the 60 percent limit of heating
    needs supplied by the active system? If so, what maxi-
    mum efficiency do you hope to achieve, and how soon?

3. What is the estimated cost for the building materials
    for your active system, per cubic foot of living space?

4. What type of metal would you recommend for use in the
    collectors in order to maximize thermal conductivity
    while minimizing construction and maintenance costs?

Your answers, along with any recent findings you can share
with me, will conclude a learning experience that I will put
into practice next summer by designing and building my own
solar heated home. In gratitude for your time and effort, I
will gladly send you a copy of my finished report, along
with the house plans I have designed. Thank you.

                              Sincerely yours,

                              Gerald Jackson

FIGURE 10-9   An Unsolicited Letter of Inquiry

posed with care, courtesy, and detail will yield positive results. For further study review Figure 10-1.

Letter of Complaint

An effective letter of complaint is difficult to write, not because of what you have to say, but because you have to find a reasonable way to say it. A complaint is an expression of your resentment, your dissatisfaction, your frustration. However, in most cases it is a mistake to begin a complaint letter with the sole intention of "telling someone off." Although everyone likes to sound off now and then, it is less important to express your dissatisfaction than to achieve a desired result: a refund, a replacement, improved service, better business relations, or even an apology. If you are genuinely enraged, lock yourself in a closet and scream for five minutes before sitting down to write.

Imagine that you have recently bought an expensive stereo component system, with top-of-the-line speakers, from a dealer in New Jersey. Three weeks after your purchase you moved to Wisconsin and five weeks later you noticed an increasing distortion of heavy base sounds in your speakers. Your first impulse might be to write a letter beginning with "I've been ripped off, you lousy crook"; however, you wisely control your temper, planning and writing your letter in line with your responses to the questions we presented earlier.

Introduction

First, identify yourself and your purpose. Maintain the "you" perspective by stating your claim *objectively* (this exercise in patience will mean that you have to choose your words carefully). Save the four-letter words for the closet. Also remember that an apologetic and meek complaint letter is no more effective — sometimes even less — than a belligerent one.

Body

In your body section, present the specific details supporting your complaint. Identify the faulty item clearly, giving serial and model numbers. Describe the deficiency and explain how it has caused you inconvenience, expense, loss of time, and so on. Propose what you consider a fair adjustment, phrasing your statement so that your reader will feel motivated to honor your request.

Conclusion

Conclude with a courteous but firm statement indicating your good will and confidence in the reader's integrity.

Figure 10-10 shows how your final revision might read. You will get positive results by addressing the reader not as an enemy or buffoon, but as a com-

534 Hartford Way
Madison, Wisconsin 20967
March 20, 1978

Manager, Stereo Components, Inc.
143 Main Street
Newark, New Jersey 10311

Dear Sir:

On December 10, 1977, I bought a stereo component system
(sales receipt #114621) from your outlet. Three weeks later
I moved to Wisconsin, and after four weeks of stereo use I
noticed increasing distortion of heavy bass sounds in my
speakers.

As a classical music lover I bought your top-of-line
speakers (Toneway 305's, #3624 and 3625) because of their
extra-wide bass range. However, their distortion of lower
ranges of percussion and keyboard sounds is increasing to
the point of actual vibration, making my expensive system
useless.

My speaker guarantee states that items for repair or replacement must be returned to the original retailer. But because
we are now hundreds of miles apart, such an arrangement would
cost me a great deal of time and money and would further
delay the use of my equipment. Under these circumstances,
could you kindly arrange for your fellow retailer in the
Madison area to honor my guarantee directly?

Your store's reputation for good service among many of my
friends and acquaintances prompted my purchase, and I am
sure that you will do everything possible to minimize my
inconvenience.

                              Yours truly,

                              Sara Fields

FIGURE 10-10   A Letter of Complaint

petent and responsible businessperson. Diplomacy is always more effective than insults. However, if your first letter elicits no favorable response, you might think of phrasing your follow-up letter a bit more strongly. For further study and practice, the Exercises section in Chapter 11 contains illustrations of a form for filing consumer complaints with the state attorney general's office.

Letter of Instruction

The purpose of a letter of instruction is to provide precise directions for carrying out a procedure you know to be important to your reader. In the introduction to such a letter you will need to explain why the particular instructions are being given. In the conclusion you will wish to provide any useful supplemental information and to express your appreciation for your reader's efforts and cooperation. The body of your letter will consist of the instructions themselves. Instructions are best written in the imperative mood. Other criteria for good instructions are discussed in Chapter 13. Be particularly careful not to take your reader's knowledge for granted. Remember that although the task for which you are giving directions is probably familiar to you and thus easy for you to perform, it is new and unfamiliar to your reader. Thus, you will need to provide *all* necessary information.

Unclear, incomplete, or inaccurate directions are frustrating and all too common. For instance, people often give poor directions for reaching a certain location because they assume that the addressee knows more about the area than he or she should be expected to know. In such cases, generalities make instructions meaningless: "down the road a piece" (how far, exactly?); "turn right at the light" (stop light, blinking light?); "You will see a house on the corner" (color, size, right, left?). Be sure that your letter delivers every detail your reader needs.

Imagine that you have obtained a lease on the wilderness property on Deerfoot Lake from the Eastern Paper Company (Figures 10-1 and 10-2). In order to apply for a building permit from the Maine Land Use Regulation Commission, you must have a site evaluation (soil depth, drainage, water table, and other elements) performed by a state-registered engineer. After speaking with the engineer by phone you send him a letter of instruction for reaching your property, which has a boat access only. You also need to pinpoint the location of your proposed log cabin. Here is how you might compose your letter, shown in Figure 10-11.

Introduction

In your opening paragraph, identify the procedure for which you are providing directions and explain the reasons for providing them. You may also use this paragraph to supply any background necessary to the reader or to call attention

154 Seaweed Lane
East Harwich,
  Massachusetts 01263
September 25, 1978

Mr. Lionel D. Kearns
Professional Engineer
3 Wright Lane
Otisfield, Maine 04572

Dear Mr. Kearns:

In our September 20 phone conversation about your upcoming
evaluation of my proposed building site on the northern
shore of Deerfoot Lake, you asked for detailed directions to
the property. Here are the instructions for reaching lots
#48 and 49. I am also enclosing a topographical map of the
area.

From the Seboomook dock, proceed approximately 4½ miles by
water in a southeasterly direction. Immediately after
passing through the channel between Seboomook Island and the
mainland (see enclosed map), look for the forest service
camping area on your left (marked by a log bench perched out
on the rock point of the mainland). My property lies 1000
feet east of the camping area. It is marked by a highly
visible granite ledge, approximately 30 feet long and 15
feet high.

LANDING CAUTION: A rock shoal along the westerly frontage of
the property extends about 30 feet from the shoreline.
Approach the shoreline carefully, from the easterly end, and
you will find a suitable landing area on a small gravel beach
immediately to your right of the ledge.

Lot boundaries are marked by yellow stakes located within a
few feet of the shoreline. Look for lot numbers carved on
yellow-marked trees adjacent to the yellow stakes.

If I can receive the results of your evaluation by early
November I will have a head start for spring building plans.
Please call me at 231-978-4568 (collect) for further information. I appreciate your help in this wilderness building
project.

                              Best wishes,

                              John M. Lannon

Enclosure

FIGURE 10-11   A Letter of Instruction

to any enclosed material — lists of materials or tools needed, charts or diagrams, maps, or the like.

Body

In your body section, describe each step of the procedure in the order of its performance. If your instructions are at all complicated, place each step in a separate paragraph and number the paragraphs sequentially. Include any cautions or warnings immediately before the steps to which they apply.

Conclusion

Conclude by mentioning the specific time or date by which the procedure should be completed (as applicable). Offer to provide further information, if needed. As a convenience, include your telephone number in case your reader has questions.

WRITING THE RÉSUMÉ AND JOB APPLICATION LETTER

Nearly everyone will eventually need to write a job application. Unless a relative promises you a job in the family company, you will have to find your job in the conventional way — through letters, résumés, dossiers, and interviews. A college degree alone will not ensure you a good job. In fact, as the desirability of any job increases so does the competition among qualified applicants. Because today's job market is, by-and-large, a buyer's market, with many applicants competing for few openings, you have only a few possible courses of action. These include: (1) jumping off a bridge and ending it all; (2) shaving your head, joining a Tibetan monastery, and transcending it all; and (3) taking the time and effort to plan and carry out an effective campaign for marketing your skills to prospective employers. For option 3 your most valuable tools are your résumé and your letter of application; both must stand out among their competitors.

Job Prospecting: The Preliminary Step

Before writing a model letter and résumé, you need to do your homework. Job prospecting is the searching and studying of the job market to identify realistically the career areas and jobs for which you qualify.

Being Selective

Many new graduates make the mistake of applying for too broad a range of jobs, including many for which they have no real qualifications. Such a shotgun approach is ambitious, but it may well decrease your chances — and it can be most discouraging. If you spend your time, energy, and optimism everywhere, you limit the time you have to concentrate on the openings for which you do qualify. Be selective in your search.

Launching Your Search

Your best bet for launching your job campaign (and a "campaign" it is: a sustained and deliberate operation with a definite goal) is to do early homework and planning. (1) Six months to one year before graduation, or even earlier, begin scanning the want-ads; large city papers often publish an entire "employment" section as part of their Sunday editions. In these supplements are descriptions, salary scales, and qualifications for just about any·job imaginable. (2) Ask your college reference librarian to point out occupational handbooks and magazines or journals in your field. (3) Visit your college placement service; here, various openings are posted, interviews are scheduled, and counselors can give you specific advice about job-hunting. (4) If possible, speak with someone now working in your career area; in this way you will get an inside view, along with some practical advice. (5) Sign up at your placement office for interviews with. company representatives who visit your campus.

If you take these steps well before your final semester you may learn that certain courses make you more marketable. In many engineering fields, for example, computer experience is desirable. Many nursing positions require counseling experience, and so on. Learn as much as you can in order to tailor your final semester's curriculum to these requirements (taking one or two introductory computer courses; taking a counseling course and doing volunteer work for a community service organization, or the like).

Being Realistic

When you do apply for jobs, be realistic. If the advertised requirements include several years of practical experience, or administrative experience, or a Master's degree, save your time and energy and look elsewhere. Sometimes, however, the gap between your own qualifications and the qualifications required by the prospective employer may not be too great. In this case, an enthusiastic, well-written letter, along with alternative qualifications (related volunteer work or pertinent outside interests) might land you the job. Rely on your good judgment and the advice of placement counselors and faculty members. Don't hesitate to ask for advice! Besides applying for advertised openings you might write to some organizations that have not advertised recently. Both solicited and unsolicited letters are discussed later in this chapter.

To conclude, unless you have influential relatives or great luck your job search will require careful planning, deliberate execution, and saintly patience (don't expect overnight results!). Once you have a clear picture of where you and your qualifications fit into the job market, you will set out to answer the big question asked by all employers: "What do you have to offer?" Your answer must be a highly polished presentation of yourself, your education, work history, interests, and special skills — in short, your résumé.

The Résumé

Your résumé is a summary of your experience and qualifications — a personal inventory which accompanies your letter of application. Written before your application letter, the résumé provides the raw materials for your letter. For ease of preparation and reading, divide your résumé into seven classes of information:

> — Name and address
> — Age, marital status, and physical characteristics
> — Career objectives
> — Educational background
> — Work experience
> — Personal activities, interests, awards, and special skills
> — References

This information provides an employer with a one- or two-page ready reference to who you are. Your application letter, in turn, will emphasize and discuss specific parts of your résumé.

Begin work on your résumé at least one month before your job search. You will need that much time to compose, revise, and polish until it represents your best effort. Your final version then can be duplicated for each of your targets.

First, list on separate sheets of paper the seven classes of information. Then brainstorm each subject (as discussed in Appendix B) to identify the important items in your background.

Name and Address

Under your first heading include your full name, street and mail address (if different), and telephone number (many interview invitations and job offers are tendered by telephone).

Age, Marital Status, and Physical Characteristics

Recent federal legislation protects you from job discrimination on the basis of sex, religion, race, or national origin. Therefore, you are not required to include a photograph (although you may) or information about these items.

Your age may affect your candidacy, and it should be mentioned. Discrimination on the basis of marital status can be illegal; however, it could be an advantage to indicate your marital status in applying for certain jobs. For example, sales jobs that require frequent traveling might best suit an unmarried person. Because some jobs have strict physical requirements, you might indicate your height, weight, and state of health.

Career Objectives

First, go back to your want-ads and make a survey of the *specific* jobs for which you are *realistically* qualified. Resist the impulse to be all things to all people; be yourself, as you really are. The key to a successful résumé is the image of *you* that it projects — disciplined and purposeful, yet flexible. State both your immediate and long-range goals, including, if possible, any plans for continuing your education:

> My immediate goal is to join the intensive-care nursing staff of an urban teaching hospital. Through on-the-job experience and part-time graduate study in crisis treatment and life-support systems I hope eventually to supervise an intensive-care unit and instruct student nurses.

Your statement of career objectives shows that you have a clear sense of purpose and have given serious thought to your future.

Educational Background

Beginning with your most recent school and working backwards, list the degrees and diplomas you have earned and schools you have attended *beyond* high school (unless you attended a high-school vocational program in specific preparation for your career). List the courses that have directly prepared you for your career. If your class rank is in the upper 40 percent, mention it; otherwise, omit this information. Include any schools attended or courses completed while you were in military service. If you financed part or all of your education by working, say so, indicating the percentage of your contribution.

Work Experience

Beginning with your most recent job and working backward, list and clearly identify each job you have held, giving specific dates of employment and names of employers. Also, state whether the job was full-time, part-time (hours weekly), or seasonal. Briefly describe your specific duties in each job and indicate any promotions or added responsibilities you received.

Personal Interests, Activities, Awards, and Special Skills

This section deserves a great deal of thought and care; it may reveal more about you *as a person* than any other section, and your prospective employer will study it carefully.

List information about hobbies, sports, and other pastimes; memberships in team, school, community, or social organizations; offices held; and any recognition for outstanding performance. Include the dates and specific types of any volunteer work. These items describe you as an individual, giving employers a revealing profile of such important traits as variety of personal interests, creative use of leisure time, concern for personal growth and community welfare, team spirit, ability to work within a group, leadership qualities, and performance capabilities. Most notably, a history of volunteer work suggests that you give freely of your time, talent, and energy without concern for material gain; thus you display a certain generosity of spirit. Employers know that a person who actively seeks a well-rounded life is likely to take an active interest in his or her job. Who you are away from work largely defines who you will be on the job.

Obviously, you will want to be selective in completing this section. List only the items that have some relevance to your field, along with those which reflect your competence and good character.

References

Often a reference letter is the major element in getting a prospective employer to want to meet you; thus, again, thought and care should enter into your selection of references.

Your list of references names four or five people *who have agreed* to write strong, positive assessments of your qualifications and personal qualities. Include your references' full names, titles, and addresses (and telephone numbers, if applying locally). Simply to state "references available on request" is a mistake; you may lose an important advantage. Most likely, one or more of your references is a well-known and respected member of your chosen field (a professor, a company officer, a supervisor, etc.). A prospective employer who sees the name of a friend or respected professional is also likely to notice *your* name. Thus, you will become a known quantity among the crowd of applicants.

Select references who can speak with authority about your competence and character. Avoid members of your family (everyone knows that grandmothers consider their grandchildren flawless), neighbors, and close friends not in your field. Choose instead among professors, previous employers, and respected community figures who know you well enough to write on your behalf. In asking for a reference keep these two points in mind:

1. *A mediocre or poor letter of reference is more damaging than no letter at all.* Therefore, don't simply ask, "Could you please act as one of my references?" A question phrased this way leaves the person little chance to say no. He or she may not know you well or may not be impressed by your work but, instead of refusing, may write a watery letter that will do more harm than good. Instead, make a detailed request: "Do you feel that you know me and my work well enough to write me a strong letter of reference? If so, would you please act as one of my references?" This second version gives your respondent the option to decline gracefully. Otherwise, it elicits a firm commitment to a strongly positive letter.

2. *Letters are time-consuming to write.* Your references are busy people with no time to write countless individual letters to every prospective employer. Therefore, ask for only one letter, addressed *To whom it may concern.* Your reference keeps a copy for his or her files; you keep the original for your personal dossier (so you can reproduce it as necessary); and a copy is sent to your placement office for inclusion in your placement dossier. Because recent legislation permits you to read all material in your placement dossier, this arrangement will provide you with your own copy of your credentials.[1] (The dossier is discussed later in this chapter.)

If one or more of the people you select as references live a great distance from you, you may wish to make your request by letter. Figure 10-12 shows a sample letter of request.

Composing the Résumé

With your vital data collected and your references lined up, you are ready to compose your actual résumé. Imagine yourself to be a twenty-two-year-old student about to graduate from a community college with an A.A. degree in Hotel and Restaurant Management. Before attending college, you worked at related jobs for over three years. You are now seeking a junior-management position with a nationwide hospitality chain while you continue your education, part-time. You have spent parts of the past two weeks compiling and selecting information for your résumé and obtaining commitments from four references. Figure 10-13 shows how your finished product might look, with items listed in parallel form and uniformly indented. Notice that this résumé mentions nothing about salary. Wait until this matter comes up in your inter-

---

[1] Under some circumstances you may — and may wish to — waive the right to examine your recommendations. Some applicants, especially those applying to professional schools as in medicine and law, do in fact waive the right to see recommendations. They do so in concession, one supposes, to a general feeling that a letter writer who is assured of confidentiality is more likely to provide a balanced, objective, and reliable assessment of a candidate. In your own case, you might want to seek the advice of your major advisor or a career counselor.

203 Elmwood Street
San Jose, California 10462
March 12, 1978

Mr. John Knight
Manager, Teo's Restaurant
15 Loomis Street
Pensacola, Florida 31642

Dear Mr. Knight:

From September 1974 to August 1976 I worked under your supervision at Teo's Restaurant as waiter, cashier, and then
assistant manager. Because I enjoyed my work I decided to
study for a career in the hospitality field.

In three months I will graduate from San Jose City College
with an A.A. degree in Hotel and Restaurant Management. Next
month I will begin my job search. Do you feel that you know
me and my work well enough to write me a strong letter of
recommendation? If so, would you be willing to act as one of
my references?

In order to save your time, may I ask that you address your
letter "to whom it may concern." If you will kindly send me
the original, I will forward a copy to my college placement
office.

Please let me know if you would like a copy of my résumé to
review my recent activities.

Thank you for your help.

                                        Sincerely,

                                        James David Purdy

FIGURE 10-12   A Letter Requesting a Recommendation

RÉSUMÉ

Name and Address   Age, Marital Status,
                                          Physical Data

    James David Purdy   22, married
    203 Elmwood Street   health: excellent
    San Jose, California 10462   height: 5'11"
    Telephone: 214-316-2419   weight: 160 pounds

Career Objectives

  My immediate goal is to obtain an entry-level position in
  the customer-relations division of a large hospitality
  chain. By continuing my education part-time and gaining
  experience in desk and dining-room management, advertising,
  and customer service, I hope eventually to assume market
  management responsibilities.

Educational Background

    A.A., Hotel/Restaurant Management--San Jose City College,
                          June 1978
              Cumulative Grade-Point Average: 3.25 of a
                                         possible 4.00
              Related Courses: Hospitality Organization and
                                Management, Psychology, Oral
                                Communication, Nutrition,
                                Food Purchasing and Cost
                                Control, Accounting, Hotel
                                Management, Business Law,
                                Quantity Food Preparation,
                                Beverage Management, Person-
                                nel Management, Physical
                                Operation and Sanitation,
                                Hotel-Restaurant Merchan-
                                dising, Marketing, Adver-
                                tising
          All my college expenses were financed by scholarship
          and my part-time job (20 hours weekly--see work
          experience).

FIGURE 10-13 A Résumé

James David Purdy's résumé--page 2

Work Experience

  9/76-present Peek-A-Boo Lodge (200 units), San Jose--began
                as desk clerk and am now desk manager (part-
                time)

  8/75-8/76   Teo's Restaurant, Pensacola, Florida--began
                as waiter, advanced to cashier, and finally
                to assistant manager

  9/73-8/75   United States Navy--food service specialist

  12/72-9/73   White's Family Inn, San Luis Obispo, Cali-
                fornia--bus boy then waiter (part-time)

  5/73-4/74   Encyclopaedia Britannica, Inc.--sales repre-
                sentative (part-time)

Personal Interests, Activities, Awards, and Special Skills

  Interests: skiing, continental cooking, travel, sailing,
              oil painting, and various wilderness sports

  Activities: member of high school varsity basketball and
               track teams (3 years); assistant scoutmaster,
               Boy Scouts, Pensacola; member of college
               student senate (2 years); member of Inn-
               keeper's Club--planned, prepared and served
               monthly dinners at the college (2 years)

  Awards: elected captain of basketball team, 9/73;
           received Lion's Club Scholarship, 4/77

  Special Skills: speak French with fluency; expert skier

References

  Dr. Walter Jones, Marketing Professor, San Jose City
     College, San Jose, California 10462

FIGURE 10-13 (*Continued*)

James David Purdy's résumé--page 3

<u>References</u> (continued)

    Mr. Melvin Hawks, Chairman, Hotel Management Program,
      San Jose City College

    Miss Olga Herst, Owner-Manager, Peek-A-Boo Lodge, San Jose

    Mr. John Knight, Manager, Teo's Restaurant, 15 Loomis
      Street, Pensacola, Florida 31642

    For dossier requests please write to me or my
      Placement Office
      Ludlow Building
      San Jose City College
      San Jose, California 10462

FIGURE 10-13 (*Continued*)

view, or later. And because James Purdy is not entering a beauty contest, he has not attached a photograph. The information, specific but concise, describes what he has to offer in less than three pages, requiring only a couple of minutes to skim. There are no meaningless statements of self-praise as "I did such a terrific job that I was promoted to manager." The facts speak for themselves.

As a final check of your résumé, look at it as a personnel director might, analyze your presentation, and if you find weaknesses strengthen them. As a guide, Figure 10-14 shows Personnel Director Mary Smith's assessment of James Purdy, in the form of a memo to her colleagues.

When fully satisfied that your résumé is precise and complete, have your model copy printed by a lithographer or printer. For less than twenty dollars you can obtain a better-looking copy than you could produce on a typewriter. This one prototype, in turn, will yield as many copies as you need. For clear, neat copies use a photocopying machine or an offset printing process; *never* send out carbon, thermofax, or mimeographed copies.

A final suggestion: avoid using a résumé-preparing service. Although professionals can use your raw materials to produce an impressive résumé, employers will often recognize the source by its style; if they do, they may conclude that you are incapable of communicating effectively on your own.

Now, with your résumé fully prepared, you are ready to plan and compose the equally important job application letter.

The Job Application Letter

Your Image

Your job application letter is one of the most important pieces you will ever write. Depending on its quality your letter will either open doors or be a waste of time and effort. Although its text is based on your résumé, you must emphasize your personal qualities and qualifications in a way that is personable and convincing. Here you will project an image of your personality. In your résumé you merely present raw facts; in your application letter you will discuss these facts. And the tone in which you discuss them suggests a good deal about the kind of person you are. The letter is your opportunity to explain how you see yourself fitting in the organization. Your purpose is to interpret the items on your résumé to show your employer how you will be valuable.

Many people are uncomfortable talking about themselves in letters to strangers. They often feel that they can say little without seeming conceited. However, the most essential ingredient in your letter is self-confidence. After all, if you don't believe in yourself, who will? Your letter is a sales letter: it markets your greatest commodity — *you*. To be effective, it *must* stand out among other applications.

TO: Members of the   DATE: January 20, 1977
     Hiring Committee

FROM: Mary Smith,
       Personnel Director

SUBJECT: Follow-up on James Purdy's
          Application (copy enclosed)

This applicant shows a sense of purpose and responsible
planning for his future. His recent background provides
detailed and specific support for his stated plans.

The fact that he financed his own education yet achieved
a high cumulative average indicates that he is both a dili-
gent and capable worker. His course of study, along with
practical experience in sales, food service, and hospitality
suggests that his career choice is based on sound knowledge
of the hotel/restaurant field and an obvious interest and
talent for direct customer contact.

His history of job promotions is clear indication that
the quality of his work has impressed his employers repeatedly.
His skiing ability and interest in cooking and sailing would
seem to make him a strong candidate for a position in one of
our northern resort facilities. His history of activities
and awards suggests that he works well with others (including
youngsters), is respected by his peers, has leadership qualities, and is willing to volunteer his time and talent without
compensation. Finally, his ability to speak a foreign
language could be an important asset to our customer relations
division.

Overall, James Purdy seems to be a well-rounded person
who knows what he wants and who can offer youth, enthusiasm,
and experience to our organization. He promises to be a
responsible employee who will continue to improve personally
and professionally. I recommend that we pursue his application.

FIGURE 10-14 A Personnel Director's Memo

Because you may feel uncomfortable talking about yourself, you could be tempted to cut your letter short, to do a rush job. This tactic reduces your immediate pain, but it also negates your chances for success. After spending years preparing for a career, you would be foolish to write anything less than a perfect letter to sell your abilities. So begin your model letter early and revise it until you are proud to sign it.

Targets

With your letter and résumé polished and complete you can apply for jobs anywhere without leaving your desk. Unlike your résumé, however, your letter should never be xeroxed. Although you can base letters to different employers on the same model — with appropriate changes — type each letter freshly.

The immediate purpose of your letter is to secure an interview. Therefore, the letter itself should make the reader want to meet you. Make your statements engaging, precise, and *original*. Borrowed phrases from textbook examples and "letterese" will not do the job.

Sometimes you will apply for positions advertised in print or by word of mouth (solicited applications). At other times you will write prospecting letters to organizations that have not advertised but might need someone like you (unsolicited applications). In either case, your letter should be tailored to the situation.

The Solicited Letter

Imagine that you are James Purdy. In *Innkeeper's Monthly* you read this advertisement and decide to apply:

RESORT MANAGEMENT OPENINGS

Liberty International, Inc. is accepting applications for several junior management positions at our new Lake Geneva Resort. Applicants must have three years practical experience, along with formal training in all areas of hotel/restaurant management. Please apply by June 1, 1978 to:

Elmer Borden
Personnel Director
Liberty International, Inc.
Lansdown, Pennsylvania 24135

Now, plan and compose your letter, using the questions in this chapter as a guide:

Introduction. Introduce yourself and create a tone of self-confidence by directly stating your reason for writing. Mention the specific title of the job you seek and the publication where you read the advertisement. Remember that you are talking *to* someone; use the pronoun "you" often (this is especially important here, where you must talk about yourself without sounding conceited). If you can, establish a direct connection by mentioning the name of a mutual acquaintance; for example, you learn that your professor of nutrition, Dr. H. V. Garlid, is a former colleague of Elmer Borden; mention of his name attracts immediate close attention to your letter. Finally, after referring your reader to your enclosed résumé, you are ready to discuss the proof of your qualifications.

Body. Concentrate on two kinds of information: (1) what you can bring to the job (your strengths), and (2) what you hope for from the job (challenge, growth, and so on). Don't come across as a jack-of-all trades. Relate your experience to *this* job. Avoid empty flattery ("I am greatly impressed by your remarkable company"). Be specific. Replace "much experience," "many courses," or "increased sales" with "three years of experience," "five courses," or "sales increased by 35 percent between June and October 1976." Show your dynamic qualities by using the *active* rather than the *passive* voice:

> *Weak*
> Increased responsibilities were steadily given to me.

> *Stronger*
> I steadily assumed increasing responsibilities.

Trim the fat from your sentences:

> *Flabby*
> I have always been a person who enjoys a challenge.

> *Lean*
> I enjoy a challenge.

Project self-confidence with your language:

> *Unsure*
> It is my opinion that I will be a successful manager because. . . .

> *Certain*
> I will be a successful manager because. . . .

Finally, avoid the use of "letterese." Write as you speak.

Conclusion. Restate your interest in the job, emphasize your flexibility and willingness to retrain (if necessary), and review briefly other important personal qualities. If your reader is nearby, end with a request for an interview; otherwise, request a telephone call, stating times when you may be reached. <u>Your strong and courteous conclusion should leave your reader with the impression that you are more than a name on a page; you are worth knowing</u>.

Revision.   *Never* settle for a first draft — or even a second or third! Perhaps by your fourth you will be approaching the best possible answers to our guide questions. And because, in any case, your letter is your model for letters serving a wide variety of circumstances, it must be your best effort. When you are sure that your letter has high-quality content, an appropriate tone, and an impeccable format, sign it. If you still feel unsure, revise it once again.

James Purdy's letter to Elmer Borden, replying to the *Innkeeper's Monthly* advertisement, was the product of his careful attention to these principles. After taking plenty of time, and making a number of revisions, he finally signed the letter in Figure 10-15. He wisely chose to emphasize his practical experience because his background is varied and impressive. An applicant with less practical experience would emphasize education instead, discussing related courses and extracurricular activities.

You should also choose the best way to describe how you will fit in. And remember that an enthusiastic tone can go a long way. In fact, the attitude you project can be as important as the background you offer. Show yourself to be an interested and interesting person with a clear sense of purpose.

The Unsolicited Letter

Ambitious job seekers will not limit their search to advertised openings. The unsolicited, or "prospecting," letter is a good way of uncovering other possibilities. Such letters have definite advantages and disadvantages.

Disadvantages.   The unsolicited approach does have two drawbacks: (1) You may waste time and energy writing letters to organizations that simply have no openings. (2) Because you don't know what the opening is — if there is one — you cannot tailor your letter to the specific requirements.

Advantages.   This cold-canvassing approach does have one important advantage: For an advertised opening you will compete with legions of qualified applicants, whereas your unsolicited letter might arrive just when an opening has materialized. If it does, your application will receive immediate attention and you just might get the job! Even when there is no immediate opening, an impressive application may be filed until an opening does occur. It may even be passed along to a colleague at a company that has an opening.

There are often good reasons for going further than the Help Wanted columns. Unsolicited letters generally are a sound investment if your targets are well chosen and your expectations are realistic.

203 Elmwood Street
San Jose, California 10462
April 22, 1978

Mr. Elmer Borden
Personnel Director
Liberty International, Inc.
Lansdown, Pennsylvania 24135

Dear Mr. Borden:

Your advertisement in the March issue of Innkeeper's Monthly
prompts my application for a junior management position at
your Lake Geneva resort. I will graduate from San Jose City
College on May 30 with an A.A. degree in Hotel/Restaurant
Management. Dr. H. V. Garlid, my nutrition professor, has
told me of his own rewarding experience as a consultant with
Liberty International, further encouraging me to write. My
background and interests, as described below and in the
enclosed résumé, seem well suited to your requirements.

For the past two years I have financed my education while
gaining practical experience by working as part-time desk
clerk and, now, desk manager at a 200-unit hotel/restaurant
facility in San Jose. This experience, combined with earlier
customer-contact work as Navy food service specialist,
waiter, busboy, and sales representative, has helped me
understand customers' needs and expectations of quality
service. As a continental cooking hobbyist, I have firsthand knowledge of the continuous effort, attention, and
patience required to maintain an outstanding cuisine. Moreover, you might find that my skiing and sailing abilities
would be assets to your resort's recreation program.

Although I have much to learn about the hospitality business,
a challenging position with Liberty International would
offer the chance I seek for professional growth and personal
involvement.

If my background, my flexibility, and my enthusiasm have
sparked your interest, Mr. Borden, please phone me at home
(214-316-2419) any weekday after 4 p.m.

                              Yours truly,

                              James David Purdy

FIGURE 10-15   A Solicited Letter of Application

Reader Interest.

Reader Interest.   Because your unsolicited letter is unexpected, attract your reader's attention early and make him or her want to read further. Don't begin: "I am writing to inquire about the possibility of obtaining a position with your company." By now, your reader is asleep. If you can't establish a direct connection through a mutual acquaintance, use a forceful opening like this:

> In six years I have pounded on strange doors as a book salesman, carried a ton of dirty dishes as a busboy, endured customer demands as a waiter, kept my patrons healthy — if not always happy — as a military cook, and juggled room assignments as a desk clerk and manager. In short, my customer-relations experience in hospitality management extends far beyond mere textbook learning.

Unlike the usual, time-worn, and plastic openings, this approach gets through to your reader immediately. Who could resist reading on? Whereas generalities and borrowed phrases make you seem like another member of the faceless mass, specific details and a vital tone help you stand out.

Figure 10-16 shows an unsolicited version of James Purdy's letter. Notice that the only major difference between the solicited and unsolicited letter is the opening paragraph. This second version also requests an interview because the employer is within easy traveling distance.

The Prototype

Most of your letters, whether solicited or unsolicited, can be versions of your one model, or prototype. Thus your prototype must represent you and your goals in the best possible light. As you approach your job search give yourself plenty of time to compose your model letter and résumé. In your actual search you might write ten letters or several hundred, depending on your field and your expectations. In any case, the quality of your application will be interpreted as an indication of the quality of work you will do as an employee. Don't sign your letter until it speaks well for you, both on the lines and between them. Work from a good model and you will succeed.

SUPPORTING YOUR APPLICATION

Your Dossier

Your dossier is a folder containing your credentials: college transcript, letters of recommendation, and any other items (such as a notice of a scholarship award or letter of commendation) that testify to your accomplishments. In your letter and résumé you talk about yourself; in your dossier others talk about you. An employer impressed by what you have said about yourself will wish to read what others think about you and will request a copy of your dossier. By collecting your letters of recommendation in one folder you spare your references from writing the same letter over and over.

203 Elmwood Street
San Jose, California 10462
April 30, 1978

Ms. Charon Kiev, Manager
Personnel Division
Happyday Inns, Inc.
Los Angeles, California 37654

Dear Ms. Kiev:

Does your hotel chain have a place for a junior manager with broad practical experience, a college degree in hospitality management, and a proven commitment to quality service and customer relations? If so, please review my specific qualifications in this letter and the enclosed résumé.

I will graduate from San Jose City College on May 30 with an A.A. Degree in Hotel/Restaurant Management. For the past two years I have financed my education while gaining practical experience by working as a part-time desk clerk and, now, desk manager of a 200 unit hotel/restaurant in San Jose. This experience, combined with earlier customer-contact work as Navy food service specialist, waiter, bus boy, and sales representative has helped me understand customers' needs and expectations of quality service. As a continental cooking hobbyist I have firsthand knowledge of the effort, attention, and patience required to maintain an outstanding cuisine. Moreover, you might find that my skiing and sailing background makes me particularly suited for work at one of your resort facilities.

Although I have much to learn about the hospitality business, a challenging position with Happyday Inns would offer the chance I seek for professional growth and personal involvement.

If my background, my flexibility, and my enthusiasm have sparked your interest, Ms. Kiev, please phone me at home (214-316-2419) any weekday after 4 p.m. I would welcome the opportunity for an interview.

Yours truly,

James David Purdy

FIGURE 10-16 An Unsolicited Letter of Application

If your college has a placement office it will keep your dossier on file, sending copies to employers who request them. In any case, keep your own copy in a manila folder. Then, if an employer writes to you, requesting your dossier, you can xerox a copy immediately and mail it out, advising your reader that the placement office copy is on the way. This is not needless repetition! Most often, employers establish a specific timetable for (1) advertising an opening, (2) reading letters and résumés, (3) requesting and reviewing dossiers, (4) holding interviews, and (5) making job offers. Obviously, if your letter and résumé do not arrive until the screening process is at step 3 you are out of luck. The same is true if your dossier arrives when the screening process is at the end of step 4. Timing, then, is crucial. Too often, dossier requests from employers sit and gather dust in some "incoming" box on a desk in the placement office. Sometimes one or two weeks will pass before your dossier is mailed out. And, of course, the only loser in this case is you.

When you receive a dossier request, you can assume that you are a semi-finalist for the position. This is no time to let up. By acting at once you retain control of the application procedure. Don't entrust your destiny to a busy placement office!

Interviews

If the employer is impressed with your collected credentials, he will phone or write to invite you for an interview. Now you can be sure that you are one of the finalists. You may meet with one interviewer, a group, or several groups in succession. You may be interviewed alone or with several candidates at once. Interviews can last one hour or less, a full day, or even several consecutive days. The character of the interview can range from a pleasant, informal chat to grueling quiz sessions resembling an inquisition. Some interviewers may antagonize you deliberately to observe your reaction ("Whatever made you imagine that you could fill this position?"). If that happens, suppress your annoyance, look your interviewer straight in the eye, and answer confidently.

Are you one of many people who dread the idea of an interview? Your library may be able to provide books containing far more detailed advice than there is space for here; because a self-confident manner is of first importance, prepare yourself by studying the techniques of being interviewed. Better yet, get some actual practice. Take as many interviews as you can. You will find your self-confidence increasing with each one.

Prepare for your interview by learning whatever you can about the company (its products, or services, recent growth, future prospects, branch locations) in trade journals and industrial registries or indexes. If time permits, request company brochures and annual reports. Be prepared to give specific answers to the obvious questions:

Why do you wish to work here?
What do you consider to be your strongest quality?
What do you see as your biggest weakness?
Where would you like to be in ten years?

Plan informative and direct answers to specific questions about your background, training, experience, and salary requirements. Project a strong sense of purpose. Prepare your own list of questions about the job and the organization; you will be invited to ask questions, and the questions you ask can say as much about you as the answers you give.

If you have done your homework well, your interview should be a stimulating experience in which you and your prospective employer can learn much about each other. Remember that the purpose of the interview is to confirm the impressions about your qualifications and personality that an employer has gained from your application. Your interviewer wants to know if you are as impressive in person as you seem on paper. Consequently, your best strategy is to be yourself. You have specific skills and a unique personality to offer. Busy people are taking the time and expense to speak with you because they recognize your worth. Knowing this, you can enter your interview with confidence.

Be sure you know the exact time and location of the interview. Come well dressed and groomed. Maintain direct eye contact most of the time; if you stare at your shoes your interviewer will not be impressed. Relax in your chair but don't lounge. Don't smoke, even if invited. Don't pretend you know more than you do; if you can't answer a question, say so. Avoid simple yes or no answers as well as complicated life stories. Make your answers detailed but to the point.

When your interviewer hints that the meeting is ending (perhaps by checking his watch), don't overstay your welcome. Make any necessary concluding comments that emphasize your interest in the job; ask when you might expect further word; thank your interviewer for his time; and leave promptly.

The Follow-up Letter

Within a few days of your interview, reinforce your candidacy with a letter thanking your prospective employer and restating your interest. This simple act of courtesy and sophistication can only help your cause. Figure 10-17 shows James Purdy's follow-up to his interview with Elmer Borden.

The Letter of Acceptance

If all goes well you will receive a job offer by phone or letter. If it is by phone, request a written offer and respond with a formal letter of acceptance. This letter may serve as part of your contract; be sure to spell out the terms of the offer you are accepting! Figure 10-18 shows James Purdy's letter of acceptance.

203 Elmwood Street
San Jose, California 10462
May 5, 1978

Mr. Elmer Borden
Personnel Manager
Liberty International, Inc.
Lansdown, Pennsylvania 24135

Dear Mr. Borden:

    Thank you for your hospitality during my two-day visit
to your Lansdown offices. After meeting with you and your
colleagues and touring the Lansdown resort, I am convinced
that I could be a productive member of your customer
relations staff.

                                Sincerely yours,

                                James David Purdy

FIGURE 10-17 A Follow-up Letter

203 Elmwood Avenue
San Jose, California 10462
May 5, 1978

Mr. Elmer Borden
Personnel Manager
Liberty International, Inc.
Lansdown, Pennsylvania 24135

Dear Mr. Borden:

I am happy to accept your offer of a position as assistant
recreation supervisor at Liberty International's Lake Geneva
Resort with a starting yearly salary of $10,500.

As you requested, I will phone Ms. Druid in your personnel
office for final instructions on reporting date, physical
examination, and employee orientation.

I look forward to a long and satisfying career with Liberty
International.

Sincerely yours,

James David Purdy

FIGURE 10-18   A Letter of Acceptance

203 Elmwood Avenue
San Jose, California 10462
May 16, 1978

Ms. Charon Kiev, Manager
Personnel Division
Happyday Inns, Inc.
Los Angeles, California 37654

Dear Ms. Kiev:

Although I was impressed by the challenge and efficiency of
your company's operation, I am unable to accept your offer of
a position as assistant desk manager of your Beirut hotel. I
have taken a position with Liberty International which will
allow me to complete the requirements for my B.S. degree in
hospitality management on a full-time basis.

Thank you for your time, courtesy, and consideration, and
best wishes for continued success.

                               Sincerely yours,

                               James David Purdy

FIGURE 10-19 A Letter of Refusal

The Letter of Refusal

All job offers are not equally attractive; you may decide to refuse several. If you do, it is good practice to write a prompt and cordial letter of refusal, explaining your reasons, and, especially, leaving the door open for future possibilities. You may find later that you are disillusioned with the job you accepted and wish to explore old contacts. Figure 10-19 shows how James Purdy handled a refusal.

CHAPTER SUMMARY

The letter is a more personal form of communication than the report; its tone must be pleasing in order to have a positive influence on your reader. As a rule of thumb, don't ever send off a letter until you feel good about signing it.

Any effective letter has an appropriate format and form, is written in conversational language with a "you" perspective, and expresses a clear purpose. The types of letters you will write most often are:

– the letter of inquiry, requesting detailed information from your reader
– the letter of complaint, written to register your dissatisfaction and to request adjustment
– the letter of instruction, explaining how to carry out a procedure

Among your most important correspondence is your résumé and job application letter. Follow these steps in writing your application:

1. Spend some time job prospecting.
2. After brainstorming on your background, begin work on your résumé and letter early, and plan on many revisions.
3. Compose your résumé as an inventory of your qualifications. Make a perfect model from which you can run off xerox copies.
4. Compose your letter, emphasizing the major qualifications from your résumé, along with your personal qualities. Project a sense of self-confidence without being pompous. Tailor your letter to fit the job and the application situation (solicited or unsolicited). Write a fresh letter (based on your prototype) for each application.

Follow these steps in supporting your application:

1. Compile your dossier and retain control of its distribution.
2. Prepare well for interviews and take as many as you can to sharpen your skills.
3. Write follow-up letters after completing interviews.
4. Request job offers in writing and respond to each with a detailed letter of acceptance.

5. For offers that you refuse, send refusal letters that leave doors open for future contacts.

REVISION CHECKLIST

Use this checklist as a guide to revision. It will ensure that you succeed in your letter-writing assignment.

1. Does your letter have an introduction-body-conclusion structure?
2. Does it contain all major parts (heading, inside address, salutation, letter text, complimentary closing, signature)?
3. Does it contain all needed specialized parts (typist's initials, enclosure notation, distribution notation, postscript)?
4. Is your letter composed in an appropriate format (good paper, neat typing, uniform margins and spacing)?
5. Does your letter follow an accepted form (semiblock or modified block)?
6. Is it phrased in conversational language (free from clichés and "letterese")?
7. Does your letter embody a "you" perspective (words chosen to establish trust, respect, and mutual understanding with the reader)?
8. Is it written in correct English (spelling, mechanics, and usage as discussed in Appendix A)?
9. Does your letter achieve its purpose?
   a. Have you identified your definite purpose?
   b. Have you given the reader all needed facts?
   c. Have you identified the name and position of your reader?
   d. Does the tone of your letter reflect your relationship to your reader?
   e. Can you expect a positive response to your letter as written?
   f. Will your reader get a favorable impression of you from your letter?
   g. Are you ready to sign your letter with confidence?

Now list those elements of your letter that need improvement.

EXERCISES

1. Bring to class a copy of a business letter that you or a friend may have received. Working in small groups, compare letters, using the principles of effective letters discussed in this chapter. Choose the most effective and the least effective letter and, as a group, compose two separate paragraphs explaining the group's choices.

2. Write and mail an unsolicited letter of inquiry about the topic that you have investigated, or will investigate, in an analytical report or research

assignment. Your letter may request brochures, pamphlets, or other informative literature, or it may ask specific questions about your subject ("What chemicals are used to clean algae, barnacles, and other marine vegetation from the cooling system's filters?" "Are these chemicals then discharged into the sea?"). Submit a copy of your letter and your addressee's response to your instructor. Plan and write this and all other letters in these exercises according to the questions at the end of the Revision Checklist.

3. Complete the following statement: "The elements that contribute to a truly distinctive letter of application are . . ." Now, use your completed statement as a topic sentence for a unified and coherent paragraph.

4. As a student in a state college you learn that your governor and legislature have cut next year's operating budget for all state colleges by 20 percent. This will cause the firing of many young and popular faculty members, a drastic reduction in student admissions, reduction in student financial-aid programs, cancellation of several new college programs, and erosion of the morale of the college community and the quality of instruction. Write a complaint letter to your governor or your legislative representative, expressing your strong disapproval of this cut and justifying a major adjustment in the proposed budget.

5. Hide a slip of paper with your name on it in some remote corner of your college campus, outside of your classroom building. Write a formal letter of instruction to a classmate, explaining how to locate the hidden item within fifteen minutes. Exchange letters and launch your fifteen-minute search. When all items have been found, critique individual instructions in class.

6. Besides providing factual data about one's background, what does a letter of application say about an applicant? Explain in a short essay titled "Reading between the Lines."

7. Write a 500-word essay explaining your reasons for applying to a specific college for transfer or for graduate or professional school admission. Be sure that your essay covers two general areas: (1) what you can bring to this school by way of attitude, background, and talent, and (2) what you expect to gain from this school in personal and professional growth.

8. Write a letter applying for a part-time or summer job. Choose an organization that can offer you experience that is directly related to your career goal. Be sure to identify the exact hours and calendar period during which you are free to work.

9. a. Identify the job that you would most like to have in two to five years. Using newspaper, library (see your reference librarian for assistance), placement office, and personal sources, write your own full description of the job: duties, responsibilities, work hours, salary range, requirements for promotion, highest promotion possible, unemployment rate in the field, employment outlook for the next decade, need for further education (advanced degrees, special training, etc.), employment rate in terms of geography, optimum age bracket (as in football, does one fade around thirty-five?), and any other items you can think of.

b. Using the same sources and your own good judgment, construct a profile of the ideal employee for this job. If you were the personnel director screening applicants, what specific qualifications would you require in an employee (education, experience, age, physical ability, appearance, special skills, personality traits, attitude, outside interests, and so on)? If you can, locate an actual newspaper advertisement describing job responsibilities and qualifications in detail.

c. Assess your own credentials against each item in the ideal-employee profile. Review the plans that you have made to prepare yourself for this job: specific courses, special training, work experience, etc. Assume that you have completed your preparation. How do you measure up, on paper to the requirements in part b? Are your goals realistic? If not, why not? What alternative plan should you formulate?

d. Using your list from part c as raw material, construct your personal résumé. Revise your résumé until it is perfect.

e. Write a letter of application for the job described in part a. Revise your letter until you feel good about signing it.

f. Write a follow-up letter to your fictional employer, thanking him or her for your recent interview and again expressing your interest in working for the organization.

g. Write a letter accepting the job offer you received from this same employer.

h. Write a letter graciously refusing this job offer.

i. Submit each of these items (job description, employee profile, newspaper ad, résumé, application letter, follow-up letter, letter of acceptance, letter of refusal), in order, to your instructor.

NOTE: Use the sample letters in this chapter for guidance but don't borrow specific expressions.

10. Assume that the following advertisement has appeared in your school newspaper:

STUDENT CONSULTANT WANTED

The office of the Dean of Students invites applications for the position of student consultant to the Dean for the upcoming academic year. Duties will include (1) meeting with fellow students as individuals and groups to discuss issues, opinions, questions, complaints, and recommendations regarding all areas of college policy, (2) presenting oral and written reports of findings to the Dean of Students on a regular basis, and (3) attending various college planning sessions in the role of student spokesperson. Time commitment: 15 hours weekly during both semesters. Salary: $2000.

Candidates for this position should be full-time students with at least one year of student experience at this college. The ideal applicant will be skilled in report writing and oral communication, will have the ability to work well with others, and will demonstrate a firm commitment to the welfare of our college community. Application deadline: May 15.

a. Compose a résumé and a letter of application for this position.

b. As a class, split into groups of six to form screening, interview, and hiring committees.

    c. Exchange your group's letters and résumés with another group in the class.

    d. As an individual committee member, read and evaluate each of the six applications you have received. Rank each application, privately, on paper, according to the criteria discussed in this chapter before discussing them with the colleagues in your group. *Note:* While screening applicants you will be competing for selection by another committee who is reviewing your own application.

    e. As a committee, select the three strongest applications and invite the applicants for interviews. Interview each selected applicant for ten minutes, after you have prepared a list of standardized questions.

    f. On the basis of these interviews, rank your preferences privately, on paper, giving specific reasons for your final choice.

    g. Compare your conclusion with those of your colleagues and choose the winning candidate.

    h. As a committee, compose a memo to your instructor, giving specific reasons for your final recommendations.

    i. Write your own evaluation of this exercise. In two or three paragraphs discuss what you have learned here.

11. Most of the following sentences need to be overhauled before being included in a letter. Identify the weakness in each statement and revise as needed.

    a. Pursuant to your ad, I am writing to apply for the position of junior accountant.

    b. I need all the information you have about methane-powered engines.

    c. You idiots have sent me a faulty carburetor!

    d. It is imperative that you let me know of your decision by January 15.

    e. You are bound to be impressed by my credentials.

    f. I could do wonders for your company.

    g. I humbly request your kind consideration of my application for the position of junior engineer.

    h. If you are looking for a winner, your search is over!

    i. I have become cognizant of your experiments and wish to ask your advice about the following procedure.

    j. You will find the following instructions easy enough for an idiot to follow.

    k. I would love to work for your wonderful company.

    l. As per your request I am sending the county map.

    m. I am in hopes that you will call soon.

    n. We beg to differ with your interpretation of this leasing clause.

    o. I am impressed by the high salaries paid for this kind of work.

12. Evaluate the following letters according to the revision checklist at the end of this chapter and make any needed changes.

Mr. Arthur Marsh
Durango Chemical Corporation
Box 278
Lakeland, Wisconsin 39765

Dear Mr. Marsh:

I was reading the local paper and came across your advertisement in regards to an opening for a crushing and grinding operator's position at your plant. At the present time I am in college, but would like to fill that opening when this semester is over. I am highly qualified for this job as I have already had two years experience in this area. I have operated both crushing and grinding circuits that provide the raw ore used in the processing of phosphate products. I also have experience in operating front-end loaders, forklifts, cats, and 30, 50, and 120-ton haul units. I have held the different positions of laborer, operator, and foreman, so I have a full understanding of this type of operation. I am a very organized and safety-minded worker that can handle myself well in emergency situations. I am a responsible and punctual employee. If you need any further information concerning my work or personal background, please contact me at the address on the envelope. I thank you for considering my application and hope to hear from you soon.

                              Cordially,

                              Raymond Manning

1289 Fourth Street
Madison, Wisconsin 86743
October 5, 1978

Mr. James Trask
Trask and Forbes, Attorneys at Law
17 Lord Street
Bartly, Michigan 47659

Dear Mr. Trask:

     Having just graduated from law school, I am looking for
an established law firm with which to join and learn. Your
firm seems to meet my requirements and I hope I meet yours.

I had thought of going into legal services, but then decided
to go immediately into a private practice. I will be able
to perform innumerable tasks while gaining invaluable
knowledge.

Your firm is considered to be one of the finest in the region
and that is another of the aspects that attracted me. Your
firm is without a junior partner or assistant at this point
in time and I feel very qualified for the position.

Enclosed please find my educational qualifications included
in my résumé. I have just passed the bar on my first attempt
and received very high grades in law school.

Should you have any questions or comments, we could discuss
them at an interview. I am available any time during the
business week from 9:00 to 5:00. Feel free to phone me at
304-756-9759 or write, as I would like to hear from you in
the immediate future.

                              Humbly yours,

                              Brendan Gaines

11

Writing
Informal Reports

CHAPTER GOALS

DEFINITION

PURPOSE OF INFORMAL REPORTS

CHOOSING THE BEST REPORT FORM
    FOR YOUR PURPOSE

COMPOSING VARIOUS INFORMAL
    REPORTS
  Typical Reports in Memorandum Form
    Survey Results
    Proposals
    Progress Reports
  Typical Reports in Letter Form
    Site Inspection Reports
    Proposals
    Work Estimates
  Typical Reports on Prepared Forms
    Travel Vouchers
    Purchase Requisitions
    Business License Applications
    Periodic Activity Reports
  Typical Reports in Miscellaneous Forms
    Minutes
    Survey Results
    Progress Reports

CHAPTER SUMMARY

REVISION CHECKLIST

EXERCISES

CHAPTER GOALS

Upon completing this chapter you will know:

- The meaning and purpose of informal reports.
- How to choose the best report form for your purpose.
- The similarities and differences among various types of informal reports.
- How and when to write effective memos.
- How and when to write effective letter reports.
- How and when to complete prepared-form reports.
- How and when to use other forms of reports broadly classified as miscellaneous.

DEFINITION

Informal reports range in length from one brief sentence to several pages. They are written daily to communicate messages within and between organizations.

In contrast to longer, formal reports, informal reports record only the tip of the information pyramid. Most of them require no long-range planning, are quickly prepared, contain little or no background information, have no supplements (title page, abstract, etc.), and have a variety of possible formats.

PURPOSE OF INFORMAL REPORTS

In the working world, where time is money, the informal report is the one item most often written and read. Its purpose is to communicate rapidly and precisely in one of these formats: the memorandum, the letter report, the prepared-form report, or a variety of other forms which fit into none of the first three categories and which we will call "miscellaneous."

On the job, you will need to communicate quickly and accurately. Your level of success may depend largely on your skill in sharing useful information with colleagues. By sharing useful information we mean that you avoid repeating information and you provide any needed additional information. Here are some of the kinds of informal reports you might write on any workday:

- A request for assistance on a work project.
- A requisition for parts and equipment.
- A proposal outlining the reasons and suggesting a plan for a new project.
- A brief set of instructions for one or more colleagues.
- A cost estimate for planning, materials, and labor on a new project.
- A report of your progress on a specific assignment.
- An hourly or daily account of your work activities.
- A voucher detailing your business travel expenses.
- A report of your inspection of a site, item, or process.
- A statement of reasons for equipment malfunction or failure to meet a deadline.
- A record of the minutes of a meeting.
- A memo describing a change in company personnel policy (vacation time, promotions, etc.)
- A report of your survey to select the best prices, materials, equipment or service among those offered by several competing firms.

These are just a few samples of the almost infinite variety of daily reports that keep companies moving. Most of these reports may be cast in a number of different forms.

CHOOSING THE BEST REPORT FORM FOR YOUR PURPOSE

Whether you decide to report your data in a memo, a letter, on a prepared form, or in any of the miscellaneous forms will depend on your purpose, reader, and situation. It is possible that the same information you cast in a memorandum to your superior will be incorporated in a letter to another company. Or, if you worked for a different company, you might put the same information in a prepared form provided by that company.

Each of the memo examples that follow, for instance, was written for technically informed readers within the writer's organization. The same information might have been written in letter form if the readers had been outside the company. The letter examples in this chapter might have been written as memos. Many of the prepared-form examples could also have been cast in memo form if prepared forms had not been available. However, certain short reports in this chapter show that data and reporting situations sometimes call for specific forms.

The point is that in any organization a great deal of working information has to be exchanged as easily as possible. This flow of information is maintained most conveniently by a variety of report forms. The more you write, the easier it will be to select the best form for your purpose.

COMPOSING VARIOUS INFORMAL REPORTS

Typical Reports in Memorandum Form

The memorandum is the most common form of in-house communication and can cover any subject. A hasty note to a colleague to arrange a luncheon meeting can be classified as a memo. So can a telephone message as shown in Figure 11-1. This kind of brief note usually is discarded immediately after it has served its purpose.

Aside from such brief pieces, most memos follow a fairly well specified format. Unless your organization provides its own prepared form for memos, follow the standard format shown in Figure 11-2. The standard memo has a heading that names the organization and identifies the sender, recipient, subject, and date. Its text follows an introduction-body-conclusion structure: first, you identify your purpose for writing the memo; next you give the specific information related to your purpose; finally, you conclude cordially with a request, a recommendation, or an offer of further assistance.

If you need a second page, list the recipient's name, the date, and the page number (Ms. Jones, 9/4/78, page 2) three spaces from the top of the page. Begin your text three spaces below. You may also need to photocopy or mimeograph your memo for distribution throughout your organization or for permanent filing. Because memos can cover just about any topic and purpose, we will look at three typical categories that can be reported in memo form: survey results, proposals, and progress reports.

Survey Results

Brief surveys to examine conditions that affect an organization are common. The memo in Figure 11-3 from a Midwest grain distributor is typical of the high-information, in-house memos written everywhere. This memo does its job by giving clear and specific information concisely. Notice the absence of background information. (An explanation of how and where these data were obtained would not be significant for this writer's purpose.) The titles of sender

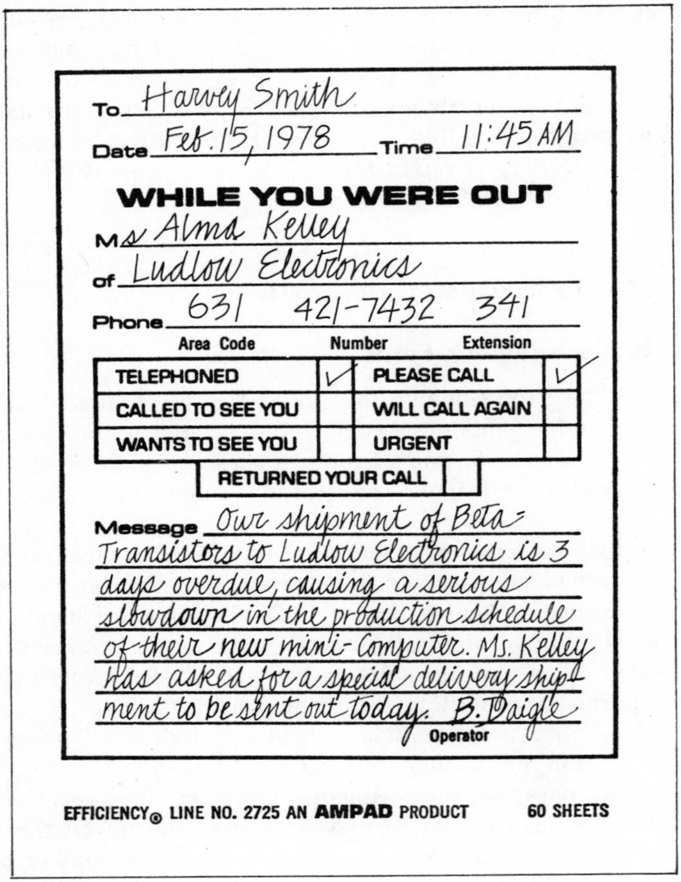

To __Harvey Smith__

Date __Feb. 15, 1978__   Time __11:45 AM__

WHILE YOU WERE OUT

M__s__ __Alma Kelley__

of __Ludlow Electronics__

Phone __631   421-7432   341__

Area Code   Number   Extension

TELEPHONED	✓	PLEASE CALL	✓
CALLED TO SEE YOU		WILL CALL AGAIN	
WANTS TO SEE YOU		URGENT	
RETURNED YOUR CALL			

Message __Our shipment of Beta-Transistors to Ludlow Electronics is 3 days overdue, causing a serious slowdown in the production schedule of their new mini-Computer. Ms. Kelley has asked for a special delivery shipment to be sent out today. B. Daigle__

Operator

EFFICIENCY® LINE NO. 2725 AN **AMPAD** PRODUCT   60 SHEETS

FIGURE 11-1   A Telephone Message

and recipient are stated clearly, and the subject heading, typed in full caps for emphasis, promises exactly what the memo will deliver. The writer signed the memo immediately after her typed name and title. She wisely has chosen to arrange her body section in a classification table to further simplify the reader's job of interpretation. The distribution enclosure (cc.) at the bottom of the page identifies all other readers receiving copies.

In your own field, you may be asked to report research findings comparing the cost or quality of items that are similar. These findings may lead to con-

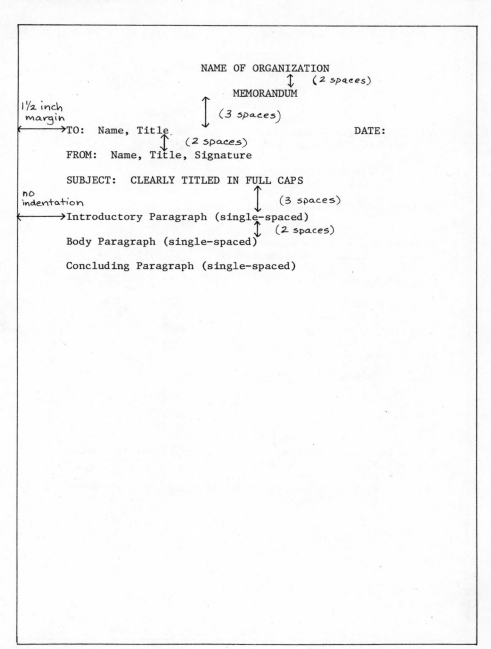

FIGURE 11-2   Standard Memo Format

ACME GRAIN WHOLESALERS INC.

MEMORANDUM

TO: Charles Jones, Manager,   DATE: April 15, 1978
      Marketing Division

FROM: Margaret Spaulding,
      Research Director

SUBJECT: FOOD-GRAIN CONSUMPTION IN U.S., 1969-72

Here are the data you requested on April 7 as part of your
division's annual marketing survey.

U.S. PER CAPITA CONSUMPTION OF FOOD GRAINS IN POUNDS, 1969-72

Corn Products:	1969	1970	1971	1972
Cornmeal and other	15.8	15.8	15.8	15.8
Corn syrup and sugar	20.3	20.8	21.4	21.7
Oat Food Products	3.2	3.2	3.2	3.2
Barley Food Products	1.2	1.2	1.2	1.2
Wheat:				
Flour	112.0	110.0	110.0	111.0
Breakfast cereals	2.9	2.9	2.9	2.9
Rye, Flour	1.2	1.2	1.2	1.2
Rice, Milled	8.3	6.7	7.7	7.0

If you have any questions or require additional information,
please call Ms. Smith at 316.

cc: Mr. C. B. Schultz, Vice-President in Charge of Marketing

FIGURE 11-3   A Memo Reporting Survey Results

tracts with certain suppliers. The student-written memo in Figure 11-4 is a good example of how useful data in memo form can serve as a practical basis for decision-making.

Proposals

Proposals can vary in length from less than one page to several volumes. Regardless of length, proposals are written to prompt the reader to take specific action or to support your suggestions or request. Your purpose in writing a proposal is to *convince* your reader: to give you permission to pursue a special project; to hire you to do a certain job; to improve existing conditions; or to otherwise lend support to your idea. The proposal in Figure 11-5 is written to generate reader concern about effective ecology. This memo contains two proposals related to the same issue of alternate energy sources. Therefore, the headings, "Philosophy" and "Costs" are used to give the reader a clear signal about the respective contents. The items in each proposal are spelled out clearly. As appropriate to a proposal on a controversial energy issue, the tone is firm and confident without being overbearing or belligerent. The writer shows that she believes in her recommendations. A less confident writer could have replaced "should" with "might possibly" throughout the memo. (How would this change affect the memo's effectiveness?) On the other hand, a more militant writer could have replaced "should" with "must." [1] (What effect would this change have?) Because a proposal is written to gain the reader's support, tone and word choice are crucial. Above all, the proposal must present a convincing case.

Sometimes, short proposals are written to obtain approval for a longer study or research project. For instance, Figure 11-6 shows a student-written proposal memo outlining her plan for completing the final term project, the analytical report. The introduction section of this memo is designed to familiarize the reader with the issue and to justify the proposed analysis. The body section includes an itemized list of areas of investigation, along with a brief description of research procedures and information sources. The conclusion describes the goal of the investigation and offers to provide additional information. Any reader's questions about *what, why, for whom, how, when,* and *where* are answered fully. This writer convinces readers that her idea is based on specific facts and common sense.

---

[1] "Must," of course, is an appropriate choice in section 3 under "Costs." This section deals with the most immediate and crucial issue (siting decisions for power plants, etc.) and not simply with the philosophy of the policy itself. Therefore, the wording must be as strong as the situation will bear in order to influence decisions that are crucial to the preservation of environmental quality. In other cases, choose words that reinforce and emphasize your point of view, without antagonizing and alienating your reader.

CALVIN COLLEGE

MEMORANDUM

TO: Professor Smith   DATE: February 15, 1978
     Technical Writing Instructor

FROM: Susan Grimes, Student

SUBJECT: CONSUMER SURVEY OF COMPARATIVE RETAIL PRICES FOR
          DILANTIN TABLETS

I conducted my informal survey of comparative prices for
filling a Dilantin prescription by calling six local pharmacies. My data are presented in the following classification
table.

SIX LOCAL PHARMACIES CLASSIFIED IN DESCENDING ORDER
OF THEIR RETAIL PRICE FOR DILANTIN

Pharmacy	Price/ 100 tablets
Hargrove Pharmacy, Harwich	$4.14
Cascade Village Pharmacy, Hyannis	4.14
Murphy's Rexall, Sandwich	4.10
Apothecary, Dennis Village	3.89
Consumer's Pharmacy, Harwich	2.79
Dunn's Pharmacy, Hyannis	2.19

These data are important to me because I must take Dilantin
every day. The 100 tablets last only about one month and the
expense of this medicine quickly adds up. From my data I
conclude that my best choice for future Dilantin purchases is
Dunn's Pharmacy in Hyannis.

FIGURE 11-4 A Memo Reporting Survey Results

MASSACHUSETTS COASTAL ZONE
MANAGEMENT COMMISSION

MEMORANDUM

TO: Members of the Commission   DATE: February 13, 1978

FROM: Judith M. Barnet, APCC Representative

SUBJECT: PROPOSAL FOR AMENDMENTS TO THE ENERGY CHAPTER OF THE
MASSACHUSETTS COASTAL ZONE-MANAGEMENT PREVIEW

A realistic energy policy should reflect the broadest possible philosophy and a detailed assessment of costs.

Philosophy

Any public energy policy written in the 1970s should begin by
encouraging conservation and development of alternate energy
sources. This commitment should be reflected in every statement made by a governmental body. To implement such an
attitude, the Association for the Preservation of Cape Cod
proposes that Massachusetts Coastal Zone Management amend its
policy as follows:

1.   Insert as one of the objectives in the energy chapter of
     the CZM plan (page 2-G/22) "to promote conservation of
     energy by every consumer -- residential, commercial,
     industrial, or municipal."

2.   Insert as one of the earliest policies and recommenda-
     tions (before present policy #29) a statement of support
     and encouragement for development and use of alternate,
     nontraditional energy sources, especially by small com-
     munities.

Costs

Any public energy policy written in the 1970s should include
a proper cost assessment, which in the CZM plan should be
implemented by appropriate discussion and tables reflecting
the following:

FIGURE 11-5   A Proposal in Memo Form

1. Environmental costs of siting energy (primarily oil and nuclear) facilities on the coast. The Program Preview does not address these costs.

2. Economic costs (best estimate) of alternate sources should be supplied, to permit comparison with economic costs of conventional sources.

3. The Energy Facilities Siting Council must routinely review all possible technologies when making siting decisions, recognizing the inherent characteristics of each. In other words, the council should not measure alternate sources by the criteria appropriate to centralized sources (i.e., that they be able to supply vast amounts of energy over vast networks).

Your implementation of these proposed amendments will help to ensure a well-balanced program of energy development in coastal areas.

FIGURE 11-5   (*Continued*)

CALVIN COLLEGE

MEMORANDUM

TO: Dr. James Granger   DATE: March 4, 1978
     Technical Writing Instructor

FROM: Anne Bickett, Student

SUBJECT: ANALYTICAL REPORT PROPOSAL

In answer to your March 2 request for an analytical report
due May 10, I propose a study of the problem of low employee
morale at the Foodstuff Supermarket in South Dennis. During
my two years as a part-time employee at Foodstuff I have seen
a high turnover and general employee dissatisfaction over the
work situation and the store's management policies. Top
management has also voiced its concern about this problem.

My analysis, written for the general reader, will cover the *(Tell who it w*
following areas: *be written f*

1. An assessment of the efficiency of Foodstuff's management
    by drawing parallels and contrasts between the actual
    management operation and principles of effective manage-
    ment that I will identify and collect from my secondary
    sources.

2. A consideration of the direct or indirect effects that
    any management problems might have on employee morale.

3. An assessment of management's effectiveness in employee
    motivation.

4. An assessment of the role of effective communication in
    management-employee relations.

My secondary research will include library and other published *(What sou*
sources of data. Primary research will include personal   *will be u*
observation, questionnaires, and interviews with both
employee and management representatives.

All conclusions and any recommendations for positive change
will be based on the collected evidence in my report. If
you have any further questions I will be happy to discuss
this proposal with you at any time.

FIGURE 11-6   A Proposal in Memo Form

Progress Reports

In large organizations, progress (or status) reports are often written daily as a way of keeping track of activities, problems, and progress made on a particular job. Such record-keeping is especially vital in a business that employs several work crews simultaneously on a variety of projects. Figure 11-16 is typical of this kind of report cast in a "miscellaneous" form.

Sometimes, you will be asked to report on your progress in compiling a longer, formal report. For instance, Figure 11-7 shows a memo describing a student's progress in collecting data for her final term project. She has partitioned her memo into four sections: work completed, work in progress, work to be completed, and date for completion. Although this writer chose a memo format, her report — like most in this chapter — might be converted to an alternate format (letter, prepared form, or miscellaneous form) as the situation dictated. Many companies in fact provide prepared forms for progress reports.

Typical Reports in Letter Form

Although memos are usually in-house correspondence, letter reports generally go to readers outside the organization. The data in a particular memo and a particular letter report may be identical but the format and tone will differ. You will often address a letter report to potential clients, colleagues, policy-making authorities, and other readers whom you may not have met. Your reader probably will file your letter as a permanent record. Therefore, be sure that your data are accurate before you sign your letter. Also, because a letter is a more personal form of correspondence than a memo, be sure that it embodies the "you" perspective (discussed in Chapter 10).

For the introductory and closing elements of your letter, follow the standard letter format discussed in Chapter 10. The only two format additions in a letter report are (1) a "subject" heading, placed two spaces below the inside address and two spaces above the salutation, and (2) other headings, if they are needed to segment your letter into specific areas of data. The following sections include examples of three typical letter forms: a report of a site inspection, a proposal, and a work estimate.

Site Inspection Reports

Like a memo, a letter report provides the most information in the least space. Figure 11-8 shows a soil engineer's evaluation of a proposed cottage site in a wilderness area. This sample contains three kinds of data: (1) a description and evaluation of the building site, (2) instructions for building a suitable waste-disposal system, and (3) instructions for completing the building-permit application forms. Each section is clearly subsumed under its own heading to

PROGRESS REPORT

TO: Dr. J. Lannon, English Professor

FROM: T. Fitzgerald, student

DATE: April 27, 1978

SUBJECT: Analytical Report
          A STUDY OF THE IMPACT OF THE SANDWICH HISTORIC
          DISTRICT COMMITTEE ON THE ZONING AND ARCHITECTURAL
          CHARACTER OF SANDWICH

WORK COMPLETED TO DATE

March 22: Completed report on Sandwich Historic
District Committee.

April 11: Obtained maps of Sandwich, legislation,
certificates of appropriateness, exemption, and appeals
from Town Hall.

April 12, 14, 15: Investigated district area by car,
noted differences in historic and nonhistoric areas.

April 18: Photographed sampling of areas in district.
Twenty photos taken, fifteen returned by developer.

April 19: Divided master map into sections, rede-
fining district.

April 20: Completed tentative outline.

April 22: Interviewed chairman of Committee, Donald
Bourne. Received new set of rules and regulations for
district.

WORK IN PROGRESS: Drawing maps of present district and
                   redefined area.

WORK TO BE COMPLETED

April 28: Interview Edward Carey, committee member.

May 2: Interview George Smith, committee member.

DATE FOR COMPLETION: May 11, 1978

FIGURE 11-7   A Progress Report in Memo Form

Telephone
312-547-9758

                        Lionel D. Kelley, P.E.
                           3 Wright Lane
                        Otisfield, Maine 04572

                                December 21, 1977

Mr. John M. Lannon
154 Seaweed Lane
East Harwich, Massachusetts 01263

SUBJECT: SITE EVALUATION--COTTAGE LOT, LITTLE "W" TOWNSHIP

Dear Mr. Lannon:

Forms HHE 200 are enclosed detailing a site evaluation conducted on your leased 30,000-square-foot lot. Below is a
summary of my evaluation, along with instructions for proceeding with your plan.

Site Description and Evaluation

The site is made up of Lots 48 & 49 and a 50- by 200-foot
extension to the rear of these lots, which are owned by the
Eastern Paper Company and shown on their maps. The report
and the design are meant to comply with the intent of the
Maine State Plumbing Code and are contingent on your
obtaining the additional land at the rear of the lots.

The site has a high ledge outcrop on the lake side and drops
off at the rear. A ridge runs perpendicular to the lake and
the waste disposal systems must be constructed on the west
side of this ridge. This area is about 5 or 6 feet above
high water of the lake.

The water supply will be hand-carried from the lake to serve
your 16- by 20-foot seasonal cottage.

FIGURE 11-8   A Site Inspection Report in Letter Form

page 2, J. M. Lannon, 12/21/77

Instructions for Building a Waste-Disposal System

To construct the gray water system, select an area across
the slope and running level between the two blue flags of
the test borings. Drive a steel rod along this 18-foot run
to determine that you have 36 inches from the surface to
the bedrock. Once this line has been established, dig a
trench 24 inches wide by 12 inches deep, grading level.
Backfill the trench with 3/4 to 3 inches of stone,
embedding a 4-inch diameter PVC perforated pipe, 18 feet
long, in the top 4 inches. Connect the pipe to a standard
16- by 36-inch distribution box, and connect the cottage
sink drain with a 1½-inch diameter polyethylene pipe. Cover
the 4-inch diameter pipe with orange building paper and
cover with 4 inches of topsoil.

To construct the privy pit, probe for bedrock, obtaining a
depth of 48 inches if possible. The ledge appears to go
downward from the ridge and we can anticipate that this
depth can be reached downslope from the first blue flag
toward Lot 50. Excavate a pit to a depth leaving 2 feet of
soil to the bedrock level. Then construct a mound to have a
pit of 36 inches deep and locate the privy as directed by
code section 9.13.

I have enclosed a waiver form to allow you the use of coarse
gravel in lieu of the graded stone. The lot location, being
in a heavily wooded, remote area, does not warrant the use
of stone and I recommend its substitution. Hand-dug test
holes at the boring sites revealed a well-draining high void
granular material which I consider adequate for your requirements. The code permits your applying for this waiver.

Instructions for Completing Building-Permit Application

I have enclosed a separate set of HHE 200 forms for you to
include as exhibit 3 of your LURC building permit application. The check marks indicate where your signature is
required. Complete and sign all copies before submitting
them to the respective agencies.

FIGURE 11-8   (*Continued*)

page 3, J. M. Lannon, 12/21/77

A plumbing inspector has not yet been assigned to this area.
LURC will advise you about proper procedure for inspection
on issuance of your building permit.

If you have any questions, please contact me at any time.
Best of luck on your project.

                                        Very truly yours,

                                        Lionel D. Kelley, P.E.

LDK/jh
Enclosures 1

FIGURE 11-8   (*Continued*)

increase readability. Notice the absence of extraneous information. The letter simply delivers what its subject heading promises. Both descriptions and instructions are easy to follow. The writer closes with a personal expression of good wishes.

Proposals

Like its memo counterpart discussed earlier, the proposal in letter form is written to bring about an action or to enlist support. It must, therefore, be convincing. Notice how the letter in Figure 11-9 uses concrete details to express the terms of the proposal. The tone is polite, yet firm and positive.

Work Estimates

A close cousin to the proposal is the work estimate, which specifies the details of a service the writer proposes to provide and estimates the cost of materials and labor. This type of report is designed to tell the customer exactly what he will and will not get for his money. Because a signed estimate can be legally binding, specifications and figures must be precise. To illustrate, the second-to-last paragraph in Figure 11-10 clearly indicates exceptions to the repairs outlined in the estimate.

Typical Reports on Prepared Forms

In an attempt to streamline communications and to keep track of various types of data, more and more companies are making prepared forms available for short reporting assignments. Such forms are useful in two ways: (1) A prepared form simplifies your reporting task by providing clear guidelines for recording data. If you complete the form correctly you are sure to satisfy your reader's needs. (2) A prepared form standardizes the data reported from various sources. Each reporter provides the same classes of data recorded in the same order. This fixed format allows for rapid processing and tabulation of data. The sample questionnaire in Figure 12-1 is a good example of the effectiveness of a prepared-form report; its data can be easily reviewed and tabulated.

The one drawback of a prepared form is its limited space for recoding data. From time to time you will need to attach your own prose statement explaining certain items on the form. A few of the kinds of information routinely recorded on prepared forms are illustrated and discussed in the following sections.

Travel Vouchers

A travel voucher is a record of expenses incurred by the writer in traveling on company business. The voucher in Figure 11-11 outlines one week's travel expenses for a junior member of an engineering consulting firm. He is reimbursed

gerald a. jackson
post office box 185
amherst, mass. 01002

March 15, 1977

Ambrose Savings Bank
South Haley Street
Weston, Massachusetts 09768

SUBJECT: PROPOSAL TO ERECT A NEW DWELLING

Attention: Charles Smith

Dear Mr. Smith:

This letter is in application for a construction loan in the
amount of $67,000, on an interest-only basis, for the con-
struction of the described residence (plans and specifications are enclosed) on Lot #6 of my Leverett property.
Anticipated sales price of the completed home is $98,000,
including the standard realtor's commission. I have already
completed clearing work and some excavation, and expect
weather conditions to permit the commencement of foundation
work within the next three weeks. Construction time is projected at approximately five months, with completion
targeted for September 1, 1977.

The quality of construction materials and workmanship will be
comparable to the adjacent three homes which you have inspected. Exterior woodwork will be executed in Western Red
Cedar, while interior finishes will comprise masonry, dry-
wall, and Philippine mahogany. All sashes, doors, flooring,
cabinets, and special millwork will be designed and custom
fabricated. Water supply and waste disposal will be
handled on-site; the appropriate permits have already been
obtained. The heating system will be oil-fired hot air,
ducted for the later addition of air conditioning. All
windows and skylights will be double-glazed and insulation
will be maximized.

FIGURE 11-9 A Proposal in Letter Form

page 2, Ambrose Savings Bank, 3/15/77

Thank you for giving this proposal your immediate attention.
I shall be pleased to provide any additional information
you may require.

                                        Very truly yours,

                                        Gerald A. Jackson

GAJ/cb
Enclosures: architect's drawings
               specifications

FIGURE 11-9   (*Continued*)

LEVERETT LAND & TIMBER COMPANY, INC. | creative land use
quality building materials
architectural construction

January 17, 1977

Mr. Thomas E. Muffin
Clearwater Drive
Amherst, Massachusetts 01002

Dear Mr. Muffin:

I have examined the damage to your home caused by the
ruptured water pipe and consider the following repairs to be
necessary and of immediate concern:

Exterior:
Remove plywood soffit panels beneath overhangs
Replace damaged insulation and plumbing
Remove all built-up ice within floor framing
Replace plywood panels and finish as required

Northeast Bedroom--Lower Level:
Remove and replace all sheetrock, including closet
Remove and replace all door casing and baseboards
Remove and repair window sill extensions and mouldings
Remove and re-install electric heaters
Re-spray ceilings and repaint all surfaces

Northwest Bedroom--Lower Level:
Remove and replace all sheetrock, including closet
Remove and replace all door casings and baseboards
Remove and re-install electric heaters
Remove and repair window sill extensions and mouldings
Re-spray ceilings and repaint all surfaces

Post Office Box 185, Amherst, Mass. 01002   413-549-6239

FIGURE 11-10 A Work Estimate in Letter Form

page 2, T. E. Muffin, 1/17/77

Family Room:
    Remove and replace sheetrock on north and west walls
    Remove and replace door casings and baseboards where
      required
    Remove and re-install electric heaters
    Remove and repair window sill extensions and mouldings
    Re-spray ceiling and paint all new work
    Repair closet door under stairs

Entry and Stairwell:
    Repair entry sill and refit doors
    Remove and replace sheetrock on north wall and par-
      tition
    Remove and re-install stair-rails
    Repair and replace stair treads
    Replace skirt boards and trim
    Replace entry landing and baseboards

Main Level:
    Remove, replace, and finish all oak floors
    Remove and re-install door casings and electric
      heaters
    Replace baseboards as required
    Repair sheetrock corners as required
    Paint all new work

This appraisal of damage repair does not include repairs and/
or replacements of carpets, tilework, or vinyl flooring.
Also, this appraisal assumes that the plywood subflooring on
the main level has not been severely damaged.

Leverett Land and Timber Company, Inc. proposes to furnish
the necessary materials and labor to perform the described
damage repairs for the amount of six-thousand-one-hundred-
and-eighty dollars ($6,180).

                          Sincerely,

                          Gerald A. Jackson
                          President

GAJ/cb

FIGURE 11-10   (*Continued*)

LOCAL TRAVEL EXPENSE STATEMENT

DATE	ACTIVITY	ODOMETER READING	MILEAGE	PARKING	MISC.	TOTAL
2/2/77	Inspect Structural Supports at Blue Hills Project	15,021	28		Tolls 1.00	3.80
2/2/77	Pick up Blue Prints at Architect Stein's Office	15,071	7	0.10		0.80
2/3/77	City Planning Conference at City Hall	15,108	12	2.00		3.20
2/3/77	Meet Job candidate at Bradley Airport	15,120	24	1.50	Tolls 1.00	4.90
2/4/77	Inspect Rockhaven Apts. Building Site	15,215	18			1.80
2/4/77	Supervise Ground-Breaking for Apco Insurance Building	15,251	31	0.60		3.70

Amount Claimed $ ___18.20___

I certify that this statement, the amounts claimed and attachments are true, correct, and complete to the best of my knowledge and belief, and that payment for the amount claimed has not been received.

___February 6, 1977___
Date

___Arthur Hatfield___
Signature of Traveler
Address (if check is to be mailed)

___Feb. 8, 77___
Date

___Susan Boss___
Approval

FIGURE 11-11 A Typical Travel Voucher

$0.10 per mile for company-related travel in his own car. Notice that the information is concise and specific. Of course, in order to complete this form, the writer has kept close track of his travel activities in a notebook reserved for this purpose.

Purchase Requisitions

A purchase requisition is a formal request made by an individual or department in an organization to purchase new equipment or supplies. Figure 11-12 shows a sample purchase requisition from the accounting department of a plastics company, filed with the purchasing agent. Notice that the "Remarks" section provides space for requesting certain items on a "rush" order or for any other important comment.

Business License Applications

If you plan to operate your own business you will need to apply for a license from the appropriate city or town. In Figure 11-13, the proposed business and its location are described. For this intended reading audience, the applicant's reasons for selecting that particular business are not significant. However, these reasons would be significant if the applicant were completing a business loan application from a local bank. For some retail businesses (such as the sale of alcoholic beverages) you will need to complete much more elaborate forms.

Periodic Activity Reports

The periodic activity report is similar to the progress report in summarizing work activities over a specified period. Your company most likely will provide a prepared form for this reporting task. The sample report in Figure 11-14 is a log of hours worked, type of work accomplished, and mileage traveled by one construction company employee during one week. Most jobs where employees carry out their responsibilities without direct supervision will require periodic activity reports from all personnel. If your company does not supply prepared forms, you can easily devise one for your own use.

Typical Reports in Miscellaneous Forms

Reports that do not follow the format of the memo, the letter report, or the prepared-form report we will call "miscellaneous." There are probably as many ways of setting up informal reports as there are subjects to report about. Some reports follow conventions; others do not because their data categories can be so variable that no conventions would serve as adequate guidelines. The reporting of "minutes" of a meeting, for instance, follows fairly standard con-

ABCO PLASTICS, INC.

PURCHASE REQUISITION

FROM: *Accounting Division* DATE: *Feb. 15, 1977*

TO: *C. H. Sawbuck, Purchasing Agent* DATE REQUIRED: *March 15, 1977*

CHARGE TO: *01 Account* EXPENSE CODE: *131-A*

QUANTITY	DESCRIPTION	PRICE (IF KNOWN)	ORDERED FROM PREVIOUSLY
2	IBM "Selectric" Typewriter, Model # A-7	579.95	Hastings Office Supplies
4	Texas Instrument Desk Calculator, Model # SR-20	42.50	Digital Suppliers Inc.
4	Acco Stapler, Large Size	11.99	Hastings Office Supplies
50	Wire-In-Dex Bound Index Cards, 5 x 3 Ruled, # 08-245	.45	National Blank Book Co.
10	CWS Index Files # 533	4.00	Conway Suppliers
2	Hamilton Desk Lamps Model # HC-13	12.50	

REMARKS: *Please submit a rush order for the Texas Instrument Desk Calculators.*

DIVISION HEAD *Marvin J. Integer*

FIGURE 11-12 A Typical Purchase Requisition

THE COMMONWEALTH OF MASSACHUSETTS

Town of _Barnstable_

APPLICATION FOR LICENSE
(GENERAL)

No. _1_   _March 1_ 19 _77_

To the Licensing Authorities:

The undersigned hereby applies for a License in accordance with the provisions of the Statutes relating thereto

Arthur J. Wiener and Martha Sunbeam

Swanky Franks Inc.
(Full name of person, firm or corporation making application)

STATE CLEARLY
PURPOSE FOR
WHICH LICENSE
IS REQUESTED

To _operate a beach concession booth, selling_
hot dogs, hamburgers, soft drinks and other
common victuals from June 15 to September 10, 1977

GIVE LOCATION
BY STREET
AND NUMBER

At _A dwelling rented from Thomas Sykes, located_
at the Sea Street entrance to Hardy's Beach
in Barnstable Village

in said ~~City~~ Town of _Barnstable_

in accordance with the rules and regulations made under authority of said Statutes.

Arthur J. Wiener
Signature of Applicant

154 Curvy Road, Barnstable
Address

Received _____ 19___

Hour A.M. _____
      P.M. _____   License Granted _____ 19___

Approved _____ 19___

FIGURE 11-13   A Typical Application for a Business License

SUMMARY OF WEEKLY ACTIVITIES

NAME   P. Daily

WEEK BEGINNING MONDAY,   April 4, 1976

DAY	JOB	TIME IN	TIME OUT	TOTAL TIME	DESCRIPTION OF WORK	TRAVEL DEST.	TRAVEL MILES
4/4/76 MONDAY	Hadley	8:00	4:00	8 hrs	frame upper level walls, block for shelving, apply plywood to east side		
4/5 TUESDAY	Hadley	8:00	4:15	8 1/4	frame upper level walls, straighten and brace walls, finish plywood sheathing, layout roof framing	Jones Lumber	10
4/6 WED.	Hadley	8:00	4:00	8	cut rafters and set north wing trusses, brace and plumb trusses for sheathing		

FIGURE 11-14 A Periodic Activity Report

DAY	JOB	TIME IN	TIME OUT	TOTAL TIME	DESCRIPTION OF WORK	TRAVEL DEST.	MILES
THURS.	Hadley	8:00	4:00	8	finish roof frame and setup for plywood, sheath roof		
FRIDAY	Hadley	8:00	4:00	8	apply roof trim and layout for shingles, set up staging and stock for shingling next week, block partitions for shelving and cabinets		
SAT.							
SUNDAY							
TOTAL TIME THIS WEEK				40¼		TOTAL MILEAGE	10

FIGURE 11-14 (Continued)

ventions. The reporting of survey results for a broad and largely nontechnical audience, however, may require the writer to invent a suitable format. If you should have to invent your own format for a report, make it neat, attractive, and readable. In the following sections we will provide a few examples of reports cast in miscellaneous forms.

Minutes

Minutes are the official records of organizational and committee meetings. Copies of minutes are distributed to all members and concerned superiors as a way of keeping track of proceedings in a large organization. The person appointed secretary records the minutes.

Minutes are filed as part of official record; therefore they must be precise, clear, highly informative, and free of the writer's personal commentary ("As usual, Ms. Jones disagreed with the committee.") or judgmental words ("good," "poor," "irrelevant," etc.). When you record minutes, identify the group, date, place, and purpose of the meeting. Next, give the names of the convener (person calling the meeting) and all members present (unless there are so many that your list would be unwieldy). Finally, record each item on the agenda in chronological order, beginning with a statement that the minutes of the previous meeting were approved (or disapproved) as written or as amended. Summarize the points made during the group's discussion of each agenda item. Name the person who makes a motion, and the person who seconds it. Record the results of votes on each motion offered, along with a full description of the motion itself. If the group votes to support a specific proposal, include a description of that proposal. Figure 11-15 shows how effective minutes can provide a valuable record for future reference.

Survey Results

A report of survey results sometimes requires a more detailed treatment than a memo but a less complex treatment than a formal report. Unlike the memos in Figures 11-3 and 11-4, written for the persons requesting them, some survey reports may speak to a broader audience — perhaps all members of your organization, both technical and nontechnical, or outside readers (for whom you will also enclose a letter of transmittal). In such reports, the raw data usually are prefaced with an explanation of when, how, and why these data were obtained. Also, all technical terms are defined for the benefit of the nontechnical readers. The report ends with detailed conclusions and interpretations.

The informal report in Figure 11-16 presents the purpose, procedure, findings, interpretations, and conclusions of a survey of comparative gas prices and octane levels among local service stations. The writer wisely chose to include a bar graph (as discussed in Chapter 9) as an aid to interpretation. By scanning

PARKS COLLEGE
Kadoka, Wisconsin 41632

Minutes of the Student Senate Meeting of October 7, 1978

Members Present

   Kevin Ames, Charles Mott, Janet Leroux, Donna Campbell,
Steve Parks, Laurie Davis, Kate Taylor, Joe Griggs, Leslie
Robett, Bill Faber, Laine Logan, Gerry Stark, Peter Jones,
Kevin Oates, Tom Reid, Tricia Kelly, Ann Kearns, Mike Wills,
Bob Moor, Tom Mackie, John Verdellini, Ann Reagan

Agenda

1. The meeting was called to order at 3:30 p.m. by President
Gerry Grimes.

2. The minutes of the September meeting were approved as
printed.

3. In his treasurer's report, Charlie Mott summarized his
meeting with Dean Bailey, in which they discussed the dean's
suggestion that the Student Senate use approximately $3800
from the President's discretionary fund for intramurals
($3000 for an equipment man and $800 for equipment). Charlie
asked the Senate to consider the idea of using the money in
this way.

4. The Black Student Union is sponsoring a play called
Black Nativity by the Alma Lewis School of Fine Arts on
December 10, at an admission fee of $100 per person. They
requested $500 from the Senate to help defray costs. A
motion was made by Donna Campbell and seconded by Tom Reid
that the Senate allocate $500 from its reserve fund to the
BSU for that purpose. (passed 15-3)

5. Arthur Burnham, bookstore manager, came before the
Senate to answer questions about the bookstore's operation.
Topics discussed were: the bookstore's rate of profit, the

FIGURE 11-15   A Report of the Minutes of a Meeting

policy for charging books, the policy on book buy-backs, and the ordering of individual books.

6. Members appointed to the commencement committee are Laine Logan, Tricia Kelly, Tom Mackie, and Joe Griggs.

7. The Nursing Club requested $160 for a field trip to a cancer research center in Boston. A motion was made by Mike Wills and seconded by Ann Reagan that the Student Senate allocate $160 to the Nursing Club for its trip. (passed unanimously)

8. Core requirements were discussed at the meeting. The decision about what courses fit core requirements is not left to individual department heads. Kevin Oates suggested that this decision be made by the Academic Curriculum Committee. Volunteers were requested in order to form a subcommittee to further study this issue.

9. In the interest of encouraging active student participation in upcoming local elections, a motion was made by Kevin Ames and seconded by Laine Logan that the Senate form a committee to establish a voter-registration drive on campus. (passed unanimously) Committee members: John Verdellini, Tom Reid, Bill Faber.

10. Mike Wills read his letter of resignation. A motion was made by Kate Taylor and seconded by Steve Parks that the Senate accept Mike's resignation with deep regret. (passed unanimously) The meeting adjourned at 5:25 p.m.

> Respectfully submitted

> Peter Jones, Secretary

cc: President Dithers
     Dean Bumstead
     All senators

FIGURE 11-15 (*Continued*)

A COMPARISON OF GASOLINE PRICES AND OCTANE LEVELS AMONG
AREA SERVICE STATIONS, AS OF FEBRUARY 24, 1978
by
Janet Cosgrove

The gasoline shortage has caused prices and octane
levels to fluctuate during the past few years.[1] This report
is written to give the gasoline consumer in the Hyannis area
a ready reference for buying high-quality gasoline at the
most reasonable price. My data are based on a survey of ten
major service stations in the area: comparative prices for
regular, unleaded, and premium gasoline and respective octane
ratings are illustrated in Figure 1.

There are three types of gasoline: regular, unleaded,
and premium. Engines that do not have high-energy requirements or elaborate pollution-control systems can use regular
gas. Generally, the four- or six-cylinder economy car
engines use regular gasoline.

Newer cars are designed to run only on unleaded gas
because of government antipollution regulations. Used in
conjunction with an emission control system, unleaded gas
causes less atmospheric pollution than conventional gasoline.

[1]The octane rating of a specific type and brand of gasoline
is a measure of its antiknock properties.

FIGURE 11-16 A Short Report of Survey Findings

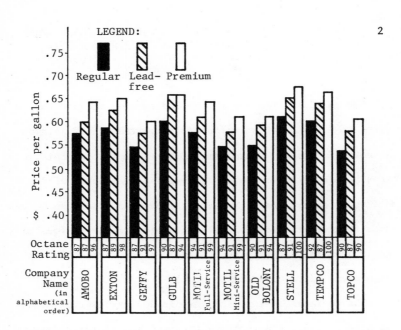

FIGURE 1.   COMPARATIVE GASOLINE PRICES AND OCTANE LEVELS
            AMONG AREA SERVICE STATIONS
            AS OF FEBRUARY 24, 1978

Some engines, generally the eight-cylinder type with a

higher compression ratio, are designed to run on premium

gasoline, which supplies higher energy needs. Premium gas,

with its higher octane rating, provides better engine per-

formance.

The octane rating of each level of gasoline -- regular,

unleaded, or premium -- is important; gasoline with an inade-

quate octane rating will cause an engine to knock and wear

FIGURE 11-16   (*Continued*)

  3

out more quickly. Therefore, consumers should know both the

type and octane level of gasoline required for their cars to

run efficiently. Figure 1 surveys the prices and octane

ratings of gas in each category. The following conclusions

can be drawn from the graph in Figure 1:

1. Motil regular has the highest octane at a price of $0.59

    per gallon at the full-service station. Consumers

    willing to buy Motil regular at the limited-service

    station (gas only) for $0.55 per gallon are getting the

    highest-rated gasoline at a most reasonable price.

2. Four companies, Geffy, Motil, Old Bolony, and Stell,

    offer lead-free gasoline with an octane rating of 91,

    at least two points higher than other competitors. Of

    these four, Geffy is the least expensive at $0.57 per

    gallon, and Stell is the most expensive at $0.65 per

    gallon.

3. In premium gasoline, Gulb offers high price and low

    octane -- $0.66 per gallon for an octane rating of 94.

    Tempco, on the other hand offers the highest octane at

    the same price -- $0.66 per gallon for 100 octane.

    Stell premium also offers a 100 octane rating at a

    slightly higher price -- $0.67 per gallon.

FIGURE 11-16   (*Continued*)

the graph, the reader can easily identify the highest octane fuel at the best price, or otherwise select the best price level and octane rating for his or her needs. This report is structured in an introduction-body-conclusion format; the raw data are explained fully to the reader.

Progress Reports

As we said earlier, progress reports are often written daily as a way of keeping track of a project's status. For such regular daily reporting, many companies provide prepared forms. When they do not, the writer is expected to invent a form, as the writer in Figure 11-17 has done, to accommodate the data categories as they might change from day to day.

CHAPTER SUMMARY

Although informal reports are only a few lines to a few pages long, and usually are prepared quickly, they form the backbone of day-to-day written communication in the working world. Depending on your subject, your reader's needs, and your company's policy, you might record your data in memo form, letter form, on a prepared form, or in a variety of other forms which we have called miscellaneous. Each format lends itself to certain reporting assignments. Unless your company specifies a format for your informal report, choose the one that best suits your purpose.

1. The report in *memo form* follows a fixed format and is best used for in-house communication. It is easily prepared and often xeroxed or mimeographed for distribution throughout the organization.

2. The report in *letter form* follows a standard letter format, with the addition of a subject line and headings as needed. It is designed for the special requirements of communicating outside your organization (most often with clients or prospective customers). Like all other letters it has a more personal tone than other types of informal reports.

3. The report on a *prepared form* follows specific guidelines for listing data so that they can be easily located, processed, and tabulated. Prepared form reports are the easiest to write, but they sometimes require an additional prose statement to explain certain entries.

4. The report in miscellaneous form does not follow the format of a memo, a letter, or a prepared form. These reports are often in-house communication such as minutes, brief survey reports, or progress reports. When sent to outside readers, they are usually accompanied by a letter of transmittal.

<u>DAILY CONSTRUCTION REPORT</u>

LEVERETT LAND & TIMBER CO., INC.   DATE: April 5, 1978
BOX 185   PROJECT: Hadley Residence
AMHERST, MASS. 01002   JOB NO: 76-0141
                                 SUBMITTED BY: D. Jenks,
                                               Sup't.

WEATHER:	Cloudy, temp. in 50s
EMPLOYEES PRESENT:	Jenks, Taylor, Barry, Smith, Reed
DESCRIPTION OF WORK:	Frame upper level walls, sheath walls, cut pilot rafters, cut and block for mechanical equipment installation. Supervise rough grading.
SUBCONTRACTORS PRESENT:	Masonry – W. Markowski, 4 men; Excavator – W. Clark, 1 1/2 yd. front-end loader with operator and 2 laborers
DELIVERIES & PURCHASES:	Jones Lumber – roof framing materials, see invoice #E-3341, LLT Purchase Order #76-567. Valley Roofing Supply – shingles, see invoice #52-564, LLT Purchase Order #76-573 W. Clark – 48 yards bank run gravel, 9 yards 3/4" stone for drains
VISITORS TO SITE:	W. Jones Lumber salesman, T. Lombardi from Ashton Real Estate, 2 casual onlookers, owner
CHANGES OR EXTRA WORK:	Enlarge master bath linen closet by 9" as requested by owner; send memo! Realign foundation drain pipes to avoid future garden area – increase of 54' of 4" perforated pipe, requested by owner; send memo!

FIGURE 11-17   A Daily Progress Report in Miscellaneous Form

EQUIPMENT FAILURES: Change air hose fittings on small
                       compressor (down-time 25 minutes);
                       check spare parts inventory. Piston
                       jammed twice on Bostitch nailgun;
                       send in for rebuild ASAP.

COMMENTS: Rain last week causing difficulty in
                       drainage work and rough grading; if
                       things don't dry out by tomorrow we
                       should delay driveway work until
                       next week. Check schedule for co-
                       ordinating roofing work with masons'
                       chimney progress.

FIGURE 11-17 (*Continued*)

REVISION CHECKLIST

Use this checklist as a guide to refining and revising your informal reports.

1. Have you chosen the best form of short report for your specific purpose?
   a. A memorandum form for in-house readers.
   b. A letter form for outside readers.
   c. A prepared form if an appropriate one is available.
   d. A miscellaneous form if your data must be supported by background information and definitions for readers who are not technically informed.
2. Does the memo have a complete heading (name of organization, name and title of sender and recipient, identification of subject, date)?
3. Does the memo text follow an introduction-body-conclusion structure?
4. Have you single spaced within paragraphs and double spaced between?
5. Have you used headings, charts, or tables wherever they are needed?
6. If more than one reader is receiving copies, does the memo include a distribution notation (cc.) to identify all other readers?
7. Does the memo give your readers what they need to know — no more and no less (including all major points and omitting minor ones)?
8. Does the letter report follow a standard letter format (as in Chapter 10), and does it include a subject heading and any needed internal headings?
9. Does the letter embody a "you" perspective?
10. In a prepared-form report, is all required data recorded accurately, neatly, and clearly?
11. For a report in miscellaneous form, is the chosen format neat, attractive, and readable?
12. Does the arrangement of data represent the best possible choice (e.g., charts, lists, etc.)?
13. Is the report written in correct standard English (grammar, mechanics, and usage, as discussed in Appendix A)?

Now list those elements of your report that need further attention.

EXERCISES

1. Write a memo to members of your college newspaper staff or to fellow members of some other campus organization, announcing the time, place, purpose, and brief agenda for an upcoming organizational meeting.

2. In a unified and coherent paragraph describe the specific informal reporting assignments that you will face in your chosen field. Explain the role that such reports play on a day-to-day basis.

3. In a brief but specific essay explain the difference between formal and informal reports. What elements do formal and informal reports have in common?

4. Compose a memo in which you outline a proposal for improving an unsatisfactory situation in the classroom, on the job, or in your dormitory or apartment (e.g., poor lighting, tension, high noise level, drab atmosphere, poor seating arrangement). Be sure to (a) give a brief background of the problem and a justification for your proposal, (b) state clearly the steps proposed to solve the problem, and (c) conclude with a statement designed to gain reader support of your proposal. Choose a problem or situation whose improvement is a matter of common sense and astute observation, rather than intensive research.

5. Compose a proposal memo to your instructor describing your plans for completing your final term project — the analytical report. Be sure to describe and define fully the subject, background, and purpose of your planned inquiry, along with your intended audience, scope of the report, and all sources of data. Remember that the intent of your proposal is to convince your reader of the soundness and validity of your project.

6. Compose a memo to your instructor outlining your progress, to date, on your final term project. Describe your accomplishments, your plans for further work, and any problems or setbacks you may have encountered; and request any assistance you might need at this point or later. Conclude your memo with a specific delivery date for your finished report.

7. a. Compose a proposal memo to your instructor describing your plans for achieving success in your career field. Describe your intended occupation, give background reasons for your choice, and list all steps of your plan to accomplish your goal.

b. Compose a memo to your instructor outlining your progress on your career project. Describe your achievements to date and any problems or setbacks encountered, and request any needed advice. Conclude your memo with a rough date for completion of your project for career success.

8. Conduct a brief survey (for example, of comparative interest rates charged by various local banks on an auto loan, comparative property tax and valuation rates among local towns, or comparative prices among local retailers for any consumer item). Arrange the data from your survey in a formal classification table (see Chapter 5) and report your findings to your instructor in a fact-finding memo that closes with specific conclusions and recommendations for making the most economical choice.

9. Construct your own prepared periodic form that will allow you to keep a one-week record of each of your daily activities. During the following week, record the time spent in each of those activities. When your prepared-form report is completed, review the data and write a one-paragraph inter-

pretation with conclusions and recommendations for better budgeting of your time.

10. Identify an area or situation on campus or in your community that is inconvenient or poses a threat to public safety (such as endless cafeteria lines, a dangerous intersection, slippery stairs, a busy street filled with pot-holes, a poorly marked railway crossing, a bus stop without a weather shelter, a poorly adjusted traffic light). Observe the problem area or situation for several hours during a peak usage period. Write a site inspection report to appropriate authorities describing the deficiencies, noting your firsthand observations, making recommendations for positive change, and enlisting your reader's support through positive action. Submit your letter report to your instructor.

11. *In class:* Divide into groups of five or six students. Choose a subject composed of several related areas (for example, *Academic Policy:* final examination policy, grading policy, core requirements, the foreign language requirement, the minimum cumulative average required for graduation, the need for specific new courses, the minimum cumulative average required for first-semester freshmen, etc.). In one class period discuss each of the items related to your subject, making proposals for positive change. *Each* member of your group should act as secretary, recording appropriate minutes of the meeting.

At home: compose your minutes in short report form (see the sample minutes in Figure 11-15) and bring them to class for comparison with the minutes written by the other members of your discussion group. Exchange copies for proofreading and revision. Are your minutes accurate, concise, and clear? Revise your report according to your proofreader's suggestions, and submit your early and final drafts to your instructor.

12. In a memorandum, compose a list of specifications and a full cost estimate of the items required for your college attendance during one full semester. Specifications should include a complete, itemized list of school fees, supplies, clothing, entertainment, travel, living arrangements (apart-ment, room, house, roommates), etc. Your final cost estimate will be a total of the costs of each of these items.

In a second memo, compose a specific proposal for financing your semester, listing each source of income and its amount.

13. The prepared form in Figure 11-18 is designed for reporting daily activities in police work. Using this form as a model, design your own form for reporting periodic work activities in your part-time or full-time job.

14. Use the prepared form for consumer complaints (Figure 11-19) as a model for your own report to the attorney general's office describing a legitimate complaint.

DENNIS POLICE - PATROL SHEET

OFFICER   SHIFT   DATE

AREA ASSIGNED - TIME CHECKED - VIS. OR MAN.

VEHICLES STOPPED

REG. NO.	LOCATION	TIME	OCCUPANT	DOB OR SSN	LOG NO.	A	C	W	V
			TOTAL STOPPED		TOTALS				

CALLS AND INVESTIGATIONS ASSIGNED

LOG NO.	RTF	NATURE OF CALL	CASE OPEN	CLOSED	REMARKS	INVEST. TIME
		TOTAL				

TOTAL CALLS & INVEST.   TOTAL ARRESTS   TOTAL P. C.

CRUISER NO.   MILEAGE START   MILEAGE END   TOTAL MILES

CRUISER CHECKLIST: OIL ☐   WATER ☐   TIRES ☐   FLARES ☐   SHOTGUN ☐

TRANSMISSION FLUID ☐   POWER STEERING FLUID ☐   FIRE EXTINGUISHER ☐

ROLL CALL BY SGT.   APPEARANCE   BRIEFING   EQUIPMENT

INITIAL _____

FIGURE 11-18 A Prepared Form for Recording Police Activities

DEPARTMENT OF THE ATTORNEY GENERAL

FOR OFFICE USE ONLY

Consumer Protection Division
One Ashburton Place, 19th Floor
Boston, MA 02108

YOUR NAME _____

ADDRESS _____ CITY/TOWN _____

ZIP _____ HOME PHONE _____ BUSINESS PHONE _____

NAME OF STORE OR COMPANY _____

ADDRESS _____ CITY/TOWN _____

ZIP _____ PHONE NUMBER _____ PERSON YOU DEALT WITH _____

INFORMATION

WAS A CONTRACT SIGNED? YES _____ NO _____ DATE _____ COST _____

PRODUCT OR SERVICE INVOLVED _____

DATE PURCHASED? _____ WAS DEPOSIT PAID? _____ AMOUNT _____

DID YOU PAY CASH? _____ LOAN _____ ON TIME _____ OTHER _____

WAS THE PRODUCT OR SERVICE ADVERTISED? YES _____ NO _____

WHERE AND WHEN WAS IT ADVERTISED? _____

DID YOU COMPLAIN TO THE COMPANY? _____ TO WHOM _____

HOW DID YOU COMPLAIN? BY PHONE _____ LETTER _____ IN PERSON _____

MAY WE SEND A COPY OF THIS COMPLAINT TO THE COMPANY? YES _____ NO _____

STATE *BRIEFLY* THE *FACTS* OF YOUR COMPLAINT

FIGURE 11-19   A Prepared Form for Consumer Complaints

12

Writing
a Description

CHAPTER GOALS

DEFINITION

PURPOSE OF DESCRIPTION

MAKING YOUR DESCRIPTION
  OBJECTIVE
  Subjective Description
  Objective Description
    Be Totally Familiar with the Item
    Record Observable Details Faithfully
    Use Precise and Factual Language

ELEMENTS OF AN EFFECTIVE
  DESCRIPTION
  Clear and Limiting Title
  Overall Appearance and Component
    Parts
  Function of Each Part
  Comparisons with More Familiar Objects
  Introduction-Body-Conclusion Structure
  Graphic Aids
  Appropriate Details

ORGANIZING AND WRITING YOUR
  DESCRIPTION
  Clearest Descriptive Sequence
    Spatial Sequence
    Operational Sequence
    Chronological Sequence
    Combined Sequences

The Outline
  Introduction: General Description
  *Body: Description and Function
    of Parts*
  *Conclusion: Summary and Operating
    Description*

APPLYING THE STEPS

CHAPTER SUMMARY

REVISION CHECKLIST

EXERCISES

CHAPTER GOALS

Upon completing this chapter you will know:

- The meaning and purpose of description.
- The differences between subjective and objective description.
- The importance of objectivity in most technical descriptions.
- How to make your description objective.
- How to evaluate a description for effectiveness.
- How to plan your description and choose the best descriptive sequence(s) according to your purpose and the physical makeup of the item.
- How to organize your description by making and working from an effective outline.
- How to proofread and revise your description for greatest effectiveness.

DEFINITION

To describe is to represent verbally or to create a picture with words. Depending on the subject, your purpose, and your reader, your description could contain some or all of these data: identification of the item; explanation of its function; portrayal of its appearance; discussion of its parts and materials; and explanations of how it works and how it has been put together.

Descriptions serve a specific purpose: to tell about an item to someone who will use it, buy it, operate it, or assemble it, or to someone who needs to know more about it for some good reason. Any subject can be described in countless different ways. Therefore, *how* you describe something — your plan of attack — will depend on your purpose or intention.

PURPOSE OF DESCRIPTION

Good description is an important part of most job-related writing. For example, people in marketing and sales use descriptions to stimulate interest in products; banks require detailed descriptions of any business venture before granting a business loan; architects and engineers describe and perfect their plans on paper before actual construction begins; medical personnel maintain periodic descriptions of a patient's condition to ensure effective treatment.

As an illustration, the questionnaire in Figure 12-1 is typically used by the police to obtain a description of a criminal suspect. When a witness provides enough details, a police artist converts the word picture into an actual sketch of the suspect. Clearly, such a description is more useful than "The suspect is tall and dark, with a medium build," or "The suspect is ugly and evil-looking."

Another illustration of description at work can be seen in job descriptions, outlining duties, responsibilities, and requirements. Your own job description will spell out exactly what the organization expects of you. If you become a manager, you might write job descriptions for newly created positions. Sometimes you will receive copies of all job descriptions within your company; then you will understand the range and limits of your colleagues' duties as well as your own. Figure 12-2 shows a job description for the director of a computer center at a community college. The details here establish the guidelines by which the employee's performance can be evaluated.

No matter what the subject, your reader will need to know the answers to some or all of these questions:

1. What is it?
2. What does it do?
3. What does it look like?
4. What is it made of?
5. How does it work?
6. How has it been put together?

These are the questions that description tries to answer. The police questionnaire, for example, is calculated to answer "What does it look like?" In this case, "it" is a person. The illustrated job description is calculated to answer the question "What is it?" which almost always requires an answer to one or more of the other questions. In this case, we need a description of the parts that make up the whole job. The purpose of description, then, is to answer as many of these questions as are applicable.

DESCRIPTION QUESTIONNAIRE

Case No: _____

Interviewer: _____   Witness: _____
Place of Interview: _____   Address: _____
Date: _____   Phone #: _____

Description of Suspect

Sex _____ Nationality _____ Age _____ Height _____ Weight _____
Build _____ Who does this person look like? _____
In what way? _____
Hair: Color _____ Long _____ Short _____ Bald _____ Curly _____
      Straight _____ Other _____
Face: Round _____ Oval _____ Square _____ Other _____
Race_____ Color Skin _____
Complexion: Light _____ Dark _____ Ruddy _____
Unusual Facial: Scars _____ Pockmarks _____ Dimples _____
               Other _____
Eyes: Color _____ Shape _____ Brows: Color _____ Bushy _____
                                       Thin _____ Average _____
Nose: Large _____ Small _____ Wide _____ Flat _____
      Pronounced _____ Nostril Shape _____
Mouth: Lip Shape _____ Large _____ Small _____ Wide _____
       Thin _____ Color _____
Teeth: Large _____ Pronounced _____ Crooked _____
       Missing _____ Stained _____
Speech: Manner of Talking _____
Words Spoken: _____
_____
Chin: Pronounced _____ Recessed _____ Wide _____ Narrow _____
      Dimple _____
Mustache: _____ Beard _____ Sideburns _____ Color _____
          Shape _____
Cheeks: Pronounced _____ Recessed _____ Flat _____ Color _____
Ears: Large _____ Small _____ Flattened _____ Protruding _____
Neck: Large _____ Thin _____ Long _____ Short _____
Shoulders: Wide _____ Narrow _____ Chest: Broad_____ Flat_____
                                        Other _____
Hand: Which used _____ Shaking _____ Calm _____
      Gloves Worn _____ Tattoos _____ Watch _____
      Unclean _____ Scars _____ Other _____

FIGURE 12-1   A Typical Descriptive Questionnaire Used by the Police

```
Fingers: Long _____ Short _____ Straight _____ Crooked _____
         Slender _____ Narrow _____ Rings _____
Fingernails: Long _____ Short _____ Clean _____ Dirty _____
Clothing: Hat Style _____ Coat Style _____ Jacket _____
          Sweater _____ Other _____ Color _____
          Material _____ Suit _____ Sport Coat _____
          Dress _____ Shirt _____ Tie _____
          Trousers _____ Socks _____ Shoes _____
Weapons: Gun _____ Knife _____ Other _____
Vehicle Used: Make _____ Model _____ Year _____
              Color _____ Reg. No. _____
              State _____ No. of Persons in Veh. _____
              No. of Doors _____ Antennas _____
              Type Tires _____ White Wall _____
              Damage to Vehicle _____
              Lights: Number _____ All Working _____
              Automatic or Standard _____
              Interior color _____ Radio Type _____
              Type of Seats _____ How Many _____
              Ripped _____ Wheelcovers _____
              Spotlights _____ Other Distinguishing
              Marks _____
              _____


Off. Signature _____  Witness Sig. _____

               _____  Date: _____
```

FIGURE 12-1 (*Continued*)

DIRECTOR OF THE COMPUTER CENTER

The Director of the Computer Center is charged with the administrative direction of the College's Computer Center.

The Director of the Computer Center is responsible to the President of the College for the proper operation of the Computer Center as a teaching resource of the College, and particularly for its data processing programs. He is also responsible for the execution of certain administrative requests for computer information. He:

Advises the President regarding the policies and procedures needed for the effective utilization of computer facilities.

Serves the College's Advisory Committee on Data Processing Program and serves as consultant for data processing programs.

Advises the College Committee on Administrative Data Processing Procedures and the College Committee on use of Computing Facilities regarding programming time allocations, new equipment and other matters related to the instructional and administrative uses of the computer.

Supervises the data processing of college computerized records.

Oversees the development of all computer programs.

Advises Divisional Chairmen, faculty and other professional staff regarding the possible application of the computer to their instructional or administrative duties.

Submits budget requests to the Dean of Administration.

Participates in local, state and national professional associations in the field of data processing.

Serves on the Administrative Advisory Council.

FIGURE 12-2   A Typical Job Description

Education: Masters Degree preferred.

Experience: Minimum 3–5 years' experience in directing com-
                  puter laboratory operations in either institu-
                  tions of higher education or in business, indus-
                  try, or government research organization.
                  Desired experience in developing systems pro-
                  grams that relate to educational computer use,
                  administrative educational computer use and
                  educational research computer use.

FIGURE 12-2 (*Continued*)

MAKING YOUR DESCRIPTION OBJECTIVE

Descriptive writing should be a familiar activity. From the earliest grades you have written descriptive paragraphs or essays. Depending on your topic, your description was mainly *subjective* or *objective* — that is, based either on opinion (a belief held without proof) or on fact (something whose existence can be shown). Subjective description emphasizes the perceiver's attitude toward the thing, whereas objective description emphasizes the thing itself.

Subjective Description

The details in a subjective description are dictated by feelings or opinions about a topic. Essays describing "My Biggest Complaint," "An Unforgettable Person," or "A Beautiful Moment" are statements of opinion; they are written from a highly personal point of view. Subjective description aims at expressing feelings, attitudes, moods, and emotions. In it you create an *impression* of your subject rather than communicating information about it ("The weather was miserable." versus "All day we had freezing rain and gale-force winds."). Besides providing little information, subjective description can be misleading; someone you have described as "an unforgettable person" might be described by someone else as a crashing bore!

Besides being seen in personal forms of writing, subjective description is found in sales and promotional literature. There it is used to create favorable impressions that influence consumer attitudes. At their best, promotional descriptions are colorful, imaginative, and valid; at their worst, they are contrived and deceptive. A good illustration is the subjective adjective "jumbo" as applied to egg size. In some stores "jumbo" eggs are really medium-sized and "extra large" eggs look like pigeon eggs. The same distortion can occur with other adjectives (new, improved, super, and so on); words like these are inevitably vague and subjective unless they are defined in terms of specified weights, dimensions, or ingredients. In fact, they are so vague that they don't really provide *descriptions* at all.

Objective Description

Objective description is largely uninfluenced by emotions or personal likes and dislikes. You are not likely to have written many objective descriptions. However, if you have ever been involved in an automobile accident you probably completed a form similar to the one in Figure 12-3, which tries to force the writer to be objective. In it you are asked to describe the physical details of the area and to give a *factual* account of the accident. Although one or more drivers involved may deny responsibility, the objective details — if honestly recorded — should speak for themselves.

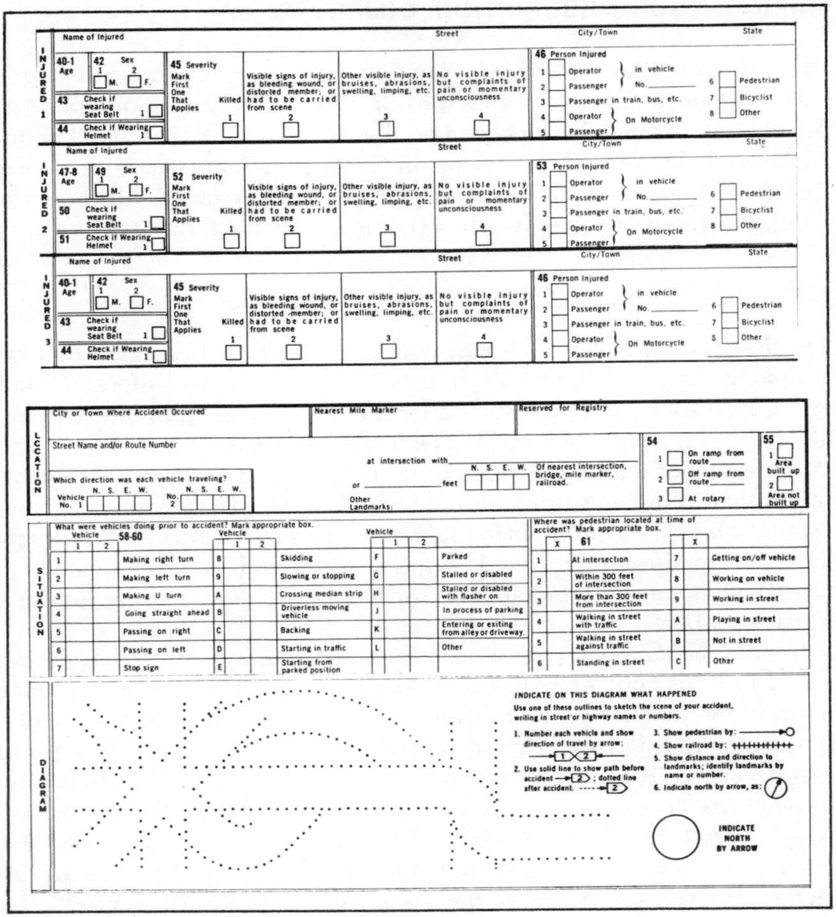

FIGURE 12-3   Portions of an Accident Report Form

If you have ever had anything stolen, you probably gave the police a description. Let us suppose that the stolen item was a tape deck. A subjective description — that the tape deck was a great source of entertainment; that it was the best money could buy; that its sound quality was superb; that it made driving a pleasure — would hardly help the investigating officer. Instead, you would need to give a list of physical characteristics: brand name, serial number, model, color, any identifying marks or scratches, method of mounting, and so on. These details describe the object itself instead of your feelings about it.

Objective description is not only concerned with concrete physical details, however. A psychologist's description of a patient's mental state is objective, insofar as it is based on demonstrable fact.

With the exception of promotional writing, most of your descriptions on the job will be objective. Your employer is less interested in your feelings about the item than about its factual details. The six questions on page 342 require objective answers. Notice that the question "What is your opinion of the item?" is not on that list. If you *are* asked to give an opinion or an interpretation, do so only *after* giving all the objective details. Base your opinions and interpretations on fact; don't confuse them with fact. Objective description records exactly what you see, which should be what another person would see. Some guidelines for maintaining objectivity follow.

Be Totally Familiar with the Item

Objective description relies on precise factual details; therefore, study the item and learn every detail before you write.

Record Observable Details Faithfully

In order to identify observable details, ask yourself these questions: What characteristics in this item could any observer recognize? What details would a camera record?

Subjective
> His office is the most depressing place I've ever seen.

What you find depressing, another may find quaint.

Objective
> His office has broken windows looking out on a brick wall, a rug with a six-inch-wide hole in the center, chairs with their bottoms falling out, missing floor boards, and a ceiling with pieces of plaster missing in three or four places.

Use Precise and Factual Language

Express details in high-information words. Name specific parts without calling them "things," "gadgets," "whatchamacallits," or "doohickeys." Avoid judgmental words (*good, super, impressive, poor*) unless your judgment is specifically requested and can be based on observable facts or statistics. The same holds true for words like *large, small, long,* and *near;* substitute *exact measurements, weights, dimensions,* and *ingredients.*

Use words that specify location: *above, below, behind, to the right, adjacent, interlocking, abutting,* and *overlapping.* Use position words: *horizontal, vertical, lateral, longitudinal, in cross section, parallel.*

Indefinite	Precise
at high speed	eighty miles per hour
a small office	an eight-by-twelve-foot office
a heavy typewriter	a fifty-pound typewriter
a late-model car	a 1978 Ford Granada two-door sedan
a high salary	$50,000 per year
long hours	sixty hours weekly
an inside view	a cross-sectional, cutaway, or exploded view
a tall mountain	with a vertical rise of 250 feet from sea level
impressive gas mileage	forty miles per gallon, city; fifty, highway
a poorly made tool	a tool with brittle plastic fittings
right next to the foundation	adjacent to the right side
partially exposed	overlapping
a small red thing	a red activator button with a one-and-a-half-inch diameter

However, don't confuse precise language with needlessly complicated technical terms. Don't say "phlebotomy specimen" instead of "blood" in describing a microscopic blood analysis. The clearest writing uses the simplest terms. Prefer nontechnical language to specialized terminology as long as the simpler terms will do the job.

The following physical description of a stethoscope is written in indefinite language:

> The standard stethoscope is an *ordinary-looking thing* which is *small* and *light* in weight. This *well-made gadget* consists of *several* parts which work together to perform an *important* function.

If you didn't know anything about a stethoscope, this description wouldn't help. It is so indefinite that it could be referring to just about any item with parts that do something. The writer has neglected his reader's need for precise details. The italicized words tell the reader nothing whatsoever.

Here is the same description effectively written:

The stethoscope is roughly twenty-four inches long and weighs about five ounces. The instrument consists of a sensitive, sound-detecting and amplifying device whose flat surface is pressed against a bodily area. This device, in turn, is attached to rubber and metal tubing that transmits the body sound to a listening device, which is inserted in the ear.

Seven interlocking pieces contribute to the stethoscope's Y-shaped appearance: (1) diaphragm contact piece, (2) lower tubing, (3) Y-shaped metal piece, (4) upper tubing, (5) U-shaped metal strip, (6) curved metal tubing, and (7) hollow ear plugs. These parts are assembled into a continuous unit.

Try to sustain this kind of objectivity and detail in all of your physical descriptions.

ELEMENTS OF AN EFFECTIVE DESCRIPTION

Clear and Limiting Title

Limit your topic by promising exactly what you will deliver — no more and no less. A title like "A Physical Description of a Typical Ten-Speed Racing Bicycle" promises a description of the entire item, down to the smallest bolt or cotter pin. If your intention, however, is to describe the bicycle's braking mechanism only, be sure that your title so indicates: "A Physical Description of a Center-Pull Caliper Braking Mechanism."

Overall Appearance and Component Parts

Allow your reader to visualize the item as a whole before you describe each of its parts. See the previous "effectively written" description of the stethoscope.

Function of Each Part

Explain the role that each part plays in the whole. In the stethoscope description, the function of the first major part — the diaphragm-contact piece — can be explained this way:

The diaphragm contact piece is caused to vibrate by body sounds. This part is the heart of the stethoscope as it receives, amplifies, and transmits the auditory impulse.

Comparisons with More Familiar Objects

The following comparison should help the reader to visualize the item:

The diaphragm contact piece is a circular metal disk roughly the shape and size of a silver dollar.

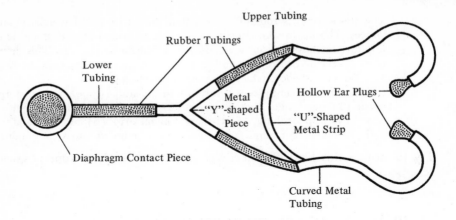

FIGURE 12-4   Stethoscope with Diaphragm Contact Piece

Introduction-Body-Conclusion Structure

Follow the structure of all good communication: (1) introduce your reader to the subject; (2) discuss the subject in detail; and (3) review what you have just discussed.

Graphic Aids

Use drawings, diagrams, or photographs whenever you can (as discussed in Chapter 9). Our overall description of the stethoscope can be greatly clarified by including the illustration in Figure 12-4 *within* the text of the discussion.

Appropriate Details

Your choice of the kinds and amount of details is crucial. On one hand, you must provide enough details to give a clear picture. On the other hand, you must avoid burying your readers in needless details. Try to identify, with precision, your readers and their reasons for reading your description.

Let us assume that you are about to describe a certain brand and model of bicycle to an uninformed person. The picture you create will depend on the details you select. How will your reader use this description? What is his or her level of technical understanding? Is the reader a customer likely to be interested in what the bike looks like — its flashy looks and racy style? Are you writing for a repair technician who needs to know the order in which the parts operate? Or is your reader a helper in your bicycle shop who needs to know how to assemble this particular kind of bicycle? Because anything could be described in at least a dozen different ways, you need to identify your specific purpose and audience.

If you can't specifically identify your reader, write for a general reader and follow these guidelines: (1) details that are less technical are more widely understood; and (2) too many details may be no better than too few.

Consider, for instance, a description of a particular brand of dishwasher that you would write for the average consumer. You can assume that your reader knows what a dishwasher looks like. On the other hand, you do not want to bury him in details that he can't possibly use. Therefore, depending on your purpose, you might describe only the parts used in operating the appliance. Or, you might describe the interior chamber so that your reader will know how many dishes the machine will clean. If your description were to be used in a repair manual for service technicians, however, you would include many more technical details.

Because you will often write descriptions for a general audience, all the sample descriptions in this chapter are so designed.

ORGANIZING AND WRITING YOUR DESCRIPTION

Before writing a word, answer these questions:

1. Why am I interested in this item?
2. Who is my reader?
3. Why do I want my reader to be interested in this item?

Your purpose in describing anything will be to tell your reader what it looks like, how it has been put together, or how it works. Sometimes your purpose will be a combination of these. Once you have identified that purpose, you will need to devise a plan of attack. What descriptive sequence is best for helping the reader picture this item? Where do you begin? What comes next?

Clearest Descriptive Sequence

Like most items, yours should have its own logic of organization, based on: (1) the way it appears as a static object; (2) the way its parts operate in order; or (3) the way its parts are assembled. We can describe these relationships, respectively, through a spatial, operational, or chronological sequence.

Spatial Sequence

To a large extent, the spatial sequence is part of all descriptions of things with physical dimensions. A spatial sequence answers these questions: What is it?

What does it do? What does it look like? What parts and material is it made of? Use this sequence when you intend your reader to visualize the item as a static object or as a mechanism at rest (a house interior, a document, the Statue of Liberty, a plot of land, a tool, an electric razor at rest, and so on). Will your reader best understand the item from outside to inside, front to rear, left to right, top to bottom? (What logical path do the parts create?) For example, a retractable pen would logically be viewed from outside to inside; a hammer, from top to bottom.

Sometimes you will want to emphasize certain parts of the item; then, you should try to design your description so those parts are either first or last in the sequence. For example, you might describe a newly designed condominium high-rise in a top-to-bottom sequence if your intention is to emphasize the more dramatic penthouse suites. If, instead, you wished to emphasize the impressive lobby, lounge, pool, and playroom on the first floor, you might follow a bottom-to-top sequence. When striving for emphasis, base your order of description on the angle of vision that you wish to create for your reader.

Operational Sequence

Like the spatial sequence, the sequence of operating parts answers the questions about identification, function, appearance, and parts and material; however, it also answers the question, How does it work? It is best used in describing a mechanism in action, such as a 35-millimeter camera, an electric razor, a smoke detector, or a stethoscope. The inherent logic of the item is reflected by the order in which its parts operate. Therefore, the choice of direction should be simple: each item has only one possible operating sequence.

For instance, in describing a solar home-heating system you would logically begin with the heat collectors in the roof, moving on through the pipes, pumping system, and tanks for the heated water, to the heating vents in the floors and walls — in short, from the source to the outlet. However, any description, unless it is concerned with something very simple, is likely to involve more than one sequence. For example, after describing the solar-heating system according to the sequence of its operating parts, you could describe each part according to a particular spatial sequence.

Chronological Sequence

In addition to answering the questions about identification, function, appearance, and parts and material, a chronological sequence answers the question, How has it been put together? The chronology is determined by the sequence in which the parts are assembled. Here again, there usually is only one possible direction.

Use the chronological sequence for an item that is best understood in terms of its assembly (such as a piece of furniture, an umbrella tent, or a prehung window or door unit). An architect might find a spatial sequence best for describing a proposed beachhouse to a client; however, he would probably use a chronological sequence for describing the house to the contractor who will build it.

Combined Sequences

If you think about the structure of the item and your intention in describing it, you should have no trouble selecting the proper combination of sequences. The short description of a trout-activated feeder mechanism in Figure 12-5 uses all three sequences; first, a spatial sequence (top to bottom) for describing the overall mechanism at rest; next, a chronological sequence for explaining the order in which the parts are assembled; finally, an operational sequence for describing the order in which the parts operate.

The Outline

A good outline is your next step in planning and organizing your description. The following model outline can be adapted to virtually all descriptive reporting assignments.

I. INTRODUCTION: GENERAL DESCRIPTION
    A. Definition, Purpose, and Background of the Item
    B. Purpose of the Report, and Specific Audience
    C. Overall Description of the Item (with graphic aid, if applicable)
    D. Principle of Operation (if applicable)
    E. List of Major Parts

II. DESCRIPTION AND FUNCTION OF PARTS
    A. Part One in Your Descriptive Sequence
        1. Definition
        2. Shape, Dimensions, Material (with specialized graphic aids)
        3. Subparts (if applicable)
        4. Function
        5. Relation to adjoining parts
        6. Manner of attachment (if applicable)
    B. Part Two in Your Descriptive Sequence
        etc.

III. CONCLUSION AND OPERATING DESCRIPTION
    A. Summary
    B. Interrelation of Parts
    C. One Complete Operating Cycle

A DESCRIPTION OF OUR TROUT-ACTIVATED FEEDER MECHANISM

The Overall Mechanism

Our trout-activated feeder mechanism was designed so trout could be fed as they became hungry. The purpose of this description is to explain the appearance, order of assembly, and order of operation of the feeder mechanism to trout hatchery owners and operators.

When trout stimulate a feeder device, food is deposited on the surface of the water, where the fish easily consume it.

The feeder mechanism is made of a plastic funnel, wooden strip, metal rod, wooden disk, and paper clip. The mechanism is a cone-shaped device with a rod passing through its two openings. The large opening of the cone is on top. Centered on the rod under the smaller opening is a wooden disk of slightly larger diameter than the opening and held to the rod by a paper clip (see Figure 1).

Order of Assembly

The plastic funnel must be large enough to hold more food than trout will need in one day. The wooden strip is

FIGURE 12-5   A Description Using Combined Sequences

2

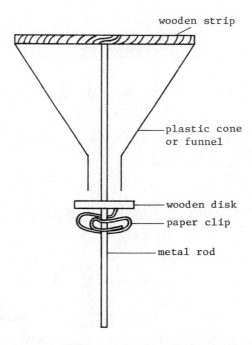

wooden strip

plastic cone
or funnel

wooden disk

paper clip

metal rod

<u>Figure 1</u>. <u>An Overall Lateral View of the Feeder Mechanism</u>

placed across the upper, large funnel opening to hold the

metal rod that runs down through the cone. This rod passes

through the bottom, smaller opening until it touches the

surface of the water. The wooden disk is connected to the

rod just under the lower opening by a paper clip (as shown

in Figure 2). The paper clip is bent twice and forms a

FIGURE 12-5   (*Continued*)

3

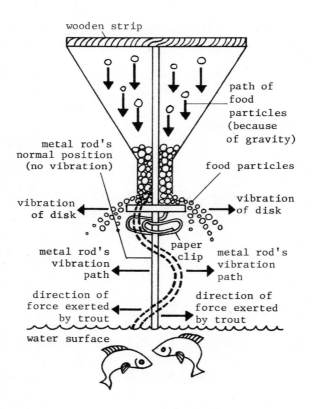

wooden strip

path of food particles (because of gravity)

metal rod's normal position (no vibration)

food particles

vibration of disk

vibration of disk

paper clip

metal rod's vibration path

metal rod's vibration path

direction of force exerted by trout

direction of force exerted by trout

water surface

Figure 2. A Lateral View of the Feeder Mechanism's Assembly and Operation

notch where the metal rod is inserted. One bend is made in

the inner section of the clip where there is a 180-degree

FIGURE 12-5 *(Continued)*

4

turn. The metal rod is inserted between the inner and outer

sections of the clip and the 180-degree head of the inner

section is bent around the rod at a 90-degree angle to the

plane of the clip. At the open end of the clip is a pointed

tip, which is bent 60 degrees straight upwards from the

clip's edge (as shown in Figure 3).

Paper Clip

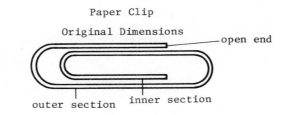

Modified Paper Clip

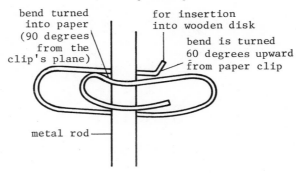

Figure 3. A Side View of a Paper Clip and of Its
          Modifications for Attachment

FIGURE 12-5 (*Continued*)

5

Mechanism in Operation

      Because trout are surface feeders they will attack any
object on the surface of the water. As the trout surface,
therefore, they strike the top of the metal rod, which is
touching the water. The force of the vibration travels up
the metal rod and shakes the disk, which is covered with
food from the funnel's gravity feed. As the disk vibrates
it causes food resting on it to fall to the water surface
where the trout can consume it (as shown in Figure 2).

FIGURE 12-5   (*Continued*)

Introduction: General Description

The introduction is the background section of your description, where you introduce your reader to the item. First, define the item, explain its purpose, and review its history. Next, explain the purpose of your description and identify your audience.

DEFINITION AND PURPOSE

The stethoscope is a listening device that amplifies and transmits body sounds to aid in detecting physical abnormalities. Its purpose is to assist doctors in diagnosing diseases.

HISTORY AND BACKGROUND

This instrument has evolved from the original wooden, funnel-shaped instrument invented by a French physician, R. T. Leannec, in 1819. Because of the modesty of his female patients, Leannec found it necessary to develop a device, other than his ear, for auscultation (listening to body sounds).

PURPOSE OF REPORT, AND INTENDED AUDIENCE

This report seeks to explain the structure and operating principle of the stethoscope to the beginning paramedical or nursing student.

Finally, give a brief, overall description of the item, discuss its principle of operation, and list its major parts. The overall description on page 351 follows an operational sequence.

Body: Description and Function of Parts

In the body you move from the general focus of your introduction to a specific description of each major part. After arranging the parts in an overall sequence, follow the individual logic of each part. Begin your description of an individual part with a definition, followed by descriptions of the part's size, shape, and material. Also, discuss any important subparts. Finally, explain the part's function in the whole, its relation to adjoining parts, and the manner in which it is attached.

DIAPHRAGM CONTACT PIECE

Definition, Size, Shape, and Material

The diaphragm contact piece is a circular metal and plastic disk, about the size of a silver dollar, which is caused to vibrate by body sounds.

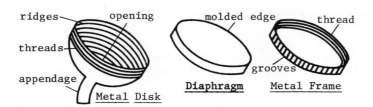

FIGURE 2   Frontal-Superior View of the Three Parts of a Diaphragm Contact
Piece

Subparts

Three separate parts make up the piece: metal disk, plastic diaphragm,
and metal frame, as shown in Figure 2.

The metal disk is made of stainless steel. Its inside surface is concave
and designed with circular ridges that concentrate sound toward an opening
in the center of the disk, then out through a hollow metal appendage.
Lateral threads ring the outer circumference of the disk in order to accommodate the interlocking metal frame. A fitted diaphragm covers the four-
inch circumference of the disk.

The diaphragm is a flat plastic disk, one millimeter thick, four inches in
circumference, with a molded lip around the edge. It fits over the metal
disk and vibrates sound toward the ridges. The diaphragm is held in place
by a metal frame that screws onto the metal disk.

The stainless steel frame is four inches in circumference around its outer
edge and three and one-half inches around its inner edge. A half-inch ridge
between the inner and outer edge accommodates threads for screwing the
frame onto the concave metal disk. The outside circumference of the frame
is covered with perpendicular grooves — like those on the edge of a dime —
which provide a gripping surface.

Function and Relation to Adjoining Parts

The diaphragm contact piece is the heart of the stethoscope as it receives,
amplifies, and transmits the auditory impulse through the system of attached
tubing.

Manner of Attachment

The diaphragm contact piece is attached to the lower tubing by an appendage on its upper end which fits inside the tubing.

Each part of the stethoscope, in turn, is described according to its own logic of
organization.

Conclusion: Summary and Operating Description

In the conclusion, you review your description briefly, explaining how the parts combine to make the item function as a whole.

Summary

The stethoscope has been described according to the sequence of its functioning parts, in sufficient detail to acquaint the reader with its physical characteristics and operating principle.

Interrelation of Parts

The seven major parts of the stethoscope provide support for the instrument, flexibility of movement for the operator, and ease in auscultation.

One Complete Operating Cycle

In an operating cycle, the diaphragm contact piece is placed against the skin to pick up sound impulses from the body surface. These impulses cause the plastic diaphragm to vibrate. The amplified vibrations, in turn, are carried through a single tube to a dividing point. From here, the sound is carried through two separate but identical series of tubes to hollow ear plugs which transmit the amplified sounds to the listener's ears.

In each of these steps, add well-labeled graphic aids whenever they will help clarify your description. Use transitional sentences to provide logical bridges between sections. As an illustration, this sentence in the description of the diaphragm contact piece leads into the description of the lower tubing:

The diaphragm contact piece is attached to the lower tubing by an appendage on its upper end which fits inside the tubing.

As long as you follow an introduction-body-conclusion structure, the outline and development of individual sections can be modified. Depending on your subject, your purpose, and your reader, you might delete or combine some of the areas of discussion. Feel free to adapt the model outline to your needs.

APPLYING THE STEPS

The descriptive report of an automobile jack in Figure 12-6, written by a student for a general reading audience, follows our outline model. As a study aid, the descriptive sequences, varying orders of headings, and transitional sentences are labeled in the margins.

DESCRIPTION OF A STANDARD FORD BUMPER JACK

OUTLINE

I.   INTRODUCTION: GENERAL DESCRIPTION

     A. Definition and Purpose

     B. Intention of Report, and Specified
        Audience

     C. Overall Description

     D. Principle of Operation

     E. List of Major Parts

II. DESCRIPTION OF PARTS AND THEIR FUNCTION

     A. The Base
        1. Definition
        2. Shape, dimensions, material
        3. Subparts
           a. stabilizing well
           b. metal piece
        4. Function
        5. Relation to adjoining parts
        6. Manner of attachment

     B. The Shaft
        1. Definition
        2. Shape, dimensions, material
        3. Function
        4. Relation to adjoining parts
        5. Manner of attachment

FIGURE 12-6 A Descriptive Report

2

    C. The Leverage Mechanism
      1. Definition
      2. Shape, dimensions, material
      3. Subparts
        a. the cylinder
        b. lower pawl
        c. upper pawl
        d. "up-down" lever
      4. Function
      5. Relation to adjoining parts
      6. Manner of attachment

    D. The Bumper Catch
      1. Definition and relation to
        adjoining parts
      2. Shape, dimensions, material
      3. Function
      4. Manner of attachment

    E. The Jack Handle
      1. Definition and function
      2. Shape, dimensions, material
      3. Relation to adjoining parts
      4. Manner of attachment

III. CONCLUSION AND OPERATING DESCRIPTION

    A. Summary

    B. Interrelation of Parts

    C. One Complete Operating Cycle

FIGURE 12-6 (*Continued*)

3

INTRODUCTION -- GENERAL DESCRIPTION

Major area
heading

Definition and Purpose

Major topic
heading

The standard Ford bumper jack is a
portable device used for raising the front or
rear end of an automobile by means of force
applied with a lever. It allows even a frail
person to lift one corner of a two-ton automobile.

Intention of the Report, and Specified Audience

This report is written for the general
reader and car owner who will sometimes need
to raise a car in order to change a flat
tire.

Overall Description

The jack consists of a molded base supporting a free-standing, perpendicular,
notched shaft, to which are attached a
leverage mechanism, a bumper catch, and a
cylinder for insertion of the jack handle
(see Figure 1). The jack is made to be

Chronological
sequence

FIGURE 12-6 (*Continued*)

4

dismantled -- except for the main shaft and

mechanism -- and to fit neatly into the auto-

mobile's trunk.

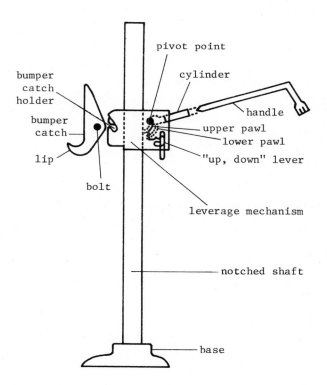

Figure 1. A Lateral View of the Standard
Ford Bumper Jack

FIGURE 12-6 (*Continued*)

5

Principle of Operation

The jack operates on a leverage principle, with the human hand traveling 18 inches
and the car only 3/8 inch during the normal
jacking stroke. Such a device requires many
strokes to raise the car off the ground but
may prove a lifesaver to a motorist on some
deserted road.

List of Major Parts

Five main parts make up the jack: the
base, the notched shaft, the leverage
mechanism, the bumper catch, and the handle.
Each part is described in detail in the   Transition
following section.

DESCRIPTION OF PARTS AND THEIR FUNCTION   Major area
                                                 heading

The Base   Major topic
                                                 heading

The rectangular base is a molded steel
plate that provides support and a point of
insertion for the shaft. (See Figure 1.)
This piece is 8 inches long and 6½ inches
wide and slopes upward 1½ inches from the

FIGURE 12-6   (*Continued*)

6

front outer edge to form a secondary plat-

form 1 inch high and 3 inches square. The

back edge of the base slopes upward more

sharply to the secondary platform.

Spatial
sequence
(bottom
to top)

Within the secondary platform is a

depression which drops 1 inch and provides a

stabilizing well for the lower end of the

shaft. Stability is further achieved by a

3/16-inch piece of steel which is 2 inches

wide and riveted and bent over to form a

cuff around the well. Together, the

depression and metal strip provide a 2-inch

stabilization zone for the end of the shaft.

As the base rests on a flat surface, the

bottom end of the shaft is inserted into

Transition

its stabilizing well.

The Shaft

Major topic
heading

The notched shaft is a steel bar which

provides a vertical track for the leverage

mechanism. This piece is 32 inches long and

forged into a trapezoidal shape. The

FIGURE 12-6 (*Continued*)

7

non-parallel sides are 1 3/8 inches long; the   Spatial
sequence
shorter parallel side of the trapezoid is   (small to
large)
3/4 inch, and the longer side 1 1/8 inches.

The notches, which enable the mechanism to

maintain its position on the shaft, are

located on the longer parallel side of the

shaft. They are 3/8 inch apart, 3/8 inch

deep and extend across the entire long side.

The shaft gives vertical support to the

raised automobile. To it is attached the

leverage mechanism, which rests on indi-   Transition

vidual notches.

The Leverage Mechanism

The leverage mechanism provides the

mechanical advantage needed for the operator

to raise the car. It is made to slide up and

down the notched shaft. The main body of

this molded steel mechanism covers 3 3/4

inches of the shaft and contains two units: Spatial
sequence
one for transferring the leverage, and one   (inside to
outside)
for holding the bumper catch.

FIGURE 12-6 (*Continued*)

8

The leverage unit consists of four main parts: the cylinder, which connects the handle and a pivot point; a lower pawl (a device fitting into the notches to allow forward or prevent backward motion), which is directly connected to the cylinder; an upper pawl, which is connected at the pivot point; and an "up-down" lever, which, by means of a spring, applies or releases pressure on the upper pawl. Moving the cylinder up and down with the handle causes the alternate release of the pawls and thus movement either up or down the shaft -- depending on the setting of the "up-down" lever. The movement is transferred by the metal body of the unit to the bumper catch holder.

The holder consists of a downsloping groove, part of which is blocked by a wire spring (see figure 1). The spring is mounted

Operational sequence

FIGURE 12-6 (*Continued*)

9

in such a way as to keep the bumper catch in   Transition

place while in operation.

The Bumper Catch

    The bumper catch is a steel device that

provides the attachment between the leverage

mechanism and the automobile bumper. This

piece is a 9-inch molded plate bent to

follow the shape of the bumper. Its distal   Spatial
                                                     sequence
½ inch is bent up in a lip (see Figure 1),   (distal to
                                                     proximal)
which hooks behind the bumper to hold the

catch in place. The two sides of the plate

are bent back 90 degrees to leave a two-inch

bumper-contact surface, and a bolt is riveted

between them. The bolt slips into the groove

in the leverage mechanism and provides the

point of attachment between the leverage unit

and the car.

The Jack Handle

    The jack handle is the steel bar that

serves as both a lever and a lug-bolt remover.

This round bar is 22 inches long, 5/5 inch in

FIGURE 12-6   (*Continued*)

10

diameter, and has a 135-degree bend 5 inches   Spatial
                                                      sequence
from the distal end. Its distal end is a   (distal to
                                                      proximal)
wrench made to fit the wheel's lug bolts,

while the proximal end is flattened for

removing the wheel covers and for insertion

into the cylinder on the leverage mechanism

which connects to the pivot point.

CONCLUSION AND OPERATING DESCRIPTION   Major area
                                              heading
Summary

The five major parts of the standard

Ford bumper jack have been described in

enough detail to give the general reader an

understanding of its construction and purpose.

Interrelation of Parts

The five main parts of the jack -- base,

notched shaft, leverage mechanism, bumper

catch, and handle -- together make up an

efficient, lightweight lifting device. This

simple tool can be used safely by the car

owner to raise a car for the purpose of

changing a tire.

FIGURE 12-6 (*Continued*)

11

One Complete Operating Cycle

The jack is quickly assembled by inserting the bottom of the notched shaft into the stabilizing well in the base, the bumper catch into the groove on the leverage mechanism, and the flat end of the jack handle into the cylinder on the leverage mechansim.

When the bumper catch is attached to the bumper, the lever set in the "up" position, and an up-down pumping motion exerted on the jack handle by the operator, the leverage mechanism gradually climbs the vertical, notched shaft until the wheel is raised from the ground. Conversely, when the lever is set in the "down" position, the same pumping motion causes the leverage mechanism gradually to descend the shaft.

FIGURE 12-6 (*Continued*)

CHAPTER SUMMARY

In describing anything, you should identify it, explain its function, portray its appearance, and list its parts and materials. Also, explain how a mechanical item works and, perhaps, how it has been put together. This kind of detailed description is a part of most job-related writing.

Although much of your earlier writing has been subjective (emphasizing your attitude toward the subject), most of your future writing will be objective (emphasizing the subject itself). To be objective, know your subject, stick to observable details, and use terms that communicate hard information about the thing itself.

An effective description begins with a clear and limiting title that promises exactly what you will deliver. First, the subject is described in terms of its overall physical characteristics; next, in terms of its component parts and their respective functions. Whenever possible, a description uses comparisons with more familiar objects. Like most good writing, the description follows an introduction-body-conclusion structure, with graphic aids used generously. The type and amount of detail should be appropriate to the subject and your reader's needs. Too many details are no better than too few, and fewer technical details are easier to understand by general readers.

Follow these steps in planning and organizing your description:

1. After defining your purpose, identify the clearest descriptive sequence. Choose one or more sequences that best follow the inherent logic of your subject.

    a. Use a spatial sequence for describing static objects or mechanisms at rest.

    b. Use an operational sequence for describing mechanisms in action.

    c. Use a chronological sequence for describing the order in which an item — either static or mechanical — has been assembled.

2. Make a detailed outline and develop your report from it.

    a. In your introduction, first define the item and explain its purpose and background. Next, discuss the intention of your description and specify your audience. Proceed to an overall description of the item and an explanation of its operating principle. Finally, list the major parts to be described in the body section.

    b. In your body section, describe and explain the function of each major part, in order, giving its definition, shape, dimensions, material, subparts, function, relation to adjoining parts, and manner of attachment.

    c. In your conclusion section, summarize the main points in the body, discuss the interrelation of the parts, and describe one complete cycle of operation.

As long as you use this three-section structure, feel free to delete or modify the internal parts to suit your subject and purpose.

REVISION CHECKLIST

Use this list to refine your report.

1. Is your description fully objective, with all important observable details recorded in precise, factual language?

2. Does it have a clear and limiting title that promises specifically what you have delivered?

3. Have you described both the item's overall characteristics and each of its component parts?

4. Have you defined each part before discussing it?

5. Have you explained the function of each part?

6. Have you used comparisons with more familiar objects whenever possible?

7. Have you used graphic aids whenever possible?

8. Does your description follow an introduction-body-conclusion structure?

9. Does your description follow your outline faithfully?

10. Will your reader be able to visualize the item from your details?

11. Are there any unnecessary or confusing details?

12. Is your description keyed to your stated purpose (will it do what it is supposed to do for your reader)?

13. Does your description follow the clearest possible sequence or combination of sequences (spatial, operational, chronological)?

14. Does the description answer all the questions on page 342 that are applicable here?

15. Are your headings appropriate and adequate?

16. Is your description written in plain English?

17. Are there enough transitions between related ideas?

18. Is it written in correct English (spelling, mechanics, and usage — as discussed in Appendix A)?

Now list those elements of your description that need improvement.

EXERCISES

1. In two or three paragraphs, discuss the kinds of descriptive writing assignments you expect to have in your field. Be as specific as possible in identifying the subjects, the situations, and the readers for whom you will

write. After giving some examples, illustrate with a detailed scenario that answers the questions about purpose on page 342.

2. Rewrite these subjective statements, making them objective by describing observable details:

    a. This classroom is (attractive, unattractive).

    b. The weather today is (beautiful, awful, mediocre).

    c. (He, she) is the best-dressed person in this class.

    d. My textbook is in (good, poor) condition.

    e. This room is (too large, too small, just the right size) for our class.

3. Write a three-paragraph subjective description titled "My Best Friend" in which you express your feelings and attitude. Next, use the sample descriptive questionnaire in Figure 12-1 as a guide for writing a physical description of the same person so that the reader could recognize him or her in a crowd. Which of these descriptions is easiest to write, and why?

4. After consulting library sources, faculty members, or workers in your field, write a one-page job description of the position you hope to hold in ten years. Or write a job description for the job that you now hold. Using the sample description in Figure 12-2 as a model, include a description of function, duties, responsibilities, and qualifications.

5. Select three of your most valuable material possessions (try to choose simple objects that can easily be described). Write a one-paragraph physical description of each in enough detail that a police officer could recognize the items if they were lost or stolen.

6. The following descriptive statements are indefinite or subjective. Choose one statement from the list and expand it into an objective description in one paragraph:

    a. Come to my place for dinner and I will cook a meal you will never forget.

    b. During my vacation, I traveled everywhere.

    c. The job opportunities in my major are numerous.

    d. I plan to be highly successful in my career.

    e. Attending a small college has (advantages, disadvantages).

    f. The room in which this course is held is (cheerful, depressing).

7. Television commercials are, supposedly, a source of factual information about various products. But do we actually learn anything from descriptions that include modifiers like *super, new, improved, jumbo, nutritious, elegant,* and *exciting?* Often, the purpose of this indefinite language is to conceal the product's similarity to other products (such as other brands of aspirin).

In class, analyze recordings or copies your instructor has made of commercials. What do you really learn from them? Try to isolate objective descriptions from subjective or downright indefinite ones.

8. Following is a list of items for description. How would each description best be organized? Map out your approach. When you have decided on your purpose, choose the descriptive sequence that best describes the overall item. Next, identify the best sequence for describing each part of the item.

For example, an overall description of a ski binding as a mechanism at rest, intended for the recreational skier, might best follow a spatial sequence that emphasized its appearance and function. In contrast, an overall description of the ski binding as a working mechanism, intended for the ski-shop technician who will repair and adjust bindings, might best follow an operational sequence.

In both cases, individual parts would be described according to their own logic of spatial organization. Choose a plan of attack that works best for you and your reader.

a handsaw	an accident
a pogo stick	a flower
a sailboat	a courtroom
a textbook	the members of your family
a retractable ball-point pen	a cigarette lighter
a steeplechase track	a bunsen burner
a pocketknife	a microscope
a pair of binoculars	a rock group

9. a. Choose an item from the following list, from exercise 8, or from your major field. Using the general outline and student-written outline in this chapter as models, outline a descriptive report. Write the report for a general reader, being sure to include a title page, major topic headings, and transitional sentences between major topics. Write one draft of the report, modify your outline as needed, and write your second draft. Proofread carefully, following the revision checklist at the end of this chapter, and exchange your report with another class member, preferably in your field, for further suggestions for revision.

a soda-acid fire extinguisher	a 100-amp electrical panel
a breathalyzer	a computer
a sphygmomanometer	a Skinner box
a ditto machine	a simple radio
a typewriter	a club or fraternity/sorority
a transit	a distilling apparatus
a saber saw	a bodily organ
a drafting table	a Wilson cloud chamber
a pet	a voodoo ritual
a blowtorch	an accomplishment

Remember that you are simply describing the item, its parts, and function; do not provide directions for its assembly or operation.

b. As an optional report assignment, you may wish to describe a place you know well. You are trying to create a visual image, not a mood; therefore, your description should be objective, simply listing the observable details and their relationships.

10. The bumper-jack description in this chapter is aimed toward a general reading audience. Evaluate its effectiveness by using the revision checklist as a guide. In one or two paragraphs, discuss your evaluation and include suggestions as to how the report might be revised, if needed.

13

Explaining
a Process

CHAPTER GOALS

DEFINITION

THE PURPOSE OF PROCESS
    EXPLANATION

TYPES OF PROCESS EXPLANATION
    Instructions
    Narrative
    Analysis

ELEMENTS OF EFFECTIVE
        INSTRUCTIONS
    Clear, Limiting, and Inclusive Title
    Logical Series of Ordered Steps
    Appropriate Level of Technicality
        Background Information
        Details
    Graphic Aids
    Warnings, Cautions, and Notes
    Appropriate Terms, Phrasing, and
        Paragraph Structure
        Active Voice and Imperative Mood
        Transitions to Mark Time and
            Sequence
        Parallel Phrasing
        Short Sentences and Paragraphs
    Introduction-Body-Conclusion Structure

ORGANIZING AND WRITING A SET OF
        INSTRUCTIONS
    Introduction
    Body
    Conclusion

APPLYING THE STEPS

ELEMENTS OF AN EFFECTIVE PROCESS
        NARRATIVE
    Clear, Limiting, and Inclusive Title
    Logical Series of Ordered Steps
    Appropriate Level of Technicality
    Graphic Aids
    Appropriate Terms, Phrasing, and
        Paragraph Structure
    Introduction-Body-Conclusion Structure

ORGANIZING AND WRITING A
        PROCESS NARRATIVE

APPLYING THE STEPS

ELEMENTS OF AN EFFECTIVE PROCESS
        ANALYSIS
    Clear, Limiting, and Inclusive Title
    Logical Series of Ordered Steps
    Appropriate Level of Technicality
    Graphic Aids
    Appropriate Terms, Phrasing, and
        Paragraph Structure
    Introduction-Body-Conclusion Structure

ORGANIZING AND WRITING A PROCESS
        ANALYSIS

APPLYING THE STEPS

CHAPTER SUMMARY

REVISION CHECKLIST

EXERCISES

CHAPTER GOALS

Upon completing this chapter you will know:

- The meaning and purpose of explaining a process.
- The differences among the three types of explanation: instructions, narrative, and analysis.
- How to select the type to suit your intentions.
- How to adjust your level of technicality to the needs of your specific audience.
- How to evaluate instructions for effectiveness.
- How to organize and write instructions by working from an effective outline.
- How to evaluate a process narrative for effectiveness.
- How to organize and write a process narrative by working from an effective outline.
- How to evaluate a process analysis for effectiveness.
- How to organize and write a process analysis by working from an effective outline.
- How to proofread and revise your report for greatest effectiveness.

DEFINITION

A process is a series of actions or changes creating an end product or a result. A process explanation, then, is an account of how these actions or changes occur.

THE PURPOSE OF PROCESS EXPLANATION

The principle of cause and effect underlies everything that happens. People and things interact in different ways to cause different effects. Each interaction is a process with a beginning, a middle, and an ending. In the manufacturing process, for example, people, machines, and raw materials interact to cause a planned effect: the production of finished goods. In a typical natural process, earth, air, sunlight, and water interact to cause the growth of plant life. In a typical chemical process, air and fuel interact in an engine's carburetor to produce a combustible vapor that will be ignited within the cylinders. Undoubtedly, you can identify many more examples.

A process explanation is designed to answer the reader's question How? — posed in one of three ways:

1. How do I do something?
2. How did you do something?
3. How does something happen?

When you explain a process you isolate and identify specific causes and their effects. For example, on the job, you might give instructions telling a colleague or a customer how to do something to achieve a certain effect: how to analyze a soil sample; how to program a computer; how to swing a golf club. (This textbook contains a collection of instructions.)

Besides explaining how to do something, you may have to give two other kinds of process explanation. You might give accounts of various procedures to an employer or client: how you repaired a piece of equipment; how you inspected a building site; how you conducted an experiment. Or, you might have to explain to a new employee how certain things happen: how the promotion system in your company works; or how the budget for various departments is determined. Each of these types is discussed in more detail in the following section.

TYPES OF PROCESS EXPLANATION

Depending on your purpose, you can design your explanation to answer one of the "how" questions, respectively, with how to do it; how I did it, or how it happens. As an illustration of how your purpose dictates the type of explanation you choose, consider Figure 13-1. Written communication occurs when these elements interact in a fixed and equal relationship. However, each type of process explanation emphasizes a different element. A set of instructions is reader-oriented; a process narrative is writer-oriented; and a process analysis is subject-oriented.

Instructions

In a set of instructions you tell your reader how to do something by explaining each step. Almost anyone with a responsible job writes instructions from time to time. And almost everyone needs to read some sort of instructions. For

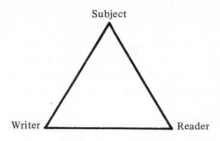

FIGURE 13-1 A Rhetorical Triangle

instance, the new employee needs instructions for operating the company's office machines; the employee going on vacation writes instructions for the person who will be filling in. An owner of a new car reads the operator's manual for servicing and operating instructions. The person who has bought a stereo-component set reads instructions for connecting the turntable, amplifier, and speakers to make a working unit. In short, instructions *emphasize the reader's role,* explaining each step in enough detail so that the reader can complete the task safely and efficiently.

Narrative

Closely related to an explanation of *how to do something* is an explanation of *how you did something* — along with a description of your results. Those of you who have written lab reports are familiar with this type of process explanation. On the job, police and fire personnel write accounts of investigations and inspections. Medical laboratory technicians write accounts of various testing procedures and their results. Construction supervisors write daily accounts of work completed on a project. This type of explanation *emphasizes your role* in such a way that the reader will understand the steps you followed and the results you achieved.

Analysis

You may often have to write explanations of how things work or how something happens by dividing the process into its parts and underlying principles. Colleagues and clients need to know such things as how stock and bond prices are governed, how fermentation occurs, how your bank reviews a mortgage application, how your town decided on its zoning laws, how radio waves are transmitted, how low-glass fiber conducts electricity, and so on. In this type of explanation, *the process itself is emphasized,* instead of the reader or writer. In effect, the process is dissected so that the reader can follow it as an "observer."

ELEMENTS OF EFFECTIVE INSTRUCTIONS

Your purpose in writing instructions is to answer all possible questions about procedure.[1] After all, your reader may well be dangling from a steel girder or surrounded by hot wires, with nothing but words on the page for directions. Therefore, obstacles to clarity are inexcusable. Make your instructions readable by including the following elements.

Clear, Limiting, and Inclusive Title

Make your title promise exactly what your instructions will deliver — no more and no less. Consider this title: "Instructions for Cleaning the Carriage, Key Faces, and Exterior of a Typewriter." It is effective because it tells the reader what to expect: instructions for performing a specific procedure on selected parts of the item. A title like "The Typewriter" would give the reader no idea of what to expect: the report might be a history of the typewriter, typing instructions, or a description of each part. On the other hand, a title like "Instructions for Cleaning a Typewriter" would be misleading, because it seems to promise instructions for cleaning the entire machine, not selected parts.

Logical Series of Ordered Steps

Good instructions not only divide the process into steps; they also guide your readers through the steps in *order,* so that they can't go wrong. For example,

> You can't join two wires to make an electrical connection before you have removed the insulation. To remove the insulation, you will need . . .

The logic of a process requires that you explain the steps in chronological order, as they are performed. Thus, instructions for building a house properly begin with the foundation, and move, in order, to the floor, walls, and roof.

Appropriate Level of Technicality

Unless you know that your reader has a technical background and technical skills, assume that you are writing for a general reader and be sure to do two things. First, give your reader enough background information to understand *why* the instructions should be followed. Second, give sufficiently detailed explanations so that your reader understands the instructions.

---

[1] To write good instructions you need to know the procedure you are explaining down to the smallest detail. Unless you have performed the task successfully, don't try to write instructions for it.

Background Information

Begin by explaining the reason for the procedure:

> Some people think that they do not have the time or skill to change their car's motor oil and engine filter. They prefer to have the changes done at a garage, service station, or car dealership. However, at today's prices, you may spend twelve dollars or more for a service you can perform yourself in thirty minutes. These instructions will help you change your oil and filter so that you can save up to seven dollars.

Also, state your assumptions about your reader's level of technical understanding:

> For constructing a wind harp, the reader is expected to have a general familiarity with hand tools and woodworking techniques in order to avoid troublesome mistakes. Also, if power tools are to be used, and used safely, a good working knowledge of their operation is essential.

Before writing the step-by-step instructions, define any special terms:

> Jogging is a kind of running — a slow trot consuming not more than seven minutes per mile.

When your reader understands *what* and *why,* you are ready to explain *how.*

Details

Most of us know the frustration of buying a disassembled item, opening the box, reading the instructions for assembly, and finding ourselves lost because the instructions are not detailed enough. Even some do-it-yourself books and gourmet cookbooks are notorious for their lack of detail and overly technical instructions. For instance, how does one "treat a rack of lamb gently with truffle essence"? Vague instructions are based on the writer's mistaken assumption that the reader has a strong technical background. Consider this set of fog-bound instructions for treating an electrical-shock victim:

1. Check vital signs.
2. Establish an airway.
3. Administer external cardiac massage if needed.
4. Ventilate, if cyanosed.
5. Treat for shock.

These instructions might be clear to the medical expert, but they mean little to the average reader. Not only are the details inadequate, but terms like "vital signs," "cyanosed," and "ventilate" are too technical for the layperson. If written for employees in a high-voltage industrial area they would be useless. The instructions need to be rewritten with clear illustrations and detailed explanations as in a Red Cross First Aid manual.

It is easy to assume that other people know more than they do about a procedure; this is especially true when you can perform the task almost automatically. Think about the days when a relative or friend was teaching you to drive a car; or perhaps you have tried to teach someone else. In many cases, the teacher becomes more and more frustrated until the student finally decides to enroll in a driving school to save the relationship! When you write instructions, remember that the reader knows less than you do. A colleague will know at least a little less; a layperson will know a good deal less — maybe nothing — about this procedure. Analyze your reader's needs carefully (as discussed in Chapter 2).

On the one hand, you will need to include enough details for your reader to understand and perform the task successfully. On the other hand, you should omit general information that the average reader can be expected to know in advance (for example, the difference between a hand tool and a power tool). Excessive details harm readability and may interrupt the sequence of steps. The following instructions contain just enough details for the general reader:

> BREAKING INTO A JOG
>
> After completing your warming-up exercises, set a brisk pace walking. Exaggerate the distance between steps, making bountiful strides and swinging your arms freely and loosely. After roughly one hundred yards of this pace, you should feel lively and ready to jog.
>
> Immediately break into a slow trot: let your torso lean forward and let one foot fall in front of the other (one foot leaving the ground while the other is on the pavement) in the slowest pace possible, just above a walk. *Do not bolt out like a sprinter!* The worst thing is to start fast and injure yourself.
>
> Relax your body while jogging. Keep your shoulders straight and your head up, and enjoy the scenery — after all, it is one of the joys of jogging. Keep your arms low and slightly bent at your sides. Move your legs freely from the hips in an action that is easy, not forced. Make your feet perform a heel-to-toe action: land on the heel; rock forward; take off from the toe.

These instructions are clear and uncluttered because the writer has correctly assessed the general reader's needs. Terms like "bountiful stride," "torso," and "sprinter" should be clear to the general reader, without elaborate definitions or graphic illustrations. In contrast, "a slow trot" is given a detailed working definition because readers might have differing interpretations of this term. When in doubt about the need to provide certain details, you are safer to risk overexplaining rather than underexplaining.

Graphic Aids

Whenever you can use a graphic aid to illustrate a step, do so (as discussed in Chapter 9). Incorporate it within your discussion of that step, as shown in this illustration of the procedure for raising the roof section of an umbrella tent:

> Lift the ridge pole by hand until the pin of the support post can be inserted into the hole that is two inches behind the cap of the ridge pole (Figure 5). Push the ridge pole up until the support post is perpendicular to the ground.

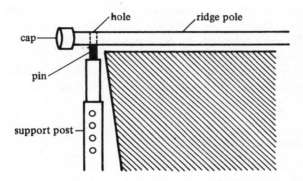

FIGURE 5   A Lateral View of the Support-Post Insertion into the Ridge Pole

Warnings, Cautions, and Notes

The only items that properly interrupt the order of steps are warnings, cautions, and notes that provide crucial information about a particular step. Refer to these in your introduction, advising your reader of their locations within the text. Place the warnings and cautions themselves, *clearly marked,* immediately before the respective steps.

> *Caution:* No one over thirty should be jogging without a doctor's approval. A person of any age who is overweight or who has not recently exercised should also have a physical checkup. Jogging, for most people, is healthful, but for some it can be deadly.

The overuse of warnings and cautions, however, might cause the reader to ignore a particularly crucial warning. Remember the boy who cried "Wolf!"

Appropriate Terms, Phrasing, and Paragraph Structure

Of all technical communication, instructions have the most crucial requirements for clear and unambiguous terminology and phrasing. Here, the words on the page are a guide to *immediate action.* Like most people, your reader probably is impatient and might not read the entire set of instructions before plunging into the first step. Poorly phrased and misleading instructions could have frustrating — or even tragic — consequences. For example, imagine astronauts being given unclear instructions during launching or reentry. Closer to home, the consequences of pilot confusion over garbled landing or take-off instructions are all too clear.

Like descriptions (Chapter 12), instructions name parts, use location and position words, and state exact measurements, weights, and dimensions. In addition, there are four elements of phrasing and paragraph development which require unusually close attention for well-written instructions. They are: (1) maintaining a consistent use of voice and mood — normally the active voice and the imperative mood; (2) using time- and sequence-marking words like *first, next, after drying,* etc.; (3) using parallel phrasing; and (4) using short sentences and paragraphs.

Active Voice and Imperative Mood

The active voice ("He opened the door.") speaks more directly than its passive counterpart ("The door was opened by him."). Likewise, the imperative mood ("Open the door.") lends more authority to your instructions than the indicative mood ("You open the door.").

> *Weak*
>
> The rudder arm should be moved toward the sail to cause the boat to "come about."
>
> The valve that regulates the flow of air is turned all the way to the right.

> *Stronger*
>
> *Move* the rudder arm toward the sail to cause the boat to "come about."
>
> *Turn* the valve that regulates the flow of air all the way to the right.

Use of the imperative makes instructions more definite because the action verb — the crucial word that tells us what the next action will be — comes in the initial position. Instead of burying your verb in the middle of your sentence, begin with an action verb — *raise, connect, wash, insert, open* — to give your reader an immediate signal.

Transitions to Mark Time and Sequence

Transitional words are like bridges between logically related ideas (as discussed in Appendix A). Some transitional words (*in addition, next, meanwhile, finally, on Tuesday morning, in ten minutes, the next day, before, the following afternoon*) are designed to mark time and sequence. They help your reader understand the task as a step-by-step process, as shown in these instructions for preparing the ground before pitching a tent:

PREPARING THE GROUND

Begin by clearing and smoothing the area that will be under the tent. This will prevent damage to the tent floor and eliminate the physical discomfort of sleeping on uneven ground. *First,* remove all large stones, branches, or other debris within a level 10 × 13-foot area. Use your camping shovel to remove half-buried rocks that cannot easily be moved by hand. *Next,* fill in any large holes with soil or leaves. *Finally,* make several light surface passes with the shovel or a large, leafy branch to smooth the area.

Parallel Phrasing

Like any other items in a series, steps in a set of instructions should be expressed in identical grammatical form, that is, in parallel construction (Appendix A). Such parallelism is important in all writing but particularly in instructions, because the repetition of the same grammatical forms can further emphasize the step-by-step organization of the instructions:

Incorrect

The major steps in sprouting an avocado pit are as follows:

1. Peeling the pit.
2. Insert toothpicks to hold the pit in position with the flat end down.
3. The water level should be maintained so that it covers two-thirds of the pit.
4. Keep the pit in a warm, dark place until the roots are developed.

Notice that step (1) is expressed as an "ing" phrase; steps 2 and 4 are expressed as complete sentences in the imperative mood; and step 3 is expressed as a complete sentence in the indicative mood. These should be rewritten so that each step is expressed as an "ing" phrase. (The instructions for performing each step will, of course, be written as imperative sentences.)

Correct

The major steps in sprouting an avocado pit are as follows:

1. Peeling the pit.
2. Inserting toothpicks to hold the pit in position with the flat end down.
3. Maintaining the water level so that it covers two-thirds of the pit.
4. Keeping the pit in a warm, dark place until the roots are developed.

Parallel construction makes the steps more readable and lends continuity to the instructions.

Although any good writer pays attention to transitions and parallelism, the urgent need of instructions to reinforce step-by-step sequences makes a failure to observe these general rules especially damaging.

Short Sentences and Paragraphs

As a rule, each paragraph should explain one major step, and individual sentences within the paragraph should explain individual minor steps. In this way you clearly separate the individual actions. Combining two major steps in a paragraph or two minor steps in a sentence will only confuse your reader. The previous instructions titled "Preparing the Ground" are a good example of effective paragraph and sentence division.

Do not shorten sentences by omitting articles (*a, an, the*) from your sentences. Instead of writing "Cover opening with half-inch plywood sheet," write "Cover the opening with a half-inch plywood sheet." Omitted articles shorten the statement, but they obscure the logic of the message.

Introduction-Body-Conclusion Structure

As in writing any good paragraph or essay, introduce your reader to the procedure, explain the steps for performance, and review your explanation. This structure is discussed and illustrated in detail in the following section.

ORGANIZING AND WRITING A SET OF INSTRUCTIONS

The introduction-body-conclusion structure can be adapted to the writing of any kind of instructions. Here is a general outline:

   I. INTRODUCTION
      A. Definition (or Background) and Purpose of the Procedure
      B. Intended Audience
      C. Knowledge and Skills Needed
      D. Brief Overall Description of the Procedure
      E. Principle of Operation
      F. Materials, Equipment (in order of use), and Special Conditions
      G. Working Definitions (*Note:* Because definitions are vital to effective performance, always place them in your introduction.)
      H. Warnings, Cautions, and Notes
      I. List of Major Steps

  II. INSTRUCTIONS FOR PERFORMANCE
      A. First Major Step
         1. Definition and purpose

2. Materials, equipment, and special conditions needed for this step
3. Substeps (if applicable)
   a.
   b.
   c.
B. Second Major Step
   etc.

III. CONCLUSION
   A. Summary of Major Steps
   B. Interrelation of Steps

This outline is only tentative. Depending on the subject of your instructions, some elements might be modified, deleted, or combined. Revise it as needed for your purpose.

All sections and subsections of this general outline are discussed and illustrated in the following pages.

Introduction

In your introduction section, give your readers the background information (when, where, why) that will prepare them for performing the task. To avoid later interruptions, define the process, identify your intended audience, and state your assumptions about the knowledge and skills needed to follow your instructions. Also, describe the process briefly and the item's principle of operation (especially if these are repair instructions). After giving your readers a solid background, identify any materials, tools, and special conditions needed to carry out the procedure. Next, define any specialized terms and give your readers any needed warnings, cautions, and notes. Finally, list the major steps for performance. At this point your readers are prepared to carry out your instructions.

As an illustration, here is an introduction from a student-written report titled "Instructions for Cleaning the Carriage, Key Faces, and Exterior of a Typewriter." As a study aid, the levels of headings and the transitional sentences are labeled in the margins.

INTRODUCTION								Major Area
										Heading
Definition and Purpose							Major Topic
										Heading
    The cleaning of a typewriter is the process of removing accumulated dirt, such as dust and eraser crumbs, from easily accessible areas so that it can operate at maximum efficiency.

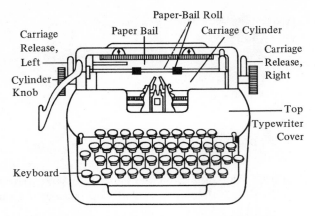

FIGURE 1   A Standard Typewriter in Frontal-Superior View

Intended Audience

These instructions are written for general readers who may be professional typists or even students typing an occasional course paper. Anyone who uses a typewriter will find that a clean typewriter will help produce a professional-looking paper.

Knowledge and Skills Required

The reader should be familiar with the parts and use of a typewriter.

General Description

Figure 1 will serve as a reference for the instructions in the next major section.

Materials

    1. a new, one-inch wide, long-handled paintbrush
    2. a bottle of rubbing alcohol
    3. two clean, soft cloths

Cautions

Pay careful attention to the "caution" notes immediately preceding steps 1, 3, and 6.

List of Major Steps

    1. brushing the dirt from beneath the carriage
    2. brushing the dirt from key faces and surrounding area

3. cleaning the carriage cylinder
4. cleaning the paper-bail rolls
5. cleaning the key faces
6. wiping dirt from the typewriter exterior
7. wiping dirt from the surrounding work area

Body

In your body section, give the actual instructions (*How*) for performance by explaining each step and substep in chronological order. Insert warnings, cautions, and notes as needed. Begin your discussion of each step by stating its definition and purpose. A reader who understands the reasons for the step probably will perform better and certainly will be more interested.

Here is the body section of the typewriter-cleaning instructions:

INSTRUCTIONS FOR PERFORMANCE

Caution: Unplug an electric typewriter before cleaning!

1. Brushing the Dirt from beneath the Carriage

Brush the dirt from beneath the carriage so that it can slide freely. Begin by pressing the right carriage release button (Figure 1) and moving the carriage completely to the right. Use the paintbrush to clear the dirt from the exposed area.

After cleaning the left undercarriage, press the left carriage release and move the carriage completely to the left. Brush the exposed area free of dirt. Finally, move the carriage back to the center position and proceed to Step 2.

2. Brushing the Dirt from Key Faces and Surrounding Area

Brush the key faces and surrounding area so that the key faces will make clean, sharp characters on your page. Use the same paintbrush as in Step 1.

In order to easily clean the keys, remove the top cover of the typewriter (Figure 1). (Some typewriter covers can be completely detached, whereas others can be slid into a position over the keyboard.) Next, brush the key faces and the area surrounding them. When these areas are clean, proceed to Step 3.

Marginal annotations:

Major Area Heading

Major Topic Heading

Transition

Transition

Caution: Do not pour rubbing alcohol directly from the bottle onto the cylinder, as excess alcohol can drip down into the machine.

3. *Cleaning the Carriage Cylinder*

Clean the carriage cylinder to remove any dirt, particularly ink, that may transfer onto your paper. Use a soft, clean cloth dampened with rubbing alcohol.

To expose the cylinder fully, lift the paper-bail roll off the cylinder into a standing position (Figure 1). Next, wipe the cylinder with the alcohol-dampened cloth, using back-and-forth motions while rotating the cylinder with the knobs (Figure 1). Continue this procedure until the cylinder has made one complete revolution. While waiting for the cylinder to dry, proceed to Step 4.

4. *Cleaning the Paper-Bail Rolls*

Because the paper-bail rolls (Figure 1) come in contact with dirt from the cylinder and ink from the typed pages, they must be cleaned.

Using the same alcohol-dampened cloth, clean each roller carefully. After the paper-bail rolls have dried (drying time: thirty seconds), place the paper bail back in its original position resting on the cylinder. You are now ready to proceed to Step 5.

5. *Cleaning the Key Faces*

Clean the key faces to remove any ink so that the imprint they make on paper is clear and well defined.

Using the alcohol dampened cloth, rub the key faces, paying particular attention to the keys that form enclosed areas: a, b, e, g, o, p, and q. After thoroughly cleaning all key faces, allow them to dry. Finally, place the typewriter cover back in its original position and proceed to Step 6.

Caution: Do not use an abrasive cleaner on the exterior of the typewriter.

6. *Wiping Dirt from the Typewriter Exterior*

Clean the typewriter exterior to remove dust and other dirt from its surfaces.

Using a soft, clean cloth, wipe the keyboard, con-

Major Topic Heading

Transition

Transition

Transition

centrating on removing the dirt that has accumulated between the keys. Next, wipe the sides, back,
and top of typewriter until all dirt has been removed.
You can now proceed to the final step.   Transition

7. *Wiping the Dirt from the Surrounding Work Area*   Major Topic
                                                             Heading
   Clean the surrounding work area so that any completed papers you place there will not become soiled.
   Using the same soft cloth ·as in Step 6, wipe the
surface of the desk or table where dust, dirt, and
eraser crumbs have accumulated. With this step
completed, you are ready to use your typewriter.

Conclusion

In your conclusion section, allow your readers to review their performance by
summarizing the major steps and discussing how they interrelate to bring about
the desired result.

CONCLUSION   Major Area
                                                             Heading
Summary of Major Steps   Major Topic
                                                             Heading
   Cleaning the exposed parts of a typewriter is a
simple process. For five minutes, once weekly, the
typewriter parts and surrounding area can be freed
of dirt, dust, and ink by several easy steps: brushing
beneath the carriage, brushing the key faces and
surrounding area, cleaning the carriage cylinder,
paper-bail rolls, and key faces with alcohol, and
wiping the typewriter exterior and surrounding work
area with a soft, clean· cloth.

Interrelation of Steps
   Your time and effort in this procedure will be
well spent: your typewriter will work more efficiently
and help you to produce clean, professional-looking
papers.

Throughout your instructions, use headings generously and appropriately to
serve as landmarks and to divide your presentation into digestible portions.
Add well-labeled graphic aids wherever they can clarify your explanation.
Use transitional sentences to provide logical bridges between sections.

APPLYING THE STEPS

The instructions in Figure 13-2 were written by a student for a general reading audience. The report is patterned after our general outline, shown earlier.

ELEMENTS OF AN EFFECTIVE PROCESS NARRATIVE

In a process narrative you explain how you did something. With a few exceptions, the elements of an effective narrative are almost identical to those of effective instructions.

Clear, Limiting, and Inclusive Title

Make your title promise exactly what your narrative will deliver — no more and no less.

Logical Series of Ordered Steps

Guide your readers through the process so they will understand — step by step — how you completed the task.

Appropriate Level of Technicality

Identify your readers precisely. As an illustration of technicality adapted to a specific audience, assume that you are an engineer who has just found a way of reducing stress on load-carrying girders in new buildings; you will explain this procedure and its results to your colleagues and supervisors. Because this explanation will be written for technically informed or expert readers you can exclude detailed background discussions. In this case, a brief summary of the underlying principles would provide enough of an introduction to your account of the procedure itself.

College lab reports are another kind of process narrative written for the informed or expert reader (your instructor). Here again, as shown in the sample report later in this chapter, introductory explanations are kept to a minimum. However, a brief discussion of the underlying theory is included to demonstrate the writer's own understanding of the procedure. The same account written for the layperson would include theoretical explanations, detailed definitions of specialized terms, equipment, and material, along with several graphic aids to illustrate equipment and special techniques. The less your reader knows, the more you need to explain.

<u>HOW TO REPLACE A WORN FAUCET WASHER</u>

OUTLINE

I.   INTRODUCTION

   A. Purpose of the Procedure

   B. Intended Audience, and Knowledge and Skills Needed

   C. Brief Description and Principle of Operation

   D. Equipment, Material, and Special Conditions

   E. Notes and Cautions

   F. List of Major Steps
      1. Shutting off the water supply
      2. Disassembling the faucet
      3. Replacing the worn washer
      4. Reassembling the faucet
      5. Turning on the water supply

II. INSTRUCTIONS FOR PERFORMANCE

   A. Shutting off the Water Supply
      1. Purpose
      2. Substeps
         a. locating the shut-off valve
         b. turning the valve in a clockwise direction

   B. Disassembling the Faucet
      1. Purpose
      2. Equipment
      3. Substeps
         a. removing the handle
         b. loosening the packing nut and washer
         c. screwing out the stem

FIGURE 13-2   A Set of Instructions

2

    C. Replacing the Worn Washer
      1. Purpose
      2. Equipment and materials
      3. Substeps
        a. removing screw holding the worn washer
        b. fastening the new washer to the stem

    D. Reassembling the Faucet
      1. Purpose
      2. Equipment
      3. Substeps
        a. screwing in the stem
        b. replacing the packing nut and washer
        c. inserting the handle

    E. Turning on the Water Supply
      1. Purpose
      2. Substeps
        a. ensuring that the faucet is closed
        b. turning the valve slowly, using half-turns

III. CONCLUSION

    A. Summary of Major Steps

    B. Interrelation of Steps

FIGURE 13-2 (*Continued*)

3

INTRODUCTION

Purpose of the Procedure

   Faucets like the ones used in most homes become wasteful

and expensive devices when improperly maintained. A leaking

faucet, caused by a worn washer, can lose up to fifteen

gallons of water per day. This loss can result in a higher

water bill, overuse of the septic system and well pump, an

increase in your hot-water bill, and rust or chlorine deposits

in your sink basin.

Intended Audience, and Knowledge and Skills Needed

   This report is a guide to replacing worn or broken

faucet washers for anyone who wishes to save the expense of

hiring a plumber. No special knowledge or skills are

necessary.

Brief Description and Principle of Operation

   The typical faucet consists of a round knob or a

handle (Figure 1) which, when turned, causes the stem to

screw down until the washer sits snugly over the seat. With

the washer in place, the flow of water is stopped. A worn

washer loses the ability to form a tight seal, causing a leak

FIGURE 13-2   (*Continued*)

4

or drip or develop. Replacing the worn washer eliminates
the leak.

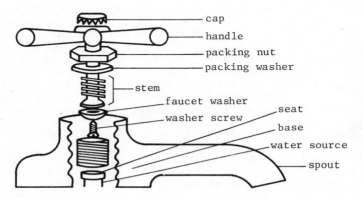

Figure 1. A Typical Faucet in Exploded View

Equipment, Material, and Special Conditions

    1. a pair of pliers

    2. a regular or Phillips (crossed head) screwdriver
       (depending on screw type)

    3. a new washer of the same size and shape as the worn
       washer

    4. a means of shutting off the water supplied to the
       faucet

FIGURE 13-2 (*Continued*)

5

Notes and Cautions

These instructions only apply to faucets that have
washers. Avoid using any excessive force on the threaded
parts, because they are made of soft metal and could easily
strip.

List of Major Steps

The major steps for replacing a worn washer are as
follows: (1) shutting off the supply of water, (2) disassembling the faucet, (3) replacing the worn washer,
(4) reassembling the faucet, and (5) turning on the supply
of water.

INSTRUCTIONS FOR PERFORMANCE

1. Shutting Off the Water Supply

Shut off the supply of water to prevent its escape
when the faucet is taken apart.

First, look under the sink or fixture for the shutoff
valve. If you are unable to find a valve in this location,
use the main shutoff valve located in the basement or beneath
the house. The water pipe (one-half to one inch in diameter)
usually originates from an inside cellar wall. Locate the
shutoff valve by following the pipe from the wall until you

FIGURE 13-2   (*Continued*)

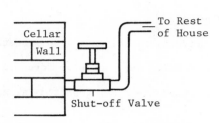

Figure 2. Location of Main Shutoff Valve

come to an attached valve, usually within a few feet of the

wall (Figure 2). Turn this valve as far as possible in a

clockwise direction. With your water supply shut off, you

can take the faucet apart.

2. Disassembling the Faucet

      The faucet is taken apart to expose the worn washer.

Before removing the handle, open the faucet enough to allow

any remaining water in the pipe to escape.

      Using your screwdriver, remove the screw located on top

of the handle. If a cap covers the screw, pry it off with a

screwdriver (Figure 1). Remove the handle.

      Next, loosen the packing nut, using the pliers to turn

the nut in a counter-clockwise direction. The flat circular

nut washer can now be lifted from the base of the faucet.

      With the packing nut and washer removed, screw the

stem out of the base by turning the faucet in the same

FIGURE 13-2   (*Continued*)

7

direction as when opening the faucet. Lift the stem out of
the base and proceed to step 3.

3. Replacing the Worn Washer

Using your screwdriver, remove the screw holding the
washer at the base of the stem (Figure 1). Remove the worn
washer causing the drip and replace it with a new one of the
same size, using the washer screw to hold it in place.
(Washers of various sizes can be purchased at any hardware
store.)

If the screw holding the washer is worn, replace it with
a new screw. When the new washer is fixed in place, proceed
to step 4.

4. Reassembling the Faucet

Reassemble your faucet before turning your water supply
back on. Follow the reverse of the sequence described in
step 2. Caution: Do not overtighten the packing nut!

First, using pliers screw the stem into the base until
it ceases to turn. Next, place the packing washer and nut
over the threads in the collar. Tighten the packing nut
using the strength of one hand. Finally, secure the handle
with your screwdriver. When the faucet is fully assembled,

FIGURE 13-2 (*Continued*)

8

turn the handle to the "off" position and proceed to step 5.

5. Turning on the Water Supply

    Turn on your water supply in order to complete your plumbing procedure. First, check to see that your faucet is fully closed. Next, turn on the water slowly (about one-half turn each time) until the shutoff valve is fully open. These slow turns are necessary to prevent a sudden buildup of pressure, which could damage the pipes.

    Your faucet should now be as good as new.

CONCLUSION

Summary of Major Steps

    To replace a worn faucet washer, follow these simple steps: (1) shut off your water supply, (2) disassemble the faucet, (3) replace the worn washer, (4) reassemble the faucet, and (5) turn on the water supply.

Interrelation of Steps

    The water is shut off to prevent leakage when the faucet is taken apart. Disassembly of the faucet allows access to the worn washer. When the washer is exposed, it can be removed and replaced. The faucet can then be reassembled and the water supply turned on.

FIGURE 13-2 (*Continued*)

Graphic Aids

Whenever you can use a drawing, photograph, or other visual illustration to clarify your narrative, do so.

Appropriate Terms, Phrasing, and Paragraph Structure

Name parts, use location and position words, and state exact weights, measurements, and dimensions. Because you are not giving the reader directions for action, but rather describing what you did, use the indicative instead of the imperative mood. Also, use the passive voice ("The experiment was performed" rather than "I performed the experiment") from time to time. Otherwise you would have to use the first person (I) continually, which seems somewhat egocentric.

Use transitions to mark time and sequence, parallel construction to emphasize the step-by-step organization, and short paragraphs to create breathing spaces between steps.

Introduction-Body-Conclusion Structure

Use an introduction-body-conclusion structure; the body section should describe the procedure in chronological order. The three sections, in order, tell the reader what you did, and why, when, and where you did it; how you did it; and what results you observed or achieved. Often the emphasis in a process narrative is on the results (as shown in the sample lab report in this chapter).

ORGANIZING AND WRITING A PROCESS NARRATIVE

The introduction-body-conclusion structure can be adapted to the writing of any process narrative. Here is how the outline is organized:

    I. INTRODUCTION
        A. Purpose of the Procedure
        B. Intended Audience
        C. Brief Description of the Procedure
        D. Principle of Operation
        E. Materials, Equipment (in order of use), and Special Conditions
        F. List of Major Steps

   II. STEPS IN THE PROCEDURE
        A. First Major Step
            1. Purpose (include a definition when writing for the general reader)

        2. Materials, equipment, and special conditions
        3. Substeps (if applicable)
           a.
           b.
           c.
    B. Second Major Step
      etc.
  III. CONCLUSION
    A. Summary of Major Steps
    B. Description of Results

Depending on your subject and audience, you might wish to modify, delete, or combine some of the elements in the sample outline. Revise it as necessary to suit your purpose.

APPLYING THE STEPS

The process narrative in Figure 13-3 is patterned after our sample outline. Because it was written by a student for her instructor and classmates, the report reflects clear assumptions about the readers' levels of technical understanding (expert and informed). This writer chose to add a subsection titled "Significance of the Experiment" to her conclusion; in it she describes her perception of the lab exercise as a learning experience.

ELEMENTS OF AN EFFECTIVE PROCESS ANALYSIS

In a process analysis you explain how something happens by breaking down the process into its individual steps. The elements of an effective process analysis are similar to those of instructions and the process narrative.

Clear, Limiting, and Inclusive Title

Again, be sure that your title lets your readers know exactly what to expect from your report.

Logical Series of Ordered Steps

Guide your readers, step by step, so that they will understand precisely how the process occurs.

REPORT OF A LABORATORY EXERCISE IN DETERMINING THE PERCENT
COMPOSITION OF ELEMENTS OF A COMPOUND

OUTLINE

I.   INTRODUCTION

     A. Purpose of the Procedure

     B. Intended Audience

     C. Principle of Operation

     D. Brief Description of the Procedure

     E. Materials, Equipment, and Special Conditions

     F. List of Major Steps
        1. Determining the weight of the compound
        2. Heating and reweighing the compound
        3. Calculating the percentages of water and salt in
           the compound

II. STEPS IN THE PROCEDURE

     A. Determining the Weight of the Compound
        1. Purpose
        2. Materials and equipment
        3. Substeps
           a. heating, cooling, and weighing the crucible
           b. weighing barium chloride hydrate and adding
              it to the crucible
           c. weighing the crucible and its contents
           d. calculating the weight of the compound

     B. Heating and Reweighing the Compound
        1. Purpose
        2. Materials and equipment
        3. Substeps

FIGURE 13-3   A Process Narrative

2

        a. heating crucible and compound for 10 minutes
           and cooling
        b. weighing the cooled crucible and compound
        c. reheating for five minutes and cooling
        d. reweighing cooled crucible and compound

    C. Calculating the Percentage of Water and Salt in the
       Compound
       1. Determining the percentage of water
       2. Determining the percentage of barium chloride
          hydrate

III. CONCLUSION

    A. Summary of Major Steps

    B. Significance of the Experiment

    C. Description of Calculations and Results

FIGURE 13-3   (*Continued*)

3

INTRODUCTION

Purpose of the Procedure

On January 28, 1977, Leslie Foye performed a laboratory experiment in determining the percent composition of elements in a compound of barium chloride hydrate. The specific purpose of the procedure was to determine the relative amounts of barium chloride salts ($BaCl_2$) and water ($2H_2O$) in the compound. This report describes that procedure and its results.

Intended Audience

The report is written for readers who have at least a basic knowledge of chemistry principles and procedure.

Principle of Operation

All compounds are homogeneous substances whose chemical compositions are determined by the definite proportions of elements they contain. These elements can be separated through appropriate chemical techniques. In the case of barium chloride hydrate, the water can be separated from the salt through heating and evaporation.

Brief Description of the Procedure

A specific amount of barium chloride hydrate was weighed, heated, and reweighed. The difference in the two

FIGURE 13-3 (*Continued*)

4

weighings equalled the amount of water in the compound.
With these data, the percentage of water (hydrate) and the
percentage of barium chloride salt in the compound were calculated. Complete recording of all data can be found on the
data sheet later in this report.

Materials, Equipment, and Special Conditions

    The following materials and equipment were used:

1. roughly three grams of a barium chloride hydrate
   sample

2. one 1½-inch diameter crucible and cover

3. one bunsen burner

4. an analytical scale

All steps were performed under supervision in a chemistry
laboratory where appropriate safety precautions were taken.

List of Major Steps

    This procedure comprised three major steps: (1) deter-
mining the weight of the compound, (2) heating and reweighing
the compound, and (3) calculating the percentages of salt and
water in the compound.

FIGURE 13-3 (*Continued*)

5

STEPS IN THE PROCEDURE

Determining the Weight of the Compound

The purpose of the first step was to determine the precise weight of the compound.

First, the crucible and its cover were heated over the bunsen burner until red hot to burn off any particles that may have interfered with their mass weight. After being allowed to cool to room temperature the crucible and cover were weighed on the analytical scale: weight of crucible and cover = 18.4128 grams.

Next, a sample of barium chloride hydrate weighing approximately three grams was added to the preweighed crucible. The covered crucible and contents were then weighed on the analytical scale: weight of crucible, cover, and sample = 21.4373 grams.

The weight of the barium chloride hydrate sample was then calculated by subtracting the weight of the crucible and cover from the weight of the crucible with contents covered (as shown on the data sheet): weight of the barium chloride hydrate sample = 3.0245 grams.

Heating and Reweighing the Compound

Heating and reweighing were performed to determine the

FIGURE 13-3   (*Continued*)

6

amount of water in the compound by causing the water to evaporate and calculating the difference in weight.

First, the covered crucible containing the compound was gradually heated over the bunsen burner for ten minutes. After being allowed to cool to room temperature, the covered crucible and contents were weighed on the analytical scale: weight of crucible, cover, and sample after primary heating = 20.9913 grams.

Next, the covered crucible and contents were heated for five minutes, allowed to cool to room temperature, and weighed on the analytical scale: weight of crucible, cover, and sample after secondary heating = 20.9912 grams.
Calculating the Percentages of Water and Salt in the Compound

The weight of the water in the compound was determined before the percentage of water could be calculated. The weight of the water was determined by subtracting the weight of the sample after the second heating from the weight of the sample before heating (as shown on the data sheet): weight of water = 00.4461 grams.

The percentage of water in the sample was calculated by dividing the weight of the water by the weight of the compound before heating and multiplying the quotient by 100

FIGURE 13-3   (*Continued*)

7

(as shown on the data sheet): <u>percentage of water in the</u>
<u>compound = 14.76 percent</u>.

Finally, the percentage of barium chloride salt in the
compound was determined by subtracting the percentage of
water from 100 percent (as shown on the data sheet):
<u>percentage of barium chloride salt = 85.24 percent</u>.

CONCLUSION

Summary of Major Steps

In this experiment, the weight of a sample of barium
chloride hydrate was determined; the sample was then heated
and reweighed twice to ensure that all water had been
evaporated; from these data, the percentages of water and
barium chloride in the compound were calculated.

Significance of the Experiment

The experiment provided practical insights into the
physical chemistry of a compound and its formation, along
with practice in the use of selected laboratory equipment.

Description of Calculations and Results

All data, calculations, and results of this experiment
are listed in the data sheet.

FIGURE 13-3 (*Continued*)

8

Data Sheet for Calculating Percent Composition of
Barium Chloride Hydrate

DATA:

Weight of crucible, cover and sample . . . . . 21.4373 grams

Weight of crucible and cover . . . . 18.4128 grams

Weight of sample before heating . . . . 3.0245 grams

Weight after primary heating . . . . 20.9913 grams

Weight after secondary heating . . . . 20.9912 grams

FINAL CALCULATIONS:

Weight of water (equals loss of weight from heating)

$$
\begin{array}{ll}
\text{weight of crucible, cover, and sample} & 21.4373 \text{ grams} \\
\underline{\text{weight after secondary heating}} & \underline{-\ 20.9912} \\
& 00.4461 \text{ grams of} \\
& \qquad\quad \text{water}
\end{array}
$$

Percentage of water

$$
\frac{\text{weight of water}}{\text{weight of compound before heating}} \times 100 = \text{percentage of water}
$$

$$
\frac{0.04661 \text{ grams}}{3.0245 \text{ grams}} \times 100 = 14.76\% \text{ water}
$$

Percentage of $BaCl_2$

$$
\begin{array}{l}
100.00 \text{ percent} \\
\underline{-\ 14.76} \ (\text{percentage of water}) \\
\ \ 85.24\% \text{ barium chloride}
\end{array}
$$

FIGURE 13-3   (*Continued*)

Appropriate Level of Technicality

Adjust your level of technicality to your specific audience. You can expect your readers to know less than you do but you need to identify their level of technical understanding precisely. As an illustration, assume that you need to write an analysis explaining the process of desalination (conversion of saltwater to freshwater). Consider your audience. Are they potential investors, political figures, or other laypersons with no apparent technical background; new members of your organization who are informed but not expert; technicians who will design the desalination apparatus; company executives who have a broad technical background but who have done no complex technical work for years; colleagues with your level of expertise who are unfamiliar with this process? The specific needs of each class of reader will differ. If you can't identify your readers or if your audience is diverse, write at the lowest level of technicality; give full background explanations, define all specialized terms, and translate technical data into plain English.

The sample analysis of color television transmission later in this chapter, intended for a general reading audience, is written at the lowest level of technicality. The same explanation for readers with a working knowledge of electronics would include schematic diagrams, symbols, wave theory, and complex equations.

Graphic Aids

Clarify your explanation with well-placed visuals whenever you can.

Appropriate Terms, Phrasing, and Paragraph Structure

Name parts, use location and position words, and state exact weights, measurements, and dimensions. Use the indicative mood throughout and the passive voice selectively.

Use transition words to mark time and sequence, parallel construction for emphasizing the step-by-step process, and short paragraphs to create breaks between individual steps.

Introduction-Body-Conclusion Structure

Use an introduction-body-conclusion structure with the body following the chronological order of the process. The introduction tells the reader what it is and why, when, and where it happens. The body tells how it happens by analyzing each step in sequence. The conclusion summarizes the steps and briefly describes one complete cycle of the process.

ORGANIZING AND WRITING A PROCESS ANALYSIS

The introduction-body-conclusion structure can be adapted to the writing of any process analysis. Here is a general outline:

    I. INTRODUCTION
        A. Definition, Background, and Purpose of the Process
        B. Intended Audience
        C. Knowledge Needed to Understand the Process as Described
        D. Brief Description of the Process
        E. Principle of Operation
        F. Special Conditions Needed for the Process to Occur
        G. Definitions of Special Terms
        H. List of Major Steps

    II. STEPS IN THE PROCESS
        A. First Major Step
          1. Definition and purpose
          2. Special conditions (needed for the specific step)
          3. Substeps (if applicable)
            a.
            b.
        B. Second Major Step
          etc.

    III. CONCLUSION
        A. Summary of Major Steps
        B. One Complete Process Cycle

Feel free to modify, delete, or combine the elements in this outline to suit the structure of the process you will describe.

APPLYING THE STEPS

The report in Figure 13-4 is patterned after the sample outline. It was written by a student to explain the process of color television transmission and reception to a general reader. Notice how the writer has effectively translated a highly technical subject into terms that any reader should be able to understand. At the same time, he has wisely omitted information that the general reader can be expected to know in advance (e.g., the definition of terms such as "antenna" or a diagram of the exterior of a TV set). In outlining his report, he has chosen to combine several elements from his introduction and to delete others which are not directly relevant to his purposes. Also, he has partitioned the major steps into substeps, and some substeps into sub-substeps.

A PROCESS ANALYSIS: HOW A COLOR-TELEVISION IMAGE IS

TRANSMITTED AND RECEIVED

OUTLINE

I. INTRODUCTION

A. Background

B. Intended Audience, and Knowledge Needed to Understand the Process

C. Brief Description and Principle of Operation

D. List of Major Steps
   1. The role played by the TV station
   2. The role played by the color-TV receiver

II. STEPS IN THE PROCESS

A. The Role Played by the TV Station
   1. Purpose
   2. Substeps
      a. scanning the scene
      b. combining the signals
         i. the color-video signal
         ii. the synchronizing signal
         iii. the color-burst signal
      c. transmitting the composite signal

B. The Role Played by the Color-TV Receiver
   1. Purpose
   2. Substeps
      a. dividing the signal
         i. picture and sound components
         ii. color burst signal
         iii. synchronizing signals

FIGURE 13-4   A Process Analysis

2

　　　　　　b. providing the voltage
　　　　　　c. generating the picture
　　　　　　　　i. color guns
　　　　　　　　ii. color dots

III.　CONCLUSION

　　A. Summary of Major Steps

　　B. One Complete Process Cycle

FIGURE 13-4　(*Continued*)

3

INTRODUCTION

Background

    Anyone who watches TV is familiar with the images
(accompanied by sound) that are generated on the screen.
Whether its source is a tape, film, or live event, the
image is transmitted by a sophisticated electronic process.
This report seeks to explain that process.

Intended Audience, and Knowledge Needed to Understand the
Process

    It should be of interest to the average TV set owner to
have a general understanding of how the set presents colorful
pictures with appropriate sound in a seemingly effortless
manner. Because the average TV owner is not an engineer or
a technician, the following explanation will be written at
the lowest level of technicality. Therefore, the reader
need possess no prior technical knowledge to understand the
process as described.

Brief Description, and Principle of Operation

    The color TV camera, located at the studio or source,
takes a continual picture of a scene. Instead of recording
the scene on film, the camera converts the image (and sound)

FIGURE 13-4 (*Continued*)

4

into a radio-type signal, which is then sent out into space.
The TV receiver then picks up this signal out of the atmosphere (through a TV antenna) and reconverts it for display
as pictures and sound. What the viewer sees on the screen
is an instantaneous representation of the scene that is
before the TV camera at that moment.

List of Major Steps

The major steps discussed in this process explanation
are (1) the role played by the TV station, and (2) the role
played by the color TV receiver.

STEPS IN THE PROCESS

The Role Played by the TV Station

The purpose of the TV station is to capture the visual
image of a scene, to convert the image into electrical energy,
to coordinate the signals needed for transmitting the image
intact, and to transmit the composite signal to receiving
antennae in the area. Figure 1 diagrams this process.

The camera shown in Figure 1 picks up the light reflected
off the objects in the scene and transforms it into electrical
energy. Specifically, the image is captured by the camera

FIGURE 13-4 (*Continued*)

5

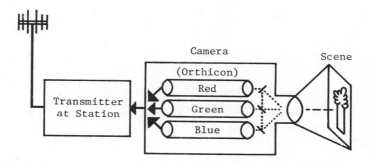

Figure 1.   A Block Diagram of the Role Played
              by the TV Station

through a scanning process whereby a beam of light moves

over the surface of the scene to reproduce an image. This

image is then sent to the image orthicon tubes which divide

the image into 525 horizontal lines, positioned one under

the other. Each bright and dark area of individual lines is

converted by the image orthicon tubes into small signal

voltages.

As shown in Figure 1, each of the image orthicon tubes

is sensitive to red, green, or blue, respectively. Thus,

three signals are generated: a red signal, a green signal,

and a blue signal. Because few scenes are simply red, green,

and blue the signals vary in intensity: for example, weak

FIGURE 13-4 (*Continued*)

6

blue, strong green, and moderate red. As when paints are mixed, depending on the <u>amounts</u> of each color, a new color is produced. Thus, each small signal is of the correct strength to later combine and yield the appropriate color.

These signal voltages are now joined to the sound (if any) and assembled into a signal group called the color video signal. In order for the combined signal to arrive at the receiver simultaneously, the TV camera at the studio and the TV receiver at home must be synchronized. For this purpose, the camera sends out synchronizing signals along with the color video signal. Thus, as each of the 525 horizontal lines mentioned earlier is being scanned, the TV set is showing the identical line at the same moment. Finally, the camera sends out a color-burst signal along with the other signals in order to tell your TV set that a program is in color.

When the composite signal is fully assembled it is sent to the TV transmitter. Here it is mixed with a very powerful voltage and hurled into space in the form of electrical energy.

FIGURE 13-4   (*Continued*)

7

The Role Played by the Color TV Receiver

The purpose of the color TV receiver is to perform
essentially the same steps performed by the TV camera in
reverse order. Figure 2 diagrams this process.

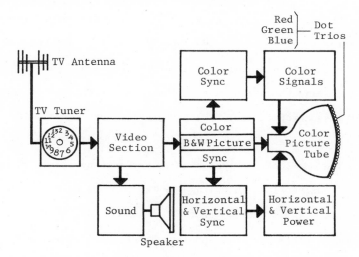

Figure 2. A Block Diagram of the Role Played
by the Color-TV Receiver

The TV tuner (controlled by the knob you turn to select
a station) takes the composite signal from the antenna and
sends it to the video section, where it is separated from
its sound components. In turn, the color-burst signal
instructs the TV set to activate its color section and to
add the color information to the black-and-white picture.

FIGURE 13-4 (*Continued*)

8

Without the color-burst signal the picture would appear in black and white.[1]

Simultaneously, the color-synchronizing signals and the horizontal and vertical synchronizing signals synchronize the set with the studio camera. If the studio camera is scanning a red scene, the set should display a red scene. If the camera is scanning line 357 (of the 525 lines) the set will display the 357th line at that instant because of horizontal synchronization. The picture is kept from rolling through vertical synchronization.

The one function that the set performs by itself is to provide extremely high voltage to the picture tube. It requires high-intensity power to present clear, bright pictures. This power is supplied by the section marked "Horizontal and Vertical Power" in Figure 2.

The video, color-burst, and synchronizing signals are channeled to the picture tube along with the power supply in

[1] As shown in Figure 2, there are actually two signals going to the picture tube: a color signal and a black-and-white signal. If the viewer turns the color-control knob completely counter-clockwise (assuming the set is not automatic-color controlled), he or she will see only a black-and-white picture.

FIGURE 13-4 (*Continued*)

9

order to generate the actual picture. Just as the color
camera has three image orthicons, the picture tube has
three sections called <u>guns,</u> one gun for each basic color --
red, green, and blue. The three color signals, in their
respective strengths, are applied to each respective gun.

The face of the picture tube is printed with colored
dots (or lines). Each gun will hit the dots that correspond
to its own color signal: the red gun will hit the red dots,
the green gun will hit the green dots, etc. The dots are
printed on the face of the tube in trios (a red dot, a blue
dot, and a green dot). Each gun hits the appropriate dot in
each trio with a high-intensity electron beam. The degree
of intensity is controlled by the strength of the signal
emitted from the image-orthicon tubes in the camera. This
varying intensity results in the correct color mixture for
the scene being scanned and, in turn, being projected as an
image on the TV screen. In short, the light energy that was
converted into electrical energy by the image orthicon tubes
is now converted back to its original form by the picture
tube to produce the actual image on the screen.

FIGURE 13-4   (*Continued*)

10

CONCLUSION

Summary of Major Steps

The color TV station captures the image, converts it into an electrical signal, combines it with other signals, and transmits it to the TV receiver. The receiver, in turn, performs the reverse order of these steps to produce the actual image on the screen.

One Complete Process Cycle

In a full cycle this process occurs as follows:

1. The station's function

   a. The studio camera scans the scene to produce a light reflection of the image.

   b. The camera then converts this light energy into color video signals and adds synchronizing and color-burst signals to form the composite-video signal.

   c. This composite-video signal is impressed on a high-voltage carrier and hurtled into space by the transmitter.

2. The receiver's function

   a. The TV antenna picks up the composite signal.

   b. The receiver properly disassembles the signal into

FIGURE 13-4 (*Continued*)

11

picture (video signal) and sound components, color-

burst signal, and synchronizing signals.

c. Assisted by high-voltage input, the picture tube con-

verts the electrical signal back to its original form

as light energy in order to display the appropriately

colored image on the screen.

FIGURE 13-4   (*Continued*)

CHAPTER SUMMARY

Because everything that happens is a series of actions or changes creating a result, you may often have to explain a specific process to someone who knows less about it than you do. Depending on your intention, you will tell the reader how to do something (instructions), how you did something (narrative), or how something happens (analysis).

When writing instructions, begin with a clear, inclusive, and limiting title that promises exactly what you will deliver. Explain each step of the procedure, in order of its performance, at a level of technicality appropriate to your audience. Use graphic aids generously and clearly indicate all warnings, cautions, and notes. Write in the active voice and imperative mood, using enough transitions to mark time and sequence, and parallel phrasing to emphasize the step-by-step explanation. Explain each major step in a single paragraph and each minor step in a single sentence so that your instructions will be easy to follow.

Follow these steps in planning and organizing your instructions:

1. In your introduction, prepare your reader for the task. First, define the process, explain its purpose, and specify your audience — stating your assumptions about the knowledge and skills your reader will need to understand your instructions. Next, describe the process briefly and mention all needed materials, equipment, and special conditions, along with the location of upcoming warnings, cautions, and notes. Finally, list the major steps to be explained in your body.

2. In your body, explain the instructions for completing the task, describing each major step and substep in chronological order. State the definition and purpose of each step, and insert warnings, cautions, and notes as needed.

3. In your conclusion, summarize the major steps in your body and explain how the steps interrelate in completing the task.

In writing a process narrative follow the same general guidelines used for effective instructions, with a few exceptions. Write in the indicative instead of the imperative mood and use the passive voice occasionally to avoid sounding egocentric. Follow an introduction-body-conclusion structure, but emphasize the results you observed or achieved.

Follow these steps in planning and organizing your narrative:

1. In your introduction, tell your reader what you did and when, where, and why you did it.

2. In your body, explain how you did it — step by step.

3. In your conclusion, summarize what you did, and describe your results.

In writing a process analysis, follow the same guidelines used for the process narrative. Write in the indicative mood and use the passive voice selectively. Again, follow an introduction-body-conclusion structure.

1. In your introduction, tell your reader what it is, and why, when, and where it happens.

2. In your body, explain how it happens — step by step.

3. In your conclusion, summarize the steps and briefly describe one complete process cycle.

Feel free to modify or delete subsections in this three-section structure to suit your purpose.

REVISION CHECKLIST

Use this list to check the quality of your work.

1. Is your process explanation keyed to your stated intention (instructions, narrative, analysis)?

2. Does your report have a clear, inclusive, and limiting title that promises precisely what you have delivered?

3. Have you given your readers enough background so that they will understand and be interested in the process?

4. Does your explanation follow the chronological order of the steps in the process?

5. Have you defined each step before explaining it (unless you are writing a narrative for an informed or expert reader)?

6. Have you written your explanation at a level of technicality your reader will understand?

7. Have you included and integrated graphic aids whenever they can clarify your explanation?

8. For instructions, have you used the imperative mood and active voice?

9. For a process narrative, have you used the indicative mood throughout and the passive voice selectively?

10. For a process analysis, have you used the indicative mood throughout and the passive voice selectively?

11. Have you used enough transitions as time and sequence markers?

12. Have you expressed the steps in parallel grammatical form?

13. Have you used a single paragraph for each major step and a single sentence for each minor step?

14. Does your report follow a fully developed introduction-body-conclusion structure?

15. Does your report follow your outline faithfully?

16. For a process narrative, does your conclusion emphasize results?

17. Are your headings appropriate and adequate?

18. Is your report written in correct English (spelling, mechanics, and usage — as discussed in Appendix A)?

Now list those elements of your process explanation that need improvement.

EXERCISES

1. Use the revision checklist to assess the effectiveness of the sample reports in this chapter. Compare your evaluation with those of your classmates in a classroom-workshop session.

2. In a three-paragraph essay, discuss the similarities and differences among the three types of process description. Give examples of each and pay particular attention to intended audience and varying levels of technicality.

3. In a short essay, discuss the type of process description that you will have to write as part of your job responsibilities. As specifically as you can, identify typical subjects, your expected audience, and its level of technical understanding.

4. Identify a situation from your own experience in which you received faulty, incomplete, or unclear instructions, either written or spoken. Describe the situation, the specific deficiency, and its consequences in two or three paragraphs.

5. In your textbooks or in library sources, locate a one- or two-page process explanation written for the general reader (or a beginning student). Using the revision checklist, evaluate the effectiveness of its organization and the appropriateness of its level of technicality in a short essay. Include any suggestions you might have for improving its effectiveness. Submit your essay and a copy of the process explanation to your instructor.

6. *In class:* Select a simple but specialized process from your major field that you understand well (how gum disease develops, how a savings bank makes a profit, how the heart pumps blood, how an earthquake occurs, how steel is made, how various petroleum fuels are made, how electricity is generated, how a corporation is formed, how a verdict is appealed to a higher court, how a bankruptcy claim is filed, etc.). Write a short essay explaining the process. Exchange your essay with a classmate who is majoring in another field. Study your classmate's explanation for fifteen minutes and then write an explanation of that process in your own words, referring back to your classmate's paper as needed. Now, evaluate your classmate's version of your original explanation for accuracy of content. Does it show that your explanation was understood? If not, why not? Discuss your conclusions in a one-paragraph essay and submit all samples to your instructor.

7. *In class:* Draw a map of the route from your classroom to your dorm, apartment, or home — whichever is closest. Be sure to include identifying landmarks. When your map is completed, write a set of instructions for a classmate who will try to duplicate your map from the information given in your written instructions. Be sure that your classmate does not see your map! Exchange your instructions and try to duplicate your classmate's map. Compare your results with the original map. In a one-paragraph essay discuss the conclusions that you have drawn from this exercise.

8. Select a recent event in which you took an active part (a lab experiment, a meeting, etc.). Make a list of all the important details of your participation. Write a process narrative, using one paragraph for each major step of your activities. Include enough details for a general reader to fully understand your role in this event.

9. Make the following instructions more readable by rewriting them in the appropriate voice, mood, phrasing, and sentence or paragraph division. Insert transitions wherever necessary.

WHAT TO DO BEFORE JACKING UP YOUR CAR

Whenever the misfortune of a flat tire occurs, some basic procedures should be followed before the car is jacked up. If possible, your car should be positioned on as firm and level a surface as is available. The engine has to be turned off, the parking brake set, and the automatic transmission shift lever placed in "park," or the manual transmission lever in "reverse." The wheel diagonally opposite the one to be removed should have a piece of wood placed beneath it to prevent the wheel from rolling. The spare wheel, jack bar, jack stand, hook, and lug-wrench should be removed from the luggage compartment.

10. Locate a technical manual in your field or a set of instructions written for a general reader. Evaluate the sample for effectiveness. Are the instructions clear and easy to follow? Are the technical terms defined? Are graphic aids used when necessary, and are they well integrated into the directions? In a paragraph, discuss the positive and negative elements of the instructions, using as criteria the points stated in the revision checklist.

11. Choose a topic from the following list or from your major field or an area of interest. Using the general outline and the student-written outlines in this chapter as models, outline a set of instructions for a process that requires at least three major steps. Write the instructions for a general reader and be sure to include a title page; a clear title; major topic headings; transitional sentences between major topics; cautions, notes, and warnings; and strict chronological organization. Write one draft, modify your outline as needed, and write a second draft. Proofread in accordance with the revision checklist, and exchange your instructions with another class member, preferably in your field, for further suggestions for revision.

achieving a golden tan
making a water pipe
growing tomatoes
filleting a fish
bleaching hair
building a bird house
beginning a food co-op

making a chowder
seeing Europe on $5.00 per day
making beer or wine at home
safely losing ten pounds in four
 weeks
taking a job interview

As an alternate assignment, expand your process explanation from exercise 6 or your process narrative from exercise 8 into a formal report.

14

Analyzing Data and Writing the Formal Report

CHAPTER GOALS

DEFINITION

PURPOSE OF ANALYSIS

TYPICAL ANALYTICAL PROBLEMS
"Will X Work for a Specific Purpose?"
"Is X or Y Better for a Specific Purpose?"
"Why Does X Happen?"
"Is X Practical in a Given Situation?"
Combining Types of Analysis

ELEMENTS OF AN EFFECTIVE
    ANALYSIS
Clearly Identified Problem or Question
A Report with No Bias
Accurate and Adequate Data
Fully Interpreted Data
Conclusions Based on Objective
    Interpretations
Clear and Careful Reasoning
Appropriate Length, Visuals, and
    Supplements

FINDING, EVALUATING, AND
    INTERPRETING DATA
Choose the Most Reliable Sources
Distinguish Hard from Soft Evidence
Avoid Specious Reasoning

PLANNING AND WRITING THE FORMAL
    REPORT
Maintain a Flexible Approach

Work from a Detailed Outline
Introduction
Body
Conclusion
Support the Text with Supplements

APPLYING THE STEPS

CHAPTER SUMMARY

REVISION CHECKLIST

EXERCISES

CHAPTER GOALS

Upon completing this chapter you will know:

- The meaning and purpose of an analysis of data.
- The similarities and differences among major types of analytical problems.
- How to evaluate an analytical report for effectiveness.
- How to select reliable data sources, evaluate evidence, and interpret it.
- How to organize and write the formal analytical report with all supplements.
- How to proofread and revise your report for more effectiveness.

DEFINITION

Analytical reports are question-answering or problem-solving reports. Analysis is basic to practically all our thinking, and in this sense all the assignments we have written have involved analysis. For instance, a summary requires an analysis of the original to reveal its significant points; expanded definition often includes an analysis of the parts of the item being defined; a physical description or a process explanation requires an analysis of the item or process. In each case, we divide the subject into its parts (partition) and group these parts within specific categories according to their similarities (classification).

The analysis of data is somewhat different from these earlier assignments: it is based not only on observation, but also on investigation and research. The subjects of earlier assignments had observable structures. For example, the stethoscope described in Chapter 12 has distinct parts and the typewriter-cleaning instructions explained in Chapter 13 have distinct steps. Your subject was wholly before you, intact, waiting only for you to discuss it clearly.

In an analysis of data, however, your subject is not a familiar item that needs describing or a process that needs explaining. Instead it is a question that needs to be answered or a problem that needs to be solved. The results of your analysis might influence a major decision. For instance, on the job, you might receive an assignment from your supervisor like this one:

> Investigate the feasibility of opening a branch of our company in Falls City and select the best available location.   .

Clearly, to get this job done, you will need to do more than observe your subject until you can describe it clearly. Decisions will depend on your findings. Therefore, you must *seek out* and *interpret* all data that will help you make the best recommendations for action. This is where you will apply the research activity discussed in Chapter 7 to an everyday situation. And it is where you will face your greatest report-writing challenge.

PURPOSE OF ANALYSIS

Most issues contain complex parts that must be unraveled to be understood. As a case in point, many Americans feel that behind several recent political assassinations there is "more than meets the eye." Analysis peels away exterior layers to expose the underlying facts; it is a process of systematic thinking that leads to valid conclusions.

In school you learn various subjects but, more important, you train your mind to think analytically. Most courses are structured to guide you through these practice runs. In English you analyze sentences by separating them into their parts, which in turn belong to specific classes of words: nouns, verbs, adjectives, pronouns, and the like. You then consider how these parts work together to form meaningful statements. In physics you learn how light projected through a prism breaks down into its color and wavelength components. In management courses you identify the personnel components that make up successful businesses and organizations. Each course teaches you to trace things to their source in order to discover and evaluate underlying principles.

After college you will apply analytical skills to problems, proposals, and other work-related questions. For example, a structural engineer analyzes material and design in evaluating the plans for a suspension bridge or a skyscraper. The wise investor analyzes economic trends, treasurers' reports, records of past performance, dividend rates, and market conditions before buying stock in a corporation. An effective legal defense is built on the attorney's analysis and logical reconstruction of facts pertaining to a case. Medical diagnosis relies on the precise identification and classification of symptoms, along with the communication of findings, interpretations, and recommendations for treatment.

On the job, you may be asked to evaluate a new assembly technique on the production line, or to locate and purchase the best machinery at the best price. Sometimes you will need to identify the cause of a monthly drop in sales, the reasons for low employee morale, the causes of an accident or fire, or the reasons for the failure of equipment. As you enter the managerial ranks you might need to evaluate a proposal for company expansion or investment. At all levels of application, the process is basically the same: (1) making a plan, (2) finding the facts, (3) interpreting the findings, and (4) drawing conclusions and making needed recommendations.

TYPICAL ANALYTICAL PROBLEMS

We analyze data to answer a question or to solve a problem. The reader may be an employer, an instructor, or some other concerned person (loan officer, client, etc.). The aim of an analytical report is to show how you have arrived at your conclusions. Your plan of attack will depend on your subject, your intention, and your reader's information needs. Here are some typical kinds of analytical problems:

"Will *X* Work for a Specific Purpose?"

Analysis can be used to answer questions of immediate practical concern. Suppose, for instance, that your employer is concerned about the damaging effects of psychological stress on his personnel. He may ask you to investigate the claim that Transcendental Meditation has therapeutic benefits — with an eye toward instituting a TM program for employees. You would design your analysis to answer this question: "Does TM have therapeutic benefits?" (See the sample report later in this chapter.) The analysis would follow a *questions-answers-conclusions* structure. Because the report might lead to decisions and specific action, you would most likely include recommendations based on your conclusions.

"Is *X* or *Y* Better for a Specific Purpose?"

Sometimes in your analysis you will compare and contrast two or more similar machines, processes, business locations, political candidates, or the like. Assume, for example, that you manage a ski lodge and you need to answer this question: "Which of the two most popular types of ski binding is preferable for our rental skis?" In a comparative analysis of the *Salamon 555* and the *Americana* bindings, you might assess the strengths and weaknesses of each in a point-by-point comparison: toe release, heel release, adjustment capability, friction, weight, and cost. Or you might use an item-by-item comparison, discussing the first whole binding, then the next. (The feasibility report in Figure 14-3 uses an item-by-item comparison.)

The comparative analysis follows a *questions-answers-conclusions* structure and is designed to help the reader make a choice. Examples are readily found in magazines such as *Consumer Report* and *Consumer's Digest*.

"Why Does *X* Happen?"

The problem-solving analysis is designed to answer questions like this: "Why do independent television service businesses have a high failure rate?" (See the sample report later in this chapter.) This kind of analysis follows a variation of the questions-answers-conclusions structure: namely, *problem-causes-solution*. Such an analysis has the following steps:

1. Identifying the problem.
2. Examining all possible and probable causes and narrowing them to more definite ones.
3. Proposing one or more solutions to the problem.

An analysis of student disinterest in most campus activities would follow the same structure. The results of a problem-solving analysis can sometimes be condensed and classified in a troubleshooting chart as shown in Figure 14-1.

Another kind of problem-solving analysis is done to predict an effect: "What will happen to me if I drop out of school?" Here, the structure is *proposed action–probable effects–conclusions and recommendations*.

"Is *X* Practical in a Given Situation?"

The feasibility analysis assesses the practicality of a plan or project: "Will the consumer tastes of Hicksville support a gourmet food and wine shop?" In a variation of the question-answers-conclusions structure, this type of analysis uses *reasons for–reasons against*, with both sides supported by statistics and other relevant data. Private business owners often use this type of analysis.

Combining Types of Analysis

You probably have noticed that these four major types of analytical problems overlap considerably. Any one study may in fact require the answer to two or more of these questions. The sample report on pages 482–506 is both a feasibility analysis and a comparative analysis. It is designed to answer these two questions: "Will a boutique pay in town?" and "If so, what location is best for it?"

GENERAL TROUBLESHOOTING CHART

If the amplifier is otherwise operating satisfactorily the more common causes of trouble may generally be attributed to the following:

1. Incorrect connections or loose terminal contacts. Check the speakers, record player, tape deck, antenna and line cord.
2. Improper operation. Before operating any audio component, be sure to read the manufacturer's instructions.
3. Improper location of audio components. The proper positioning of components, such as speakers and turntable, is vital to stereo.
4. Defective audio components.

Following are some other common causes of malfunction and what to do about them.

PROGRAM	SYMPTOM	PROBABLE CAUSE	WHAT TO DO
AM, FM or MPX reception	a. Constant or intermittent noise heard at certain times or in a certain area.	* Discharge or oscillation caused by electrical appliances, such as fluorescent lamps, TV sets, D.C. motors, rectifier and oscillator. * Natural phenomena, such as atmospherics, static, and thunderbolt. * Insufficient antenna input due to reinforced concrete walls or long distance from the station. * Wave interference from other electrical appliances.	* Attach a noise limiter to the electrical appliance that causes the noise, or attach it to the power source of the amplifier. * Install an outdoor antenna and ground the amplifier to raise the signal-to-noise ratio. * Reverse the power cord plug-receptacle connections. * If the noise occurs at a certain frequency, attach a wave trap to the ANT. input. * Place the set away from other electrical appliances.
	b. Needle of the tuning meter does not move sharply.	* Needle movement is not necessarily related to the sensitivity of the amplifier.	* Tune the set for maximum signal strength.
AM reception	a. Noise heard at a particular time of day, in a certain area or over part of the dial.	* Natural phenomenon.	* Install an antenna for maximum antenna efficiency. See "ANTENNA" in the Operating Instructions. * In some cases, the noise can be eliminated by grounding the amplifier or reversing the power cord plug-receptacle connections.

Reprinted by permission from Sansui Electric Company, Ltd.

FIGURE 14-1 A Sample Troubleshooting Chart

Regardless of the question or problem, your analytical report differs from the general research report discussed in Chapter 7. The research report is simply designed to *inform* your readers — not to move them to direct action. Although the analytical report relies on the same data-collecting techniques, it is designed both to *inform* and to *advise* your reader. Thus you are expected to come up with hard answers and sound advice.

ELEMENTS OF AN EFFECTIVE ANALYSIS

Your analytical report will incorporate many of the writing strategies learned in previous assignments, along with the guidelines that follow.

Clearly Identified Problem or Question

If you know exactly what you are looking for, you will produce the best possible report at the least expense of time and energy. For instance, if your car's engine fails to turn over when you switch on your ignition, you would wisely check your battery and electrical system before dismantling the entire engine. The same logic holds true for any report topic.

Earlier in this chapter, an employer posed this question: "Will transcendental meditation help reduce psychological stress among my employees?" The question obviously requires the answers to three other questions: "What are the therapeutic claims of TM? Are they valid? Will TM work in this situation?" How transcendental meditation got established, how widespread it is, who practices it, whether it is taught in schools, and any of the countless other questions that are sometimes asked about transcendental meditation are not directly relevant to the problem at hand (although some questions about background might be useful in the report's introduction). The point is that it is important to define the central questions and to think through any subordinate questions they may imply. Only by doing so can you determine the kind of data or evidence you need.

With the central questions clearly identified, the writer of the report on TM can formulate her statement of purpose:

> This report examines some of the claims about therapeutic benefits expressed by practitioners of Transcendental Meditation and communicates its findings to the general reader.

The writer might have begun instead with this statement:

> This report examines Transcendental Meditation and communicates its findings to the general reader.

But notice how her purpose statement effectively narrows her approach by expressing the *exact basis* of her analysis: not Transcendental Meditation (a huge topic), but the alleged *therapeutic benefits* of TM.

The best way to define your purpose is to condense your approach to a basic question: Does TM have therapeutic benefits? or Why have our sales dropped steadily for the past three months? You can then easily restate the question as a declarative sentence in your purpose statement.

A Report with No Bias

Be sure to interpret all evidence objectively. Stay on track by beginning with an unbiased title. Consider these two title versions:

> 1. The Accuracy of the Talmo Seismograph in Predicting Earth Tremors
> 2. An Analysis of the Accuracy of the Talmo Seismograph in Predicting Earth Tremors

The first version suggests that the report will discuss the Talmo Seismograph as an accurate predicting device. In contrast, the second version precisely signals the reader that the report will provide answers to certain questions about the device's accuracy. Evaluating the quality of an item is far different from arguing that its quality is a foregone conclusion. Throughout your analysis, rely on your evidence; do not force personal viewpoints on your material.

Accurate and Adequate Data

Do not misrepresent your data by excluding vital points found in the original. Assume, for example, that you are asked to select the best brand of chain saw for a tree-cutting company. As you review the reports of various tests, you come across this information:

> The Bomarc chain saw proved the easiest to operate of all six brands tested. However, it also had the fewest safety features of all brands.

If you decide to cite these data, present both points, not simply the first — even though you may personally prefer the Bomarc brand.

Reserve any personal comments or judgments for your conclusion. As space permits, include the full text of any interviews or sample questionnaires in appendixes.

Fully Interpreted Data

When you interpret you explain the meaning of your data. You emphasize certain facts and explain the relationship between them. Interpretation is the heart and substance of the analytical report. For example, you might interpret the chain-saw data this way:

> Our cutting crews often work suspended by harness, forty to sixty feet above the ground. Furthermore, much of their work is done in highly remote areas. This means that safety features should be our first concern in selecting chain saws. Despite its ease of operation, the Bomarc saw is not suitable for our purposes.

By saying "This means ..." you are helping your reader grasp the essential message suggested by your evidence. *Simply listing your findings is not enough.* You are responsible for explaining the meaning of your data. Spell it out.

Conclusions Based on Objective Interpretations

An effective conclusion appeals not to *emotion* ("You will love this device") but to *reason* ("This device will best serve your needs"). When analyzing a controversial subject, be especially careful to remain objective. Assume, for example, that you work in law-enforcement administration and have been asked to study this question: "Is the prisoner furlough system working in our state?" Do justice to this topic by making sure that your data-gathering is complete, that your interpretations are not colored by prior opinion, and that your conclusions and recommendations are based on the facts.

When you do reach conclusions, state them with assurance and authority. Avoid statements that hedge or seem noncommittal ("It would seem that ..." or "It looks as if ..."). Be direct ("The earthquake danger at our proposed plant site is high").

As we discussed in Chapter 7, your reader will be convinced by the quality of your evidence and the reasoning behind your conclusions. Strong emotional statements that have no basis in fact are worthless. If your mind is made up before you begin you can hardly expect to interpret data objectively. Keep an open mind.

Clear and Careful Reasoning

Technical reporting is not simply a mechanical process of collecting and recording information. If it were, machines could be programmed to handle the job. At each step of your analysis you need to make careful judgments about what to record, what to exclude, and where to go next. Even the planning stage requires reason and creativity in selecting the best approach to your subject (problem-solving, feasibility, comparison, etc.). As you evaluate your data (Is this reliable and important?), interpret your evidence (What does it mean?), and make recommendations based on your conclusions (How should the reader act?), you might have to make several adjustments in your original plan. Because you cannot know what you will find until you have searched, your original plan may change in the light of new evidence. Like an architect, you must be flexible enough to revise your plan as conditions dictate.

Appropriate Length, Visuals, and Supplements

Depending on the problem or question, your analysis may range from one or two paragraphs in memo form to dozens of pages in formal report form. Whatever form you use, make your report long and detailed enough to show your reader how you have arrived at your conclusions.

Review Chapter 9 and use visual aids whenever you can. Graphs are especially useful in an analysis of trends (to show the rise or fall in sales, radiation levels, and the like). Tables, charts, photographs, and diagrams work well in comparative analyses.

Unless your analysis is short enough to report in memo form, use a formal report format with all supplements: letter of transmittal, table of contents, table of illustrations, abstract, glossary, appendixes, and list of references. These items are fully discussed in Chapter 8.

FINDING, EVALUATING, AND INTERPRETING DATA

Information sources and search techniques are discussed in Chapter 7. But the search is only part of your task. As you sort out the pieces and rearrange them in logical form, you must evaluate the quality of your evidence as well as interpret its content. As you know, facts or statistics out of context can be interpreted in many ways. As a writer, you are ethically bound to find truthful answers and to communicate your findings without distortion. To do so, choose reliable sources, distinguish hard from soft evidence, and avoid specious reasoning.

Choose the Most Reliable Sources

Whether you gather data through reading, listening, or experiencing, make sure that each source is reputable, objective, and authoritative. Assume, for example, that you are analyzing the question about the alleged benefits of Transcendental Meditation. You could expect claims made in a reputable professional journal, such as the *New England Journal of Medicine*, to have scientific reliability. Also, a reputable magazine written for the technically informed (not necessarily expert) reader, such as *Scientific American*, would be a dependable source of data. On the other hand, you might wisely suspect the claims cited in glamour or movie magazines. Even claims made in monthly "digests," which offer simplistic, reductive, and largely undocumented "wisdom" to mass reading audiences, should be taken lightly.

Make sure that any interview information is obtained from people who have practiced TM for a long time. Anyone who has practiced for only a few weeks could hardly be expected to assess bodily changes reliably. And to the extent that you rely on personal-experience reports, even from those who have practiced TM for a long time, you need a representative sample of people. Even favorable reports from ten successful practitioners would be a small sample unless those reports were supported by formal laboratory and test data. However, with a hundred reports from people ranging from college students to judges and doctors, you might not have "proved" anything, but your evidence would be fairly persuasive.

Your own experience, also, is not a valid base for generalizing. We cannot tell whether our personal experience is in fact representative, regardless of how long we may have practiced meditation. If you have practiced TM with success, interpret your experience within the broader context of your collected sources.

Some social, political, or economic issues (e.g., the prisoner furlough system or causes of inflation) are always controversial. Such issues will never be resolved. That is, we can get verifiable factual data and we can reason fairly persuasively on some subjects. However, no amount of close reasoning by any expert and no supporting statistical analysis will, in the same sense, "prove" anything on a controversial subject. Somebody's thesis that the balance of payments is at the root of the inflation problem cannot be proved. Likewise, one could only *argue* (more or less effectively) that federal funds would or would not alleviate poverty or unemployment. In other words, some cause-and-effect problems are more resistant to certain solution than others, no matter how reliable the resources.

Given these difficulties, you should resist the temptation to report easy but misleading answers. You do better to report no answers at all than incorrect ones. In any case, try not to take any claims for granted. Cross-check your data through all available sources.

Distinguish Hard from Soft Evidence

Hard evidence consists of observable facts. It can stand up under testing because it is fact and is verifiable. Soft evidence consists of opinion. It may collapse under testing unless the opinion is authoritative and unbiased.

Base your conclusions on hard evidence whenever possible. For instance, early in your analysis you might read an article that makes positive claims about the effects of TM; however, the article provides no data from scientific measurements of pulse, blood pressure, or metabolic rates. Although your own experience and opinion might fully agree with the author's, you should not hastily conclude that TM is beneficial to everyone. So far, you have only two opinions — yours and the author's — without any scientific support (e.g., tests of a representative cross-section under controlled conditions). Any conclusions at this point would rest dangerously on soft evidence. Only after a full survey of reliable sources can you decide which conclusions are supported by the bulk of your evidence.

Until evidence proves itself hard, consider it soft. Suppose, for instance, that a local merchant claims that a certain vacant shop is the best business location in town, but does not support that assertion with facts. Before renting the shop you would be wise to cross-check with several other sources and to observe customer traffic in adjoining businesses at first hand. On the other hand, if the previous owner gave you the same judgment, even though he did not support it with fact, you probably could take it very seriously — particularly if you knew that he was honest and that he had vacated the shop because he had purchased a $125,000 retirement home at the age of fifty-five.

A related difficulty in assessing evidence is the confusion of probable, possible, and definite causes in a problem-solving analysis. Sometimes a definite cause can be identified easily (e.g., "The engine's overheating is caused by a faulty radiator cap"). But, most often, a good deal of searching and thought are needed to isolate a specific cause. Suppose, for instance, that you set out to tackle this question: "Why are there no children's day-care facilities on our state college campus?" A private brainstorming session (Appendix B) yields this list of possible causes:

- lack of need among students
- lack of interest among students, faculty, and staff
- high cost of liability insurance
- lack of space and facilities on campus
- lack of trained personnel
- prohibition by state law
- lack of legislative funding for such a project

Assume that you proceed with interviews, questionnaires, and research into state laws, insurance rates, and local availability of qualified personnel. In the course of your inquiry, you rule out some items, but others emerge as probable causes. Specifically, you find a need among students, high campus interest, an abundance of well-qualified people for staffing, and no evidence of state laws prohibiting such a project. Three probable causes remain: lack of funding, high insurance rates, and lack of space. Further inquiry shows that lack of funding and high insurance rates *are* issues. However, these causes can be eliminated by creating other sources of revenue: charging a fee for each child, soliciting donations through fund-raising drives, diverting funds from other campus organizations, and so on. Finally, after careful examination of available campus space and after consultation with school officials, you arrive at one definite cause: lack of adequate space and facilities.[1]

Early in your analysis you might have based your conclusions hastily on soft evidence (e.g., an opinion — buttressed by a newspaper editorial — that the campus was apathetic). Now you can base your conclusions on solid, factual evidence. You have moved from a wide range of possible causes to a narrower range of probable causes, then to a definite cause. Because you have covered your ground well, your report and recommendations speak with credibility and authority.

Sometimes it is difficult to trace a problem to a single cause, but this reasoning process can be tailored to most problem-solving analyses. Although very few except the simplest effects will have one cause, usually one or more principal causes will emerge. By narrowing the field you can focus on the real issues.

Avoid Specious Reasoning

Reasoning that is specious seems correct at first glance, but is not so when scrutinized. Reasoning based on soft evidence is often specious. Sweeping generalities are often the product of specious reasoning. Conclusions that have been speciously derived fail to stand up under testing. Assume, for example, that you are an education consultant. A local community has asked you to analyze the accuracy of IQ testing as a measure of intelligence and as a predictor of students' performance. Reviewing your collected evidence, you find a positive correlation between low IQ scores and low achievers, and vice versa. You then verify your own statistics by examining a solid cross-section of reliable sources. At this point you might feel justified in concluding that IQ tests do measure intelligence and predict performance accurately. However, this conclusion would be specious unless you could show that:

1. Neither parents, teachers, nor the children tested had seen individual test scores and had thus been able to develop biased attitudes.

2. Children testing in all IQ categories had later been exposed to an identical curriculum at an identical pace. In other words, they were not channeled into tracked programs on the basis of their test scores.

Your total data could be validly interpreted only within the context of these two variables (items having different values under different conditions).

---

[1] Of course, one could argue that the lack of adequate space and facilities is somehow related to the problem of funding. And the fact that the college is unable to find funds or space may be related to the fact that student need is not sufficiently acute or interest sufficiently high to exert real pressure. However, lack of space and facilities emerges as the *immediate* cause.

Even hard evidence can be used to support specious reasoning unless it is interpreted precisely, objectively, and within a context that accounts for all variables.

PLANNING AND WRITING THE FORMAL REPORT

Maintain a Flexible Approach

Your analysis will develop its own direction as it proceeds, depending on what you find at each point in your search for facts. Because you will be writing and revising while searching, you will need clear points of reference to remain on track. Pose and answer the following questions at various points in your search and in your writing:

1. What am I looking for?
2. How should I structure my inquiry to obtain this information?
3. How will I best communicate my process of inquiry and my findings?

These are ongoing questions whose answers can constantly change as you work your way through the research and the writing. Initially, question 1 will be answered in your statement of purpose; question 2 will be answered in your tentative or working outline; and question 3 will be answered in your formal topic or sentence outline — the blueprint for your actual report. However, as you search and write you might find these answers changing. Be flexible enough to modify your approach in case the unexpected happens. Here are a few possibilities:

1. Near the end of your research you uncover issues additional to those described in your statement of purpose (e.g., you discover that TM has no effect on certain people). Thus you need to expand your original statement of purpose.
2. You think of new major topics that are not included in your working outline or find that information on one of your original topics is unavailable. As a result, your working outline might need additions, deletions, or shuffling of parts in order for you to stay on track.
3. As you write your first draft, you find that your report does not hang together well. Before writing another draft you need to rearrange the sections in your formal outline.

Your finished report will be the product of many decisions and revisions. Review your approach often to maintain control. Revise and reshuffle as often as needed.

Work from a Detailed Outline

An effective report grows from a good outline. The following model outline can be adapted to most analytical reporting assignments:

I. INTRODUCTION
    A. Definition, Description, and Background of the Question, Issue, Problem, or Item
    B. Purpose of the Report, and Intended Audience
    C. Sources of Information
    D. Limitations of the Study
    E. Working Definitions (here or in a glossary)
    F. Scope of the Inquiry (with topics listed in ascending or descending order of importance)

II. COLLECTED DATA
    A. First Topic for Investigation
        1. Definition
        2. Findings
        3. Evaluation of findings
        4. Interpretation of findings
    B. Second Topic for Investigation
        1. First subtopic
            a. definition
            b. findings
            c. evaluation of findings
            d. interpretation of findings
        2. Second subtopic
           etc.

III. CONCLUSION
    A. Summary of Findings
    B. Comprehensive Interpretation of Findings
    C. Recommendations and Proposals (as needed)

This outline is only tentative. Revise it as you need to.

The three sample papers that follow are built on the framework of this model outline. The first paper, "Survival Problems of Television Service Businesses," is not reproduced in its entirety; however, each major section (introduction, body, and conclusion) is illustrated and preceded by a brief explanatory comment. The second paper, "Analytical Report on the Therapeutic Benefits of Transcendental Meditation," has marginal comments calling attention to the function of various sections of the report. The third paper, "An Analysis to Determine the Feasibility and the Best Location for Opening a Boutique in Pelham, Massachusetts," has been included for further study and discussion.

Each of the three reports responds to a slightly different question or problem. The first tackles the question, "Why does X happen?" The second, "Will X work for a specific purpose?" The third tackles two questions: "Is X practical in a given situation?" and "Is X or Y better for a specific purpose?" At least one of these reports should serve as a model for your own analysis.

Introduction

As for all kinds of reports, the introduction makes clear the subject of the report, describes and defines the question or problem, and explains whatever background is necessary and relevant. Be sure to identify your intended reader and to discuss briefly your sources of data, along with reasons for omitting certain data (e.g., key person not available for interview). List working definitions, unless you have so many that they need to be placed in a glossary. If you do use a glossary and appendixes, refer to them at this point. Finally, define the scope of your report by listing all major topics that you will discuss in the body.

SURVIVAL PROBLEMS OF TELEVISION
SERVICE BUSINESSES

INTRODUCTION

Definition, Description, and Background

A television service business is an enterprise specializing in the repair of selected home entertainment products. The modern household contains TV sets, master antenna systems, and related electronic equipment, which require periodic inspection and service to remain in good repair.

The "TV repairman" (who prefers to be called an electronics technician) has become a household necessity. Like the family plumber, electrician, physician, and lawyer, the electronics technician is considered one of the professionals who keep the American home functioning.

Because of their recent arrival (TV has been in general use for just over twenty-five years) the professional personality of technicians escapes analysis by the public. Service costs that are regarded as excessive cause public distrust. Many feel that the TV service field is lucrative and that the technicians are sometimes less than honest. Technicians are aware of this public image.

Coupled with the public relations problem is the history of a technology that constantly changes. Service technicians are perennially engaged in a struggle against obsolescence. "The state of the art" is the phrase constantly ringing in their ears and diverting attention from the need for sound business management. Poor public relations, efforts to keep up with an ever-changing technology, and poor financial management practices all contribute to the high rate of TV service business failure.

Purpose of Report, and Intended Audience

This analysis has been prompted by the fact that TV service businesses have ranked second only to auto service stations in bankruptcies. The purpose of this report is to give the public a better understanding of this important element of today's service technology. It is also written to direct the attention of technician–shop owners to some of the potentially fatal problems that may plague their businesses.

Sources of Information

The main source of information for this report is a study of a small business with which this writer has had considerable contact for several years. An interview with the present owner is attached to this report in Appendix A. A second interview with another local shop owner is also attached in Appendix B. The Department of Labor Statistics and several trade magazines and journals round out the sources of information. Published material on this subject is understandably scarce.

Limitations of Study

This study is limited by the narrow sampling possibilities within our geographical area. More importantly, it is limited by the reluctance of many small-business owners to "tell it like it is." Owners of TV service shops, specifically, are most hesitant to disclose financial records. The owner of a very large TV and appliance center that does its own servicing refused an interview. Unfortunately, it was the only large facility in our area.

Working Definitions

Television service shop: The conventional TV service shop is essentially a service center for home entertainment products. Items routinely serviced include TV sets, radios, stereo equipment, and antenna systems. Service businesses exist with or without sales. Some businesses refuse to sell equipment because of the added bookkeeping and inventory problems involved.

Service technician: An electronics service technician is a person trained to service home entertainment products. Outside technicians make service calls, and inside technicians do the bench work. According to the Department of Labor, in 1965 there were some 115,000 people engaged in radio and television service. One-third of these were self-employed. Of the remainder, two-thirds worked in TV shops and the others were employed by manufacturers.[1] In 1972, the number of technicians was reported at 140,000 with roughly the same breakdown as in 1965.[2] In 1974, the Department of

Labor listed the number of technicians at 135,000 with the same breakdown.[3] This last figure is striking because it shows a marked decrease in a field considered by the Department of Labor to have a scarcity of personnel. The rapid drop also occurred in a decade when the population and the number of items to be serviced by technicians increased greatly.

Scope

The topics of investigation in this report are, in ascending order of importance, the history of television service businesses, the problem of public relations, the demand for growing technical competence, and the problems of financial management.

Body

The body contains the partition of a complex subject into components that are easier to understand. Here you will discuss all topics and related subtopics, ranked in order of their importance (ascending or descending).

Your purpose is to achieve a rational and useful partition of the subject into its main parts and those, in turn, into their appropriate subparts. Carry your division as far as you can to make sense of the topic. In the sample that follows, the major topic, "The Problems of Financial Management," is divided into two subtopics: "Technician versus Manager" and "Cash Flow." This last subtopic, in turn, is divided into three more precise topics: "Sales," "Collection for Service," and "Credit Arrangements." These divisions and subdivisions keep the writer on track and help the reader follow the inquiry. Be sure that your reader can draw conclusions identical to your own on the basis of the evidence in your body section. The logic of a problem-solving analysis requires that you discuss all possible causes while narrowing your focus to probable and then definite causes. Sift, evaluate, and interpret clues to reach a valid conclusion. The process might be diagrammed like this:

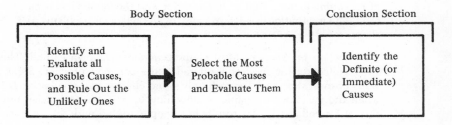

One major topic of the television service report follows. To save space, the other major topics are omitted.

COLLECTED DATA

The Problems of Financial Management

Technician versus Manager

Technician-owners cannot function productively as both full-time technicians and full-time business managers. Without improving their technical proficiency, they cannot keep the quality of their service up to professional standards. On the other hand, they must maintain the detailed financial records that are the backbone of any successful business. Shop owners' usual decision has been to attend evening courses and to leave their workbenches for a part of the day to attend to the management of their business. A shop with several technicians can easily permit this arrangement. However, in a one- or two-man shop these multiple commitments portend disaster.

Some small shops have now secured the services of outside bookkeeping and accounting agencies. Computerized methods have reduced the cost of these services, to the relief of the harried shop owner. However, many shops showing only a marginal yearly profit cannot afford to pay for outside help. Their only recourse is to request assistance from the Small Business Administration, which provides advice, financial analysis, and small loans. But these services are only offered on a limited, first-come, first-served basis.

Cash Flow

The cash flow of a small service business is affected by sales, collection for service, and credit arrangements.

Sales. Some service shops also sell TV sets, stereos, and other home-entertainment products. In many cases this policy has resulted in their downfall. Business failure is due to the owner's lack of financial discipline. Most manufacturers, or their representatives, permit "floor plans." For example, TV sets are consigned to a seller for a small down payment (usually 10 percent of the retail price). It is the seller's responsibility to pay for each item *as it is sold*, or within specified time limits. Many shop owners use this money to finance their operation and it is just a matter of time before the day of reckoning arrives. Full payment is due and the money has been spent. This too-familiar situation has led to many of the financial problems of TV service shops.

Collection for Service. Most shops generate their own capital. Therefore, strict collection for services rendered is the common practice. Signs on the walls of most shops ask for cash only — no charges and no checks. However, when the customer is unable or unwilling to pay, the technician must hold the set for collateral. This results in a shop cluttered with sets that are generating no capital.

Credit Arrangements. Most individual service work is done on a cash-on-delivery basis. Only warranty work (paid for by manufacturers) is done on credit. Manufacturers are dependable and usually pay for warranty work on a monthly schedule. Checks totalling between $500 and $1000 per month are quite welcome and generally cover most of the fixed monthly costs (rent, utilities, etc.) of a small service business.

Evaluation and Interpretation

Some owners use cash that they owe to manufacturers. Others have their shops cluttered with items being held as collateral. However, the overriding problem in financial management stems from inadequate record-keeping. This is where technician-owners were found to be weakest. They simply do not have time to tear themselves away from the bench work to attend to the "paperwork." And without good records they are unable to keep track of and manage their cash flow.

Conclusion

Your conclusion is the culmination of your report. In the body, you divided your subject into its components for investigation. Here you pull together your findings from each part. Your conclusion is likely to be of most interest to your reader because it answers the questions posed in your introduction.

Now you can summarize, interpret, and recommend. Although you have interpreted evidence at each step of your analysis, your conclusion pulls the strands together in a broader interpretation and outlines a plan of action, where appropriate. Because of its all-important function, this final section must be consistent in three ways:

1. Your summary must reflect accurately the body of your report.

2. Your overall interpretation must be consistent with the findings expressed in your summary.

3. Your recommendations must be consistent with the purpose of the report, the evidence presented, and the interpretations expressed.

Your summary and interpretations should lead logically to your recommendations. Here is the conclusion section of the television service report:

CONCLUSION

Summary of Findings

The History of Television Service Businesses

Many of the survival problems in today's service business have to do with early habits and traditions. Virtually all early television technicians were armed services veterans who had been trained as "radio mechanics." They moved into their shops and went right to work with little or no business training. Indeed, their management expertise was confined to a working knowledge of a very active cash register.

Public Relations

Price-gouging practices, which occasionally occurred in the early years have been eliminated by the profession's development of ethical standards. However, suspicions linger, largely because customers have little technical understanding of the electronic repairs needed for their sets. As a result, many customers turn to service departments in larger stores. Among the businesses studied, there seemed to be an embarrassing lack of public relations effort. The reasons given for this deficiency were lack of time and lack of funds for advertising.

The Demand for Technical Competence

The shop owners studied were all technicians of the highest caliber, who continually upgrade their skills. Realistically, a shop cannot endure without maintaining strong professional standards. Customers simply would not return. In shops with several technicians, individuals have begun to specialize. One shop has a TV department, an auto radio and stereo department, and a commercial electronic department that services such items as microwave ovens and motel master systems for signal distribution. All technicians surveyed feel that specialization will improve individual competence and purpose.

Financial Management

Shop owners who insist on doing the bench work themselves and who neglect the daily management of the business are unable to maintain proper financial records or to stabilize their cash flow. With few exceptions, unsound financial management leads to business failure.

Comprehensive Interpretation of Findings

The areas of public relations and financial management pose threats to the welfare of independent TV service businesses.

Public Relations

Official and consumer attitude toward this profession still reflects the "radio mechanic" days of the postwar years. Technicians are still viewed as "TV repairmen" who have easily learned a simple trade and who keep customers uninformed so that they can overcharge them. Consumers' lack of familiarity with the product and servicing techniques is compounded by technicians' unwillingness or inability to better inform their customers.

Financial Management

Unsound financial management is the largest cause of TV service business failures. When the books are not balanced no business can survive for long.

Recommendations

There has been a puzzling lack of initiative on the part of the service technician to erase the "radio mechanic" and "TV repairman" image. This attitude and the owner-technician's hesitancy to become a real "businessman" are the major problems of the independent electronics service industry. Positive action must be taken in both areas.

Collective action by shop owners is the best way to strengthen relations with the consumer public. Local technicians' guilds should design and sponsor advertising to inform the consumer and improve the technician's image. Even though work may continue to be plentiful, technicians owe it to themselves to convince their customers that they are competent, reliable, and trustworthy.

Service shop owners must adopt more efficient practices for operating their business. Early in their business venture they should enroll in one or more business courses at a local college. Helpful courses would include primary management, accounting, and business methods. Properly trained, they will understand such important items as balance sheets and income statements. Furthermore, they will understand their responsibilities in the tax accounting of their business. This professionalism in management will show immediate results. Any problems with financing or cash flow will become immediately obvious, thus enabling shop owners to take effective remedial action.

Support the Text with Supplements

Submit your completed report with these supporting documents, in order:

- title page
- letter of transmittal
- table of contents
- table of illustrations
- abstract
- report text (introduction-body-conclusion)
- glossary (as needed)
- appendixes (as needed)
- footnote page ⎫
- bibliography ⎭ (or alphabetical or numbered list of references)

Each of these supplements is discussed in detail in Chapter 8. Footnotes and other forms of documentation are discussed in Chapter 7.

APPLYING THE STEPS

The two analytical reports in Figures 14-2 and 14-3 were written by students for general reading audiences. Each is patterned after our model outline. The first report is designed to answer a practical question. It includes an outline and marginal commentary. The second is a good example of a combined comparative analysis and feasibility analysis. To illustrate an alternative to the MLA method of documentation, the second report uses a numbered list of references.

ANALYTICAL REPORT ON THE

THERAPEUTIC BENEFITS

OF

TRANSCENDENTAL MEDITATION

Prepared for

Dr. John Lannon
Technical Writing Instructor
Cape Cod Community College
West Barnstable, Massachusetts

by

Bonnie Kelly
Student

December 29, 1977

FIGURE 14-2   An Analytical Report

December 29, 1977

Professor John Lannon
English Department
Cape Cod Community College
West Barnstable,
  Massachusetts 02632

Dear Professor Lannon:

With this letter you will find the analytical   Introduction and
report on Transcendental Meditation which you   statement of
requested in class the week of December 1,   purpose
1977. The report examines some of the claims
for therapeutic benefits expressed by practitioners of Transcendental Meditation and
communicates its conclusions to the general
reader.

After examining much of the medical evidence   Brief outline of
on the subject and interviewing a person who   research and
claims such benefits, I have concluded that   conclusions
there may be some justice to such claims,
especially in the areas of hypertension,
bronchial asthma, and peptic ulcers. My
report includes graphs which clearly
illustrate the results of some important
research on TM. Also, in an appendix you
will find the complete text of the interview
I conducted.

If you have any questions regarding this   Courteous
report, its contents, or its conclusions,   closing
please feel free to discuss them further
with me at any time.

Sincerely,

Bonnie Kelly

FIGURE 14-2 (*Continued*)

3

TABLE OF CONTENTS

Page

LETTER OF TRANSMITTAL   2

TABLE OF FIGURES   4

INFORMATIVE ABSTRACT   5

OUTLINE   6

INTRODUCTION   8
  Definition   8
  Background   8
  Description   9
  Purpose   10
  Data Sources   10
  Working Definitions   10
  Scope   10

COLLECTED DATA   11
  Function of the Mantra   11
  Function of the "Dive"   12
  Physiological Effects of TM   14
    Lowering of blood pressure   15
    Relief from bronchial asthma   15
    Decrease in metabolism   16
  First-Person Testimonials   18
  Continuing Research   19

CONCLUSION   21
  Summary of Findings   21
  Comprehensive Interpretation of
       Findings   21
  Recommendation   22

GLOSSARY   23

APPENDIX   24

BIBLIOGRAPHY   26

FIGURE 14-2   (*Continued*)

4

TABLE OF FIGURES

Page

1. Schematic Representation of a
    TM Dive   13

2. Changes in Oxygen Consumption
    during TM   17

FIGURE 14-2 (*Continued*)

5

INFORMATIVE ABSTRACT

The technique of Transcendental Meditation, as taught by Maharishi Mahesh Yogi, has given rise to therapeutic claims by many of its practitioners. Scientific research on the physiological changes that accompany meditation supports these therapeutic claims, especially in the areas of hypertension, bronchial asthma, and metabolism. Research and interview data suggest that Transcendental Meditation may have important future applications in the medical field. Those claims by meditators that TM lowers blood pressure and helps the meditator to achieve a more relaxed and productive life style should generally be believed. Anyone wishing to relieve his or her physiological stress should consider practicing TM.

FIGURE 14-2 (*Continued*)

6

OUTLINE OF REPORT

I. INTRODUCTION

   A. Definition, Background, and
      Description of TM

   B. Purpose of the Report and Intended
      Audience

   C. Sources of Information

   D. Working Definitions (in glossary)

   E. Major Topics for Investigation
      1. Function of the <u>Mantra</u>
      2. Function of the "Dive"
      3. Physiological effects of TM
      4. First-person testimonials
      5. Continuing research

II. COLLECTED DATA

   A. Function of the <u>Mantra</u>
      1. Definition
      2. Findings
         a. evaluation
         b. interpretation

   B. Function of the "Dive"
      1. Definition
      2. Findings
         a. evaluation
         b. interpretation

   C. Physiological Effects of TM
      1. Reduction of hypertension
      2. Relief from bronchial asthma
      3. Decrease in metabolism rate

FIGURE 14-2 (*Continued*)

7

D. First-Person Testimonials
   1. Findings
   2. Interpretation

E. Continuing Research
   1. Findings
   2. Interpretation

III. CONCLUSION

A. Summary of Findings

B. Comprehensive Interpretation of
   Findings

C. Recommendation

FIGURE 14-2   (*Continued*)

8

INTRODUCTION

Definition

Transcendental Meditation is an act of intense contemplation during which one's consciousness rises above common thoughts or ideas.

Background

The man behind the spread of Transcendental Meditation is a Hindu monk with a long, grey beard and a relaxed, friendly manner, known as the Maharishi Mahesh Yogi; his style is an interesting combination of Eastern spirituality and Western paganism and incorporates a revival of some of the ancient Vedic tradition of India (based on oldest, sacred Hindu writings), which he absorbed from his teacher, Guru Dev.[1] It is generally believed that TM has caught on

[1] "The TM Craze: Four Minutes to Bliss," Time, 13 Oct. 1975, p. 71.

Major area heading
Major topic heading

FIGURE 14-2 (*Continued*)

9

so quickly because the Maharishi has been
able to present Eastern culture in a way that
is compatible with Western life styles and
values.

Description

TM is simple to learn and practical and
convenient to practice; and it seems to work
even if you don't believe that it will. The
individual TM technique is as simple as
getting into a comfortable upright position,
closing the eyes, and relaxing for twenty
minutes each morning and evening. While
relaxing, the meditator repeats an assigned
mantra.[2] The technique is easy, yet meditators universally agree that the benefits
are enormous. The physical benefits, in
particular, have attracted the interest of
the scientific world. Accumulating scientific
evidence of the benefits of meditation seems

[2] See Glossary.

FIGURE 14-2   (*Continued*)

10

to be convincing skeptics in all walks of
life that TM may indeed hold the answer to a
number of physiological and related psychological problems.

Purpose

    This report examines some of the claims   Statement
                                                           of purpose
for therapeutic benefits expressed by prac-
titioners of TM and communicates its findings
to the general reader.

Data Sources

    Information for this report was compiled
from a broad sample of reputable publications
and from a personal interview with a long-
time practitioner of TM.

Working Definitions

    Working definitions are included in the
Glossary.

Scope

    The major topics of inquiry in this
analysis are as follows: function of the
mantra, function of the "dive," physiological
effects of TM.

FIGURE 14-2   (*Continued*)

11

COLLECTED DATA

Major area
heading

Function of the Mantra

Major topic
heading
Definition

The mantra is a sacred formula -- a
collection of syllables that parallels the
individual's specific rhythm of pulse and
respiration, when silently repeated over and
over again (see Glossary). The Maharishi
himself feels that the mantra is vital to the
whole technique of TM. He contends that the
vibrations of the mantra arise just from
thinking the sound, and thereby affect the
nervous system by dissolving stress and
freeing the mind to pursue more "subtle
levels of awareness."[3] One could compare
this effect to the vibratory effect of
rocking the cradle to soothe a baby, or
contrast it to the vibratory shock of modern
music. Resonance frequency, according to

[3] Anthony Campbell, Transcendental Meditation: Seven States of Consciousness
(London: Victor Gollancz, 1973), p. 56.

FIGURE 14-2   (Continued)

12

Dr. B. Glueck, director of a Connecticut

psychiatric hospital, can have a quieting

and stabilizing effect on the nervous system.[4]

Dr. Herbert Benson, one of the leading

researchers of TM, suggests that the mantra

acts to shut off outside distracting sounds

and the individual's related feelings.[5] To

date, scientific evidence seems to support

the Maharishi's theory that the mantra exerts

an important calming effect.

Findings
(with
evaluation
and
interpretation)

Function of the "Dive"

Second major
topic heading
Definition

While relaxing comfortably and thinking

the mantra sound over and over, the meditator

experiences what is called a "dive."[6] It is

as though a swimmer is paddling along on the

surface of a pool and then plunges into the

[4] "Thousands Finding Meditation Eases
Stress," The New York Times, 11 Dec. 1972,
p. 13, cols. 4-5.

[5] Ibid.

[6] See Glossary.

FIGURE 14-2   (*Continued*)

13

deepest part, only to emerge again on the

surface again a few minutes later, refreshed

and relaxed. The drawing in Figure 1 shows

how this concept might be expressed graphically.

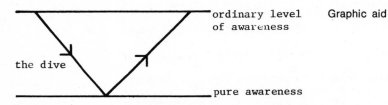

ordinary level   Graphic aid
of awareness

the dive

pure awareness

Figure 1.   Schematic Representation of a TM
            Dive

Source: Anthony Campbell, <u>Transcendental
          Meditation: Seven States of Con-
          sciousness</u> (London: Victor Gollancz,
          1973), p. 56.

    While the mediator is experiencing this

dive -- equivalent, researchers say, to several

hours of deep sleep -- several physiological

changes occur in his body, including lowered

oxygen consumption and lowered blood pressure.[7]

[7] R. K. Wallace and H. Benson, "The Physi-
     ology of Meditation," <u>Scientific American
     Offprint #1242</u>, from <u>Scientific American</u>,
     226, No. 2 (February 1972), p. 7.

FIGURE 14-2   (*Continued*)

14

These biochemical changes, in many cases,

lead to better mental and physical health.

Researchers, most prominently Dr. Herbert

Benson of Harvard and Dr. R. K. Wallace of

UCLA, who have collaborated on a number of

studies, have published many articles in

scholarly, scientific, and medical journals

to document these physiological changes in

meditators. Maharishi International Uni-

versity, recently established in Iowa, has

collected these scientific findings into a

pamphlet of charts and graphs with accom-

panying documentation.[8] This collected evi-

dence strongly suggests that the mantra and

the dive are real events with profound

physiological effects.

Findings
(with
evaluation
and
interpretation)

Physiological Effects of TM

Third major
topic heading

    Although it is not within the scope of

[8] Fundamentals of Progress: Scientific
Research on the Transcendental Meditation
Program (Ames, Iowa: Maharishi Inter-
national University Press, 1975).

FIGURE 14-2   (*Continued*)

15

this report to analyze all medical findings,
interpretations are included which present
the effects of TM on hypertension, asthma,
and body metabolism.

Lowering of Blood Pressure

First
subtopic
heading

The blood pressure of twenty-two hypertensive patients was recorded 1119 times
before and after they learned TM. The
decrease in blood pressure after practicing
TM was statistically significant.[9] These
findings suggest that TM is of clinical value
in helping hypertensive patients control
their blood pressure.

Findings
(with
evaluation
and
interpretation)

Relief from Bronchial Asthma

Second
subtopic
heading

Ninety-four percent of bronchial
asthmatic patients who learned TM showed
improvement as determined by the

Findings

[9] Benson and Wallace, "Decreased Blood
Pressure in Hypertensive Subjects Who
Practiced Meditation," Supplement II to
Circulation, 45 & 46 (October 1972),
p. 10. Reprinted in Fundamentals of
Progress, p. 35.

FIGURE 14-2 (Continued)

16

physiological measurement of airway resistance.

Sixty-one percent showed improvement as

reported by their physicians, and the same

percentage of patients made personal reports

of their own improvement.[10] These findings

indicate that TM has a positive effect on   Interpretation

bronchial asthmatic patients.

    <u>Decrease in Metabolism</u>   Third
                                                             subtopic
                                                             heading

    Research has shown that oxygen consump-

tion and metabolic rate markedly decrease   Findings

during meditation, indicating a state of deep

rest. Furthermore, Benson and Wallace report

that the partial pressure of oxygen and carbon

dioxide in the blood remain essentially

constant during meditation; thus, the decrease

in total oxygen consumption during TM is not

caused by a manipulation in breathing pattern

[10] R. Honsberger and A. F. Wilson, "The
Effects of Transcendental Meditation
upon Bronchial Asthma," <u>Clinical Research</u>,
22, No. 2, 1973, p. 124. Reprinted in
<u>Fundamentals of Progress</u>, p. 36.

FIGURE 14-2 (*Continued*)

17

or a forced deprivation of oxygen.   The

decreased consumption of oxygen is a normal

physiological change caused by a lowered

requirement for oxygen by the cells during

this effortless process.   Figure 2 shows some

of the changes in oxygen consumption that

occur while a person practices TM in com-

parison to undergoing hypnosis or sleeping.

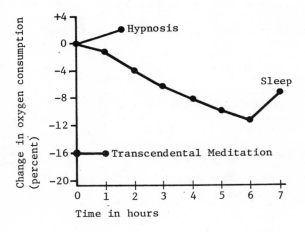

Figure 2.   Changes in Oxygen Consumption
            during TM

Source: R. K. Wallace and H. Benson, "The
          Physiology of Meditation," Scientific
          American, 226, No. 2 (February 1972),
          p. 90.

FIGURE 14-2   (*Continued*)

18

The graph shows that oxygen consumption in-   Interpretation

creases slightly under hypnosis, whereas it

decreases by 8 percent after five hours'

sleep. However, during TM, oxygen consump-

tion is reduced by 16 percent within a few

short moments. Again, this evidence supports

the theory that TM exerts a major relaxing

influence on the mind and body.

First-Person Testimonials   Fourth major
                                                    topic heading

    This writer has spoken personally with

two practitioners who insist that TM is of   Findings

great assistance in controlling their particu-

lar ailments. Jane Smith, age thirty-three,

insists that her controlled diabetic condition

is managed by the practice of TM. Ms. Smith

has practiced TM for three years. Martha

Corey, a middle-aged woman who was seriously

troubled by high blood pressure and circulatory

difficulty thirteen months ago, has lowered

her blood pressure and lost the sense of numb-

ness in her hands and one leg as a result, she

FIGURE 14-2 (*Continued*)

19

claims, of her meditation sessions. I have

personally noticed that this woman is becoming

more alert and seems to have more energy than

she had two years ago. The full text of this

writer's interview with Ms. Corey is contained

in the Appendix of this report, and again

reinforces the positive claims made for TM.

Evaluation
and
interpretation

Continuing Research

Thousands of businesspersons, scientists,

teachers, and homemakers have taken up the

practice of TM, reporting such beneficial

effects as freedom from tension, mental well-

being, heightened energy, and increased

creativity. Doctors and researchers at

leading hospitals are investigating TM as a

treatment for certain diseases and as a means

of therapy for drug addition.[11] Yet, despite

the Benson-Wallace research and that of other

Findings

[11] Gurney Williams III, "Transcendental
Meditation: Can It Fight Drug Abuse?"
Science Digest, 71, No. 2 (February 1972),
pp. 74-79.

FIGURE 14-2 *(Continued)*

20

scientists, no one is quite sure of how TM

works, and many are still skeptical about its

therapeutic claims. It has been demonstrated

that definite physiological changes do take

place during meditation but so far there have

not been any definitive studies on how TM

works on specific emotional problems. To

answer this question, researchers at the

Institute for the Living in Hartford, Connec-

ticut have begun a three-year study of the

specific effects of TM on emotional dis-

turbances.[12] This continuing professional

interest indicates that psychologists have

been sufficiently impressed by the physiologi-   Interpretation

cal findings to make further studies on TM's

influence on the emotions.

[12] Ellen Graham, "Transcendent Trend: Medi-
tation Technique, Once Haven of Young,
Gains Wider Following," The Wall Street
Journal, 31 Aug. 1972, p. 3, cols. 2-3.

FIGURE 14-2 (Continued)

21

CONCLUSION

Major area
heading

Summary of Findings

First major
topic heading

In this report I have analyzed some of the claims for therapeutic benefits of Transcendental Meditation made by its practitioners. Findings indicate scientific support for the theory that the mantra and "dive" have measurable and beneficial effects in three physiological areas: TM lowers blood pressure in hypertensive patients, decreases airway resistance in asthmatic patients, and slows overall metabolism by reducing oxygen consumption. These scientific findings have been further validated by interviews with two TM practitioners, and personal observations. Continuing scientific research suggests that TM may have further application in the treatment of emotional disorders.

Comprehensive Interpretation of Findings

Second major
topic heading

TM is not a panacea for all the problems of life, or a treatment for all mental and

FIGURE 14-2   (*Continued*)

22

physical disturbances. However, it is
apparent from the evidence that TM does produce definite and measurable physical changes
in meditators. The uses to which TM may be
put in the future to combat some of our
modern illnesses are as yet unknown. However,
we do know that the claims of TM practitioners
are being seriously considered by scientists,
and we will watch closely for the results of
their research and the subsequent application
of TM to various human disorders. In general,
TM seems to offer the possibility of a more
relaxed and productive lifestyle for its
practitioners.

Recommendation

Claims made about the therapeutic benefits of Transcendental Meditation are convincing. Anyone wishing to relieve physiological stress should seriously consider
practicing TM.

FIGURE 14-2 (*Continued*)

23

GLOSSARY

Dive: an experience in transcendental medi-
       tation when the attention of the
       meditator "passes from the super-
       ficial to deeper levels of thought and
       then frequently beyond, into the state
       of pure awareness." (Campbell,
       p. 56.)

Mantra: a word or phrase, usually Hindu,
         meaningless to the user, which is
         assigned by the teacher to the medi-
         tator to be used in his meditation
         sessions as a vehicle by which to
         obtain a more subtle level of
         thought. The choice of a specific
         mantra is considered most important
         and is based on the personality of
         the individual meditator. Once
         assigned, the mantra is not to be
         disclosed for fear it will be used
         by individuals for whom it was not
         intended.

FIGURE 14-2 (*Continued*)

24

APPENDIX

Personal interview with M. C. of Radford,
Massachusetts, who has been practicing
Transcendental Meditation for two and one-
half years, with brief intervals of nonmedi-
tation.

Question: Did you begin practicing TM with
the idea of losing weight or for any other
health reason?

Answer: No, I actually started because the
instructor had been a regular house guest
for several months. When he started a TM
group in town, I decided to enroll -- but I
had no specific expectations.

Question: Have you noticed any change in
your health since you have been practicing
TM?

Answer: Yes, my blood pressure has remained
within normal range. For years earlier, it
had been difficult to control and highly

FIGURE 14-2 (*Continued*)

25

unpredictable. Also I now find it much
easier to relax.

Question: Are you aware of any other changes?

Answer: Yes, I feel much more alert and ener-
getic than I had been before becoming a meditator.

Question: Would you say that TM is effective
medical therapy for a person who tends to be
nervous and hypertensive?

Answer: It's as effective as a lot of pills
and shots that doctors are so quick to give
out, and it's much more pleasant.

FIGURE 14-2 (*Continued*)

26

BIBLIOGRAPHY

Campbell, Anthony. "Toward Pinning Down
    Meditation," Hospital Times, 54 (May
    1970), 112-156.

Campbell, Anthony. Transcendental Meditation:
    Seven States of Consciousness. London:
    Victor Gollancz, 1973.

Elkus, W. A. "Prisoners Potentially Rehabili-
    tated by Transcendental Meditation,"
    Harvard Law Record, 58, No. 6 (March 15,
    1974), 46-62.

Fiske, E. B. "Thousands Finding Meditation
    Eases Stress," New York Times (Decem-
    ber 11, 1972), 13:4-5.

Fundamentals of Progress: Scientific
    Research on the Transcendental Medita-
    tion Program. Ames, Iowa: Maharishi
    International University Press, 1975.

Graham, Ellen. "Transcendent Trend: Medita-
    tion Technique, Once Haven of Young,
    Gains Wider Following," Wall Street
    Journal, 31 Aug. 1972, p. 6, cols. 1-2.

Kiel, Paul. "Pillar to Post," California
    Business, 41 (January 4, 1971), 39-42.

Livingstone, Richard. "Business Tries Medi-
    tating," The New Englander, 20, No. 2
    (June 1973), 15-18.

Schultz, Terri. "What Science is Discovering
    About the Beneficial Effects of Medita-
    tion," Today's Health, 15, No. 4 (April
    1972), 20-25.

FIGURE 14-2 (Continued)

27

"The TM Craze: Four Minutes to Bliss,"
        Time, 13 Oct. 1975, pp. 70–71.

Wallace, Robert. "Physiological Effects of
        Transcendental Meditation," Science,
        27 Mar. 1970, 6–10.

Wallace, R. K., and Herbert Benson. "The
        Physiology of Meditation," Scientific
        American, 226, No. 2 (February 1972),
        84–90.

Williams, Gurney. "Transcendental Meditation:
        Can It Fight Drug Abuse?" Science Digest,
        71, No. 2 (February 1972), 74–79.

FIGURE 14-2 (*Continued*)

AN ANALYSIS TO DETERMINE THE FEASIBILITY AND
THE BEST LOCATION FOR OPENING A
BOUTIQUE IN PELHAM, MASSACHUSETTS

Prepared for
Dr. John M. Lannon
Technical Writing Instructor
Cape Cod Community College
West Barnstable, Massachusetts

by
Paula-Jean Sweetman
Student

May 12, 1977

FIGURE 14-3 An Analytical Report

156 Cape Dory Way
East Yarmouth,
   Massachusetts 02453
May 12, 1977

Professor John Lannon
English Department
Cape Cod Community College
West Barnstable, Massachusetts 02668

Dear Professor Lannon:

With this letter you will find my analysis to determine the
feasibility and the best location for opening a boutique in
Pelham, Massachusetts. The report first examines marketing
opportunities in the Cape Cod area and goes on to compare
site possibilities on Main Street, Pelham, with those in the
Pelham Mall.

After reviewing my findings I reached the conclusion that
Main Street in Pelham is a more suitable location for my
boutique than the Pelham Mall. However, there is not
presently a suitable building available on Main Street in
which I could set up shop. I hope some attractive rental
possibilities will emerge shortly.

If you have any questions about my report, its contents, or
my conclusions, please feel free to discuss them further with
me at any time. I can be reached at 324-8740.

                              Sincerely,

                              Paula-Jean Sweetman

FIGURE 14-3   (*Continued*)

3

TABLE OF CONTENTS

LETTER OF TRANSMITTAL 2

INFORMATIVE ABSTRACT 5

INTRODUCTION 6

    Definition, Background, and Description
    of a Typical Boutique 6

    Description of Proposed Boutique 7

    Purpose of Report, and Intended Audience 9

    Data Sources 9

    Limitations of Study 10

    Working Definitions 10

    Scope 10

COLLECTED DATA 11

    Market Opportunities in Pelham, Massachusetts 11

    Site Possibilities at the Pelham Mall 13

    Site Possibilities on Main Street, Pelham 16

CONCLUSION 22

    Summary of Findings 22

    Comprehensive Interpretation of Findings 23

    Recommendations 24

REFERENCES 26

FIGURE 14-3 (*Continued*)

4

TABLE OF ILLUSTRATIONS

Figure 1.   Proposed Free-Flow Layout of
            P. J. Sweetman's Boutique 8

Table 1.   P. J. Sweetman's Potential Target
            Market Population (year-round) 12

FIGURE 14-3   (*Continued*)

5

INFORMATIVE ABSTRACT

The feasibility of P. J. Sweetman's proposal to open a boutique in Pelham, Massachusetts, depends on the adequacy of the target market (women between the ages of twenty-one and forty-five) and the availability of desirable retail space. Cape Hope's present target market is large enough to support the operation of this proposed boutique. The Pelham Mall is not presently the best location for P. J. Sweetman's because of disinterested consumers and high rents. Main Street, Pelham, is a better location because of the boutique and specialty shop customer traffic and lower rents. However, there are presently no suitable sites available on Main Street.

Because the proposed boutique is clearly a feasible venture, more detailed plans for the actual operation should be made. Inquiries with rental agents and periodic newspaper advertisements might soon yield a desirable site within the central business district. If P. J. Sweetman's eventually develops a substantial clientele in its Main Street location, the Pelham Mall should be reevaluated as a possible site for a second shop.

FIGURE 14-3 (*Continued*)

6

INTRODUCTION

Definition, Background, and Description of a Typical Boutique

A boutique is a small, informal specialty shop that specializes in wearing apparel and accessories for women.

The boutique originated in France in the early 1960s. Parisian designers created these shops as places for displaying their ready-to-wear apparel. Drenched in perfume and prestige, the designer-owned boutique is the place to shop for clothing in France. Most boutiques are decorated from ceiling to floor with striking merchandise displays and unusual, exotic artifacts. Shopping here is an experience in itself. An alluring element of these French boutiques is that the clothes are precisely fit to the customer. The boutiques offer one or two free fittings, which is one of the reasons why the prices are so high (1:30).

On the simpler side of the international boutique scene are the Italian shops, which seem to concentrate more on merchandise and less on decor. Their approach to merchandising is simple, practical, and relatively inexpensive. Impact display is confined to the shop windows. Brand-name labels are boldly printed on shop doors and windows to

FIGURE 14-3 (*Continued*)

7

attract attention to the merchandise before the customer
enters the shop. Often the circle display is used. Here,
merchandise complements other merchandise in several distinct circles of clothing, each making a different fashion
statement. Although not as elaborate as the French boutique,
the Italian boutique provides a pleasant, relaxing atmosphere
in which to shop (1:31-32).

The boutique boom hit the United States during the early
1960s. In New York City, specialty shops of every imaginable
shape, size, and style opened. In essence, the American
adaptation of the boutique is a shop that offers highly
specialized, ready-to-wear or made-to-order apparel in
unusual styles. Also offered are exotic artifacts, a wide
variety of accessories, and the widest possible range of
prices (2:27).

Description of Proposed Boutique

P. J. Sweetman's is an informal, one-room boutique that
specializes in clothing for young to middle-aged women.
Figure 1 illustrates a free-flow layout (without parallel
aisles). The ideal shop is 28 feet wide and 32 feet long,
for a total of 896 square feet. Selling space occupies 754
square feet of the shop. This includes the entry way, all
displays, racks, cases, counter, dressing rooms and the

FIGURE 14-3 (*Continued*)

8

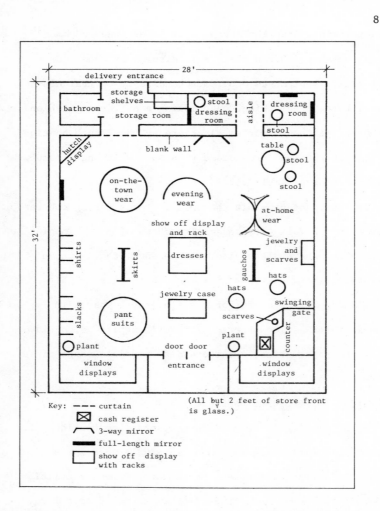

Figure 1.   The Proposed Free-Flow Layout of P. J. Sweetman's

FIGURE 14-3   (*Continued*)

9

customer sitting area. The remaining 142 square feet consists of the employees' bathroom and a small storage room,
both of which are nonselling space. The small storage room
is adequate, because all merchandise will be on the selling
floor. The storage area will be used mainly to store gift
boxes, hangers, bags, etc.

P. J. Sweetman's carries a low volume of high-quality
merchandise, which falls into three categories: career
sportswear, evening wear, and accessories.

Purpose of Report, and Intended Audience

This report has two purposes: (1) to determine the
feasibility of opening a boutique in Pelham, and (2) to
identify the best location for such a shop. The areas considered are Main Street in Pelham and the Pelham Mall, two
miles from downtown. The report is written for the general
reader and should prove helpful to anyone planning to open
a shop in either of these areas.

Data Sources

Data sources for this report include magazines, books,
demographic charts, personal observation, and several interviews and discussions with local businesspeople. I wish to

FIGURE 14-3 (*Continued*)

10

extend special thanks to Mr. Irving Jackson, owner of El

Tarantula; Mr. Edward Talbot, manager of the Pelham Mall;

and Mr. Robert Howard, President of the Downtown Pelham

Association. These gentlemen were all generous with their

time and help.

Limitations of Study

　　　Limitations of this study include a few uncooperative

interviewees and unavailable population and income statistics

for the recent year. Also, firsthand observation was limited

to the winter/spring season.

Working Definitions

1.　Anchor stores: The major department stores which draw

　　　the bulk of mall shoppers because of wide variety and

　　　moderate prices.

2　　Target market: the group of customers, classified

　　　according to age, sex, or income bracket, whom the

　　　retailer wishes to serve.

Scope

　　　This investigation centers around three major topics:

marketing opportunities in Pelham, Massachusetts; site possi-

bilities at the Pelham Mall; and site possibilities on Main

Street in Pelham.

FIGURE 14-3　(*Continued*)

11

COLLECTED DATA

Market Opportunities in Pelham, Massachusetts

Definition

P. J. Sweetman's potential target market consists of the
women between the ages of twenty-one and forty-five who live
in Bailey County year round. Their number would have to
approach 10,000 in order to make this proposed boutique
feasible.

Findings

Recent census figures indicate that an estimated 12,700
women between the ages of twenty-one and forty-five live in
Bailey County year round (3:7). During summer months,
tourism swells this number to over 50,000 (4:206). Table 1
breaks down P. J. Sweetman's year-round target market by area
and town.

Evaluation and Interpretation of Findings

Because these census figures are very recent, they can
be considered a reliable indicator of the distribution by
town and area of P. J. Sweetman's target population. Table 1
indicates that most women between the ages of twenty-one and
forty-five live in the Upper and Mid-Cape areas. Both of

FIGURE 14-3 (*Continued*)

12

TABLE 1.   P. J. SWEETMAN'S POTENTIAL TARGET MARKET POPULATION
           (year-round)

LOCATION	POPULATION
Upper Cape Area	5,225 total
Barnard[a]	2,066
Fitchfield	2,325
Monroe	199
Shoreville	635
Mid-Cape Area	4,814 total
Pelham	2,578
Deary	746
Youngville	1,490
Lower Cape Area 1	1,920 total
Brewsville	207
Colrain	496
Elwood	268
Hashby	594
Orono	355
Lower Cape Area 2	782 total
Princeton	408
Thames	148
Warren	226

[a]Excluding Orange Air Force Base

Source: Cape Hope Planning and Economic Development Com-
          mission, Census Population and Housing, 1976.

FIGURE 14-3   (*Continued*)

13

these areas are within twenty miles (a half-hour's driving
time) of Pelham. Only Lower Cape area 2, with the smallest
target population, is over thirty miles distant. Because
mild winters make the roads on Cape Hope quite navigable,
the bulk of the target population would have quick and easy
access to P. J. Sweetman's on a year-round basis.

Site Possibilities at the Pelham Mall

An analysis of the possibility of locating P. J. Sweetman's in the Pelham Mall is based on two considerations: the
type and number of competing businesses, and the availability
and cost of desirable space.

Competing Businesses

Definition. Competing businesses are those retail
operations already in the Pelham Mall which offer merchandise similar to that offered by P. J. Sweetman's. Direct
competition would be offered by stores specifically designed
as boutiques and catering to the same customer tastes and age
bracket. Indirect competition would be offered by larger
stores with one or two departments offering some styles and
prices roughly similar to P. J. Sweetman's.

Findings. There is one retail operation in the Pelham

FIGURE 14-3   (*Continued*)

14

Mall that would be in direct competition with P. J. Sweetman's. El Tarantula is a small boutique chain that
specializes in extravagant clothing and accessories for
women. El Tarantula began on Main Street in Pelham during
the 1960s. Following the success of this shop, a second
shop was opened in the Pelham Mall. Owned and operated by
Barbara and Irving Jackson, El Tarantula caters to the top
5 percent of the consumer income range. Ms. Jackson does the
buying, window displays, and shop layouts. She goes to
market three times yearly -- twice to Europe and once to New
York. According to Mr. Jackson, $1\frac{1}{2}$ percent of their merchandise is designer merchandise. The remainder, he states, are
just "high quality goods." Aside from an occasional radio
ad, this boutique does very little advertising (5).

There are two retail stores in the Pelham Mall that
would be indirectly competing with P. J. Sweetman's. The
first, Mason's, a federated department store, moved to the
Pelham Mall from Main Street in 1970. Because it is a
department store, Mason's will not be a major competitor.
Mason's career sportswear department may be in competition
because it carries similar merchandise and price lines. The

FIGURE 14-3   (*Continued*)

15

second indirect competitor would be Smith and Turner, a
department store specializing in apparel for young to middle-
aged women. Smith and Turner will not be a major competitor
because it carries such a variety of styles. In a few sportswear lines, however, it may compete indirectly.

Interpretation of Findings. Competition at the Pelham
Mall is not a major concern for P. J. Sweetman's. The only
direct competitor, El Tarantula, prices its merchandise two
to three times higher than P. J. Sweetman's and therefore
caters primarily to a higher-income market. The indirect
competitors are both department stores. Because of their
"department store" images they do not draw the specialty
shop clientele.

Availability and Cost of Desirable Space

Definition. As mentioned earlier, the proposed layout
for P. J. Sweetman's requires roughly 900 square feet of
space. The Pelham Mall provides for one-stop shopping in a
pleasant environment. It is clean, well lit, climate controlled, and tastefully decorated. These positive features
cause retail space to be scarce and expensive.

Findings. There is presently no retail space available

FIGURE 14-3 (*Continued*)

16

in the Pelham Mall. However, within the present calendar
year, construction will be completed on an addition to the
mall. On completion of the new wing, rental space will be
available. The exact size and number of shops has not yet
been determined.

Rental fees at the Pelham Mall now range from $7.00 to
$14.00 per square foot per year depending on the store
location. According to Mr. Talbot, future tenants of the
new wing, however, will most likely be paying $15.00 per
square foot regardless of location. Increased construction
costs and competition for space are cited as the reasons for
this rental increase (6).

Interpretation of Findings. Retail space in the Pelham
Mall should become available within two months before the
proposed opening date of P. J. Sweetman's. However, the
high rental costs would have to be passed along to the consumers in higher merchandise costs. These higher prices could
drastically affect the volume of sales in a new, unestablished
business.

Site Possibilities on Main Street, Pelham

Again, the type and number of competing businesses, and

FIGURE 14-3 (*Continued*)

17

the cost and availability of desirable space govern the
possibility of locating P. J. Sweetman's on Main Street in
Pelham.

Competing Businesses

Definition.   The competing businesses can again be
defined as direct or indirect competitors.

Findings.   There are two ladies' apparel boutiques on
Main Street directly competing with P. J. Sweetman's.   The
first is El Tarantula, located at 352 Main Street.   It is
identical to its sister shop in the Pelham Mall.   The second
is Entropy, a small, ladies' apparel boutique located at 604
Main Street.   Entropy specializes in casual sportswear for
young women.   Its merchandise and prices are similar to P. J.
Sweetman's.   However, Entropy concentrates on the eighteen-
to twenty-five-year-old market instead of the twenty-one to
forty-five market.

Some indirect competition might stem from two larger
stores.   First is Drake's, located at 585 Main Street.
Drake's carries a few lines similar to those that will be
carried by P. J. Sweetman's.   However, this store cannot be
regarded as a major competitor because it caters to an older,

FIGURE 14-3   (*Continued*)

18

higher-income market. The second is Hanley's, located at

326 Main Street. Hanley's carries a few similar lines, but

not enough to be a direct competitor. This store caters

primarily to a lower-income market in a variety of areas

such as little girls' wear, nightwear, etc. (7).

Interpretation of Findings. Competition on Main Street

is not a primary concern for P. J. Sweetman's. The first

direct competitor, El Tarantula, sells high-priced merchan-

dise. The second, Entropy, has merchandise and prices

similar to P. J. Sweetman's but our target markets barely

overlap. The two indirect competitors cater either to

different age groups or to different income markets.

Availability and Cost of Desirable Space

Findings. The following locations are presently avail-

able for leasing on Main Street:

1. At 564 Main Street, on the corner of Main and Brown

    Streets, is a two-family house that has been converted

    into two individual 100-square-foot shop areas. One

    shop is occupied by a delicatessen and the other is

    vacant. Situated in the center of the business district

    where the traffic flow is heaviest, this building has an

FIGURE 14-3 (*Continued*)

19

excellent location. The rental is $250.00 monthly, excluding utilities. However, the site has several disadvantages:

a. The building exterior is in very poor condition.

b. The adjacent delicatessen would not complement P. J. Sweetman's.

c. Because the building is set back twenty feet from the street, foot traffic would automatically be limited.

2. Located at 638 Main Street, in the West End, is an 800-square-foot vacant shop situated between a pizza parlor and a laundromat. The building appears to be relatively new both inside and out. The rental is $175.00 monthly, excluding utilities. However, this location has several disadvantages:

a. The building is approximately thirty feet from the sidewalk, making access inconvenient.

b. The location itself is far west of the central business district.

c. The adjacent businesses do not complement P. J. Sweetman's.

d. The adjacent businesses do not generate much traffic flow.

FIGURE 14-3 (*Continued*)

20

3. Located at 598 Main Street is a large, two-family house that has been converted into two 850-square-foot shops. Both the interior and exterior of the building are in good condition. One of the shops is occupied by a waterbed store and the other is vacant. Both the size and condition of this shop are ideal for P. J. Sweetman's needs. The rent is $200 monthly, excluding utilities. However, because of its location the site has two disadvantages:

   a. The building is far west of the central business area.

   b. The building is set back about twenty feet from the sidewalk.

4. Located at 502 Main Street is the Mini Mall. This is an old department store that has been remodeled inside and sectioned off into numerous small shop areas. The building is in good condition both inside and out. It is clean, well lit, heated, air conditioned, and in the process of being carpeted. Individual shops are rented on a seasonal or yearly basis. The largest shop available is 550 square feet, rented on a yearly basis at $175.00 monthly, including utilities. The business

FIGURE 14-3 (*Continued*)

21

location of this shop is good but there are certain
disadvantages:

a. The vacant shop is not large enough to serve P. J.
    Sweetman's needs.

b. The handmade kit shop next to the vacant shop would
    not complement P. J. Sweetman's.

c. There is already an apparel shop within this
    building, Doomsday Designs, specializing in wrap-
    around skirts.

d. Most of the shops in this building seem designed to
    cater to tourists by offering inexpensive, souvenir-
    type goods.

Interpretation of Findings. The yearly rental for each
of these sites on Main Street is substantially lower than
that for a shop of equivalent size in the Pelham Mall. However, none of these possibilities offers the combination of
good location, easy foot-traffic access, adequate floor
space, and overall desirability needed by P. J. Sweetman's.

FIGURE 14-3   (_Continued_)

22

CONCLUSION

Summary of Findings

Market Opportunities

An estimated 12,700 women between the ages of twenty-
one and forty-five live in Bailey County year round, with
the figure swelling to over 50,000 in the summer. The
majority of the year-round target population lives within
twenty miles of Pelham.

Site Possibilities at the Pelham Mall

The one direct competitor with P. J. Sweetman's in the
Pelham Mall caters to a higher-income market. The two
indirect competitors are department stores that do not
generally draw specialty-shop clientele. With completion of
a new wing, retail space will soon be available at an approximate cost of $15.00 per square foot per year (cost for 900
square feet = $13,500 per year).

Site Possibilities on Main Street, Pelham

The two direct competitors with P. J. Sweetman's on Main
Street either cater to a higher-income market or to a
generally younger age group. The two indirect competitors
are larger stores that cater to different age groups and

FIGURE 14-3   (*Continued*)

23

income markets. Several retail sites are available with
yearly rentals ranging from $2100 (with utilities) to $3600
(without utilities). However, each of these sites has some
disadvantages in regard to location, foot-traffic access,
floor space, or overall desirability.

Comprehensive Interpretation of Findings

Market Opportunities

The present target market in the Cape Hope area is
clearly large enough to support the operation of this proposed
boutique.

Site Possibilities at the Pelham Mall

The Pelham Mall is not presently the best location for
P. J. Sweetman's. Most consumers come to the mall to shop in
the anchor stores, not to browse through the small shops.
In order to afford the high rent, the small shops are forced
to charge higher prices for their merchandise. Thus consumers tend to avoid the boutiques and other specialty shops.
Instead, they shop in the department stores where the prices
are lower and the styles less exotic. P. J. Sweetman's, as a
new, unknown business, would not have an established
clientele for some time. By beginning its operation in the

FIGURE 14-3   (*Continued*)

24

mall, P. J. Sweetman's might never develop a following of established customers.

Site Possibilities on Main Street, Pelham

Main Street, Pelham, is the best location for P. J. Sweetman's. Consumers come to Main Street primarily to browse through the boutiques and specialty shops. Shop rentals on Main Street are not nearly as high as those in the mall. Therefore, the Main Street shops need not charge such high prices for goods comparable to those offered in mall shops. However, although Main Street is the best location for the proposed boutique, there are presently no suitable sites available.

Recommendations

1. Because P. J. Sweetman's has an adequate target market and is clearly a feasible venture, we should proceed from the proposal stage to the planning stage by carefully surveying current fashion trends and by contacting the appropriate designers, importers, and wholesale distributors.

2. We should ask all local rental agents to alert us immediately of sites that become available for rental

FIGURE 14-3   (*Continued*)

25

within the central business district of Main Street.
Periodic advertisements describing our site needs should
also be placed in the local newspaper.

3. If, following the success of P. J. Sweetman's on Main
    Street, we have established a substantial clientele, we
    should reevaluate the mall possibilities and perhaps open
    another shop at the mall. But we must establish a pre-
    dictable customer flow before taking this step.

    Note: Because of space limitations the appendixes con-
    taining the full text of three interviews and illustra-
    tions of various boutique displays, and a map have
    been deleted.

FIGURE 14-3 (*Continued*)

26

REFERENCES

1. Sloane, Carole. "The Little Boutiques of Roma and

     Firenze." <u>Stores</u>, December 1976, pp. 30-32.

2. Carey, Susan. "Boutiques Bustling All Over Town."

     <u>New York Times</u>, 2 Jul. 1966, p. 27, col. 2.

3. Haskel Associates Estimates. <u>U.S. Census of Population</u>,

     Volume PC (1)-B23, 1970.

4. Cape Hope Planning and Economic Development Commission.

     <u>Census of Population--General, Social, and Economic</u>

     <u>Characteristics</u>, 1970.

5. Jackson, Irving F., Owner of El Tarantula Boutique.

     Interview. Pelham, Massachusetts, February 21, 1977.

6. Talbot, Edward, Manager of Pelham Mall. Interview.

     Pelham, Massachusetts, May 4, 1977.

7. Howard, Robert, President of the Downtown Pelham Associa-

     tion. Interview. Pelham, Massachusetts, May 6,

     1977.

FIGURE 14-3   (*Continued*)

CHAPTER SUMMARY

Analytical reports are question-answering or problem-solving reports. An analysis of data requires that you collect evidence from various sources and use this evidence to draw specific conclusions and make specific recommendations. As you plan your report consider which of these questions or combination of questions your analysis is intended to answer:

1. Will X work for a specific purpose?
2. Is X or Y better for a specific purpose?
3. Why does X happen?
4. Is X practical in a given situation?

Condense your approach to a basic question and then restate it as a declarative sentence in your statement of purpose. Sometimes you will work with a combination of these approaches.

After you have identified the problem or question, be sure to interpret all data objectively and fully in order to reach valid conclusions. At each step of your analysis, make careful decisions about what to record, what to exclude, and where to go next. Make the report itself long and detailed enough to show your reader how you have arrived at your conclusions. Use visual aids generously and, except for a memo report, use a formal report format with all supplements.

As you sift through data and write your report, choose the most reliable sources, distinguish hard from soft evidence, and avoid specious reasoning.

Follow these steps in planning and writing your analysis:

1. Pose and answer these questions at various points in your search and in your writing:
   a. What am I looking for?
   b. How should I structure my inquiry to obtain this information?
   c. How will I best communicate my process of inquiry and my findings to my reader?
   Remain flexible enough to modify your approach as you go along.
2. Make a detailed outline and develop your report from it:
   a. In your introduction, make clear the subject of the report, describe and define the problem or question, and explain whatever background is necessary and relevant. Identify your intended reader and discuss briefly sources of data, along with any reasons for omitting certain data. List working definitions or place them in a glossary. If you do use a glossary or appendixes, mention them. Finally, list all major topics to be discussed in your body.
   b. In your body section, divide your subject into major topics and related

subtopics. Carry your division as far as you can to make sense of the topic. At each level of division, define the topic, discuss your related findings, and evaluate and interpret the findings.

c. In your conclusion, summarize the major findings in the body, explain the overall meaning of your findings, and make recommendations based on your overall interpretation.

Revise your outline as needed and submit your final-draft report with all necessary supplements.

REVISION CHECKLIST

Use this list to refine your report.

1. Is the report written at an appropriate level of technicality for its intended audience?

2. Does the report grow from a clear statement of purpose (researching a topic, answering a practical question, examining quality, solving a problem, measuring feasibility)?

3. Is its title unbiased and accurate?

4. Are visual aids used whenever possible?

5. Is the report's length appropriate to its subject (e.g., long enough to show how you arrived at your conclusions)?

6. Are all limitations of the report spelled out?

7. Is each topic defined before it is discussed?

8. Is the analysis based on credible sources of data?

9. Is it based on hard, rather than soft, evidence (no unsupported opinion)?

10. Is it free from specious reasoning?

11. Are all data accurate?

12. Are all data unbiased?

13. Are all data complete?

14. Are all data well documented?

15. Are all data fully interpreted?

16. Are recommendations based directly on objective interpretations of data?

17. Is the report accompanied by all needed supplements (title page, table of contents, etc.)?

18. Are headings appropriate and adequate?

19. Are there enough transitions between related ideas?

20. Is the report written in correct English (spelling, mechanics, and usage as shown in Appendix A)?

Now list those elements of your report that need improvement.

EXERCISES

1. Make a list of five or six college courses you have taken. Explain briefly the kinds of analytical processes you practiced in each course. *Hint:* Course syllabi may provide an outline for each discussion.

2. *Self-help analysis:* Choose a problem in your life (low grades, poor love life, insufficient time for relaxation, feelings of depression, frequent anxiety, etc.). Define the problem clearly in several sentences. In a private brainstorming session (see Appendix B), compile a list of possible causes. After carefully evaluating each possible cause, compile a list of probable causes, thereby narrowing your original list. Now, evaluate each probable cause in an attempt to emerge with one or more definite causes. Summarize your findings; draw conclusions based on your evidence, and formulate specific recommendations for solving the problem.

3. *In class:* Divide into groups of about eight students. Choose a subject for group analysis — preferably, a campus issue — and partition the topic through a group brainstorming session. Next, select major topics from your list and classify as many items as possible under each major topic. Finally, draw up a working outline that could be used for an analytical report on this subject.

4. Prepare a questionnaire based on your work in exercise 3 and administer it to members of your campus community. List the findings of your questionnaire and your conclusions in clear and logical form.

5. Explain, in detail, how analysis forms the basis of each of the technical writing techniques studied in this course.

6. In the periodical section of your library, find examples of reports or articles that use each of the following types of analysis:

   a. Answering a practical question (Will X work for a specific purpose?).

   b. Comparing two or more items (Is X or Y better for a specific purpose?).

   c. Solving a problem (Why does X happen?).

   d. Assessing feasibility (Is X practical in a given situation?).

Provide full bibliographical information, along with a *descriptive* abstract (page 48) of each article.

7. In the periodical and newspaper section of your library, compile a list of sources, by title, ranked in general order of reliability: (a) List five highly reliable sources. (b) List five sources that are less reliable. Briefly explain the reason for each choice by discussing your criteria for judgment.

8. The following statements are followed by false or improbable conclusions. In order to prevent specious generalizations, what specific supporting data or evidence would be needed to justify each conclusion?

   a. Eighty percent of black voters in Alabama voted for George Walrus as governor. Therefore, he is not a racist.

    b. Fifty percent of last year's college graduates did not find desirable jobs. Therefore, college is a waste of time and money.

    c. Only sixty percent of incoming freshmen eventually graduate from this college. Therefore, the college is not doing its job.

    d. He never sees a doctor. Therefore, he is a healthy person.

    e. This house is expensive. Therefore, it must be well built.

9. Writing the Analytical Report

    a. Choose a subject for analysis from the list at the end of this exercise, from your major field, or from an area of personal interest.

    b. Identify the problem or question so that you will know exactly what you are looking for.

    c. Restate the major question as a declarative sentence in your statement of purpose.

    d. Hold a private brainstorming session (Appendix B) to generate major topics and subtopics.

    e. Use the topic to make an outline, based on the model outlines in this chapter. Carry the division of the outline as far as you can to identify all points of attack.

    f. Make a list of all the sources that you will investigate in your analysis.

    g. Write a proposal memo to your instructor (pages 305–309), describing the problem or question and your plans for attacking it. Attach a working bibliography (pages 159–160) to your memo.

    h. Use your working outline as a guide to research and observation. Evaluate your sources and evidence and interpret all evidence fully. Modify your outline as needed.

    i. Submit a progress report to your instructor (pages 310–311), describing work completed, problems encountered, and work remaining.

    j. Write the report for a general reader and include major topic headings and transitional sentences between topics. Work from a clear statement of purpose and be sure that your reasoning process is clearly expressed. Verify that your evidence, conclusions, and recommendations are consistent.

    k. After writing your first draft, make any needed changes in your outline and revise your report according to the revision checklist. Include all necessary supplements.

    l. Exchange reports with another class member for further suggestions for revision.

Here are some possible subjects for your analysis:

- The effects of a vegetarian diet on physiological energy.
- The causes of student disinterest in campus activities.
- The student transportation problem to and from your college.
- Two or more brands of tools or equipment from your field.
- The alcoholism or divorce problem in a specific rural area.
- Noise pollution from nearby airport traffic.
- The effect of the new supersonic jumbo jets on the atmosphere.

- The feasibility of opening a particular business.
- The best location for a new business.
- Causes of the high drop-out rate of students in your college.
- The pros and cons of condominium ownership.
- The feasibility of moving to a certain area of the country.
- Job opportunities in your career field.
- Effects of the 200-mile limit on the fishing industry in your coastal area.
- The effects of budget cuts on public higher education in your state.
- The best nonprescription cold remedy.
- The adequacy of zoning laws in your town.
- Radio and TV interference caused by electrical devices through 115 VAC (60 hz) power lines.
- Effect of population increase on your local water supply.
- Adequacy of your student group health insurance policy.
- The feasibility of using biological pest control as an alternative to pesticides.
- The best method for controlling the gypsy moth.
- The feasibility of large-scale desalination of sea water as a fresh water source.
- Effective water conservation measures that can be employed in your area.
- The effects of legalizing gambling in your state.
- Effective measures for relieving the property-tax burden in your town.
- The causes of low employee morale in the company where you work part-time.
- Effective measures for improving the tourist trade in your area.
- Causes of poor television reception in your area.
- The effects of thermal pollution from a local nuclear power plant on marine life.
- Effective measures for the reclamation of strip mined land.
- The feasibility of using wood as an energy source.
- Two or more brands of wood-burning stove.
- The feasibility of converting your home to solar heating.
- The adequacy of police protection in your town.
- Effective measures for improving the fire safety of your home.
- The best energy-efficient, low-cost housing design for your area.
- Effective measures for improving productivity in your place of employment.
- Reasons for the success of a specific restaurant (or other business) in your area.
- The feasibility of operating a campus food co-op.
- The job outlook for college graduates over the next decade.
- The best investment (real estate, savings certificates, stocks and bonds, precious metals and stones, etc.) over the past ten years.
- The problem of water supply and waste disposal for new subdivisions in your town.

15

Oral Reporting

CHAPTER GOALS

DEFINITION
Advantages
Disadvantages

PURPOSE OF ORAL REPORTS
Informal Reports
Semiformal Reports
Formal Reports

IDENTIFYING THE BEST TYPE OF FORMAL REPORT
The Impromptu Delivery
The Memorized Delivery
The Reading Delivery
The Extemporaneous Delivery

PREPARING THE EXTEMPORANEOUS DELIVERY
Know Your Subject
Identify Your Audience
Plan Your Report
Statement of Purpose
Homework
Introduction-Body-Conclusion
Sentence Outline
Delivery Time
Practice Your Delivery
Feedback
Organization
Tone
Anticipate Audience Questions

DELIVERING THE EXTEMPORANEOUS REPORT
Use Nervous Energy to Advantage
Use Natural Body Movements and Posture
Speak with Confidence, Conviction, and Authority
Moderate Voice Volume, Tone, Pronunciation, and Speed
Maintain Eye Contact
Read Audience Feedback
Be Concise
Summarize Effectively
Leave Time for Questions and Answers

CHAPTER SUMMARY

REVISION CHECKLIST

EXERCISES

CHAPTER GOALS

When you have completed this chapter, you will know:

- The meaning and purpose of oral reporting.
- The differences among informal, semiformal and formal oral reports.
- The differences among the impromptu, memorized, reading, and extemporaneous deliveries.
- How to prepare the extemporaneous delivery.
- How to practice your delivery.
- How to evaluate your plan and practice run for effectiveness.
- How to revise your plan and refine your delivery.
- How to deliver the extemporaneous report.

DEFINITION

An oral report is any spoken factual statement requiring some preparation and forethought. In this broad sense, oral reports can be anything from a brief, informal discussion, to highly prepared formal speeches or lectures. This chapter will discuss the more formal reporting situations, which require planning and preparation.

Like the written report, the oral report must be clear, informative, and technically appropriate for its audience. But the oral report has both advantages and disadvantages compared to its written equivalent.

Advantages

1. Instead of facing a blank and silent page, you have the advantage of audience feedback; real people are listening and responding to your delivery. As you interpret these responses, you can adjust the content, style, and pace of your presentation.

2. Your personality will influence audience interest in your delivery. No longer are you the faceless author of a written report. A pleasing personality usually elicits a warm audience response.

3. Because your spoken delivery is three-dimensional, a good oral report has a stronger effect and is thus more memorable than its written equivalent.

4. An oral report can save time. Instead of individually reading a written version, many people can receive your message simultaneously.

5. In the question-and-answer period after your report, you can clarify any foggy points immediately.

Disadvantages

1. A written report is easier to polish and refine, because you write it in privacy, proofreading and revising at your leisure. In speaking, on the other hand, nervousness could cause you to garble the message.

2. An oral report is extremely limited in the complexity of information it can communicate. In a written report, on the other hand, readers can study complex data as long as they need to.

3. Your readers move through the written report at the pace they need to understand the message, perhaps skimming some parts and studying others. However, in oral reporting, you establish the pace and emphasis, thereby creating the chance of "losing" or boring your listeners.

4. An oral report is also more difficult to review because it is given only once.

To summarize: an oral report is more personal, may be more effective, is an overall time saver, and elicits direct audience response; in contrast, a written report is easier to refine and organize, can be more complex, can be studied at the reader's own pace, and can be easily reviewed.

Keep these distinctions in mind in planning any oral presentation.

PURPOSE OF ORAL REPORTS

In a thousand different ways, everyone communicates facts by speaking. Your own oral reports will vary in style, range, complexity, and formality in various situations.

Informal Reports

At the least formal level, your oral report may consist of a one-to-one discussion with someone else. For example, you might be describing a new hull design to a fellow sailor, outlining the agenda of an upcoming convention to a colleague, or briefly describing your progress on a project to a supervisor. These reporting situations usually occur spontaneously and take only a few minutes.

Semiformal Reports

At a slightly more formal level, you may need to "brief" colleagues or work crews (giving a brief schedule of daily activities and making specific job assignments). Or you may give periodic reports about company policies and prospects to members of your department. In such cases, you will address a group, basing your delivery on rough notes jotted down as reminders.

Formal Reports

Your most formal level of oral reporting may include convention speeches, reports at national sales meetings, reports to officers and other company personnel about a new proposal or project, speeches to civic groups in your community, political speeches, and so on.

These formal talks may be designed to _inform_ (e.g., to describe a new procedure for handling customer complaints), to _persuade_ (e.g., to convince company officers to vote a pay raise for employees), or to do both. In any case, the higher your status, on the job or in your community, the more you will have to give formal talks. To speak well, you will need a clear purpose, a detailed plan, and a well-practiced delivery.

Regardless of its level of formality, each oral report must communicate _information that people will use._

Because a full discussion of each type of report is beyond the scope and intention of this chapter, we will emphasize the formal report, designed to inform and persuade.

IDENTIFYING THE BEST TYPE OF FORMAL REPORT

The techniques used for delivering an oral report greatly determine its effectiveness. Here are the possibilities:

The Impromptu Delivery

The impromptu delivery is also know as the "off-the-cuff" delivery, and is good only for informal reports. It is difficult to be unified, coherent, and informative without an outline, notes, and a rehearsal or two; effective structure rarely emerges out of thin air. Avoid this unstructured approach for formal speaking situations. Don't comfort yourself by saying "It's all in my head." Get your plan down on paper.

The Memorized Delivery

In the memorized delivery, you first write out your report in full, and then memorize every detail. Although this approach is structured, you will probably sound like a parrot. Moreover, if you happen to forget a word, phrase, or line, disaster strikes! Because your personality and body language greatly influence audience interest, you can hardly expect to be an effective, natural speaker while mechanically reciting your lines.

The Reading Delivery

Sometimes, you may simply read from your written report, an approach that is structured but sometimes boring. Without maintaining eye contact with your audience, and varying your gestures and tone of voice at the right times, you might look like a robot. If you *do* plan to read your report, study it well and practice aloud to decrease reliance on the text. Otherwise, you may slur or mispronounce your words or keep your nose stuck to the text throughout your talk, in fear of losing your place.

The Extemporaneous Delivery

An extemporaneous delivery is carefully planned, practiced, and based on notes which keep you on track. This is the most widely used and effective type of speaking technique. By following a set of notes in sentence-outline form, you stay in control of your material. Also, you speak in a natural, conversational style, with only brief glances at your notes. Because an extemporaneous delivery is based on ideas (represented by topic sentences to jog your memory) rather than fully developed paragraphs to be read or memorized, you can adjust your pace and diction as needed. In other words, instead of coming across as a droning, mechanical voice, you are seen as a distinct personality speaking to other personalities. This way, you won't stare at the ceiling as you recite memorized lines, or at your report as you read it word for word.

PREPARING THE EXTEMPORANEOUS DELIVERY

Plan your report step by step to stay in full control and to build your confidence. Some suggestions follow.

Know Your Subject

A sure way to appear ridiculous is to speak on a subject that you don't fully understand or that you know too little about. Do your homework, *exhaustively*, beforehand. Be prepared to explain and defend each assertion and statement of opinion with fact. When you know your subject, you can avoid tentative and equivocating statements that begin with *I feel, I guess, I suppose, I imagine, and so on.* Your audience has come to hear a knowledgeable speaker. Don't disappoint them.

Identify Your Audience

Everyone has sat through some classroom lectures or other talks that were either boring or confusing. Surely you don't want to impose this kind of agony on your own audience. Just as you expect a speaker to be interesting, informative, and clear, try to live up to these same expectations for your audience. At one extreme, speakers who oversimplify and belabor obvious or trivial points are boring; at the other extreme, those who speak in vague generalities or who do not explain complex information are confusing. Adjust the amount of detail and the level of technicality to your particular audience.

Many audiences contain people with varied levels of technical understanding. Therefore, unless you know the background of each person, prepare a report that speaks to a general audience (as discussed in Chapter 2). A typical classroom of mixed majors provides a good practice sample.

Plan to translate all complicated technical data by fully interpreting them and by explaining all significant details. When in doubt, you would do better to overexplain than to underexplain.

As you plan your report, answer these questions about your audience:

1. What major points do I wish to make?
2. How can I develop each of these points to ensure interest and understanding?

If your subject is controversial, consider carefully the average age, political views, educational level, and socioeconomic status of most audience members. Then decide how to speak effectively without offending anyone.

Plan Your Report

Statement of Purpose

Formulate, on paper, a statement of purpose, no more than two or three sentences long. Why, specifically, are you speaking on this subject? To whom are you speaking? What purpose do you wish to achieve?

Homework

If you haven't previously spoken or written on your subject, begin gathering data well ahead of time. Use the techniques of effective summarizing discussed in Chapter 3 to identify and organize major points.

If, on the other hand, your oral report is simply a spoken version of your written report, you'll need substantially less preparation. Simply expand your outline for the written report into a full-sentence outline. For our limited purposes, we will assume that your oral report is based on a written report.

Introduction-Body-Conclusion Sentence Outline

Figure 15-1 shows a typical sentence outline for an oral report. It is based on a written report about twenty pages long. Each sentence in this outline serves as a topic sentence for a paragraph that the speaker will develop in greater detail. (Review outlining techniques in Chapter 6.) When you have made your outline, review each part to identify areas where visual aids might help. Flip charts and drawings on overhead projectors are especially effective for small (classroom-size) audiences.

Before practicing your delivery you may wish to transfer your speech outline to 3 × 5 notecards, which you can hold in one hand and shuffle as needed to keep on track. Otherwise, your best bet is to insert the pages of your outline in a looseleaf binder so they can easily be turned. In either case, type or print your material clearly, leaving substantial white space between statements, so that you can locate material at a glance.

At this point, your plan for delivery should include three steps:

1. Introducing your audience to your subject.
2. Talking about your subject.
3. Reviewing what you have just talked about.

Delivery Time

Because your oral report is, in effect, a summary of your written version, aim for a maximum delivery time of twenty minutes. Longer talks may cause your

```
                          ORAL REPORT OUTLINE


  Intention:   By informing Cape Cod residents about the dangers
               to the Cape's fresh water supply posed by rapid
               population growth, this report is intended to
               increase local interest in the problem.

    I.  INTRODUCTION

        A. Do you know what you are drinking when you turn on

           the tap and fill a glass?

        B. The quality of our water is high, but not guaranteed

           to last forever.

        C. The somewhat unique natural storage facility for our

           water supply creates a dangerous situation.

        D. The Cape's rapidly increasing population could

           easily pollute our water.

        E. In fact, pollution in some towns has already begun.

   II.  BODY

        A. The ground water is collected and held in an aquifer.

           1. This water-bearing rock formation forms a broad,

              continuous arch under the entire Cape (Graphic

              Aid 1).

           2. The lighter fresh water flows on top of the

              heavier salt water.

        B. With increasing population, vast amounts of sewage
```

FIGURE 15-1 A Typical Outline for an Oral Report

and solid waste from landfill dumps invade the
aquifer.

   1. As wastes flow naturally toward the sea, they
      sometimes invade the drawing radii of various
      town wells (Graphic Aid 2).

   2. The Cape's sandy soil causes rapid seepage of
      wastes into the ground water stored in the
      aquifer.

C. Increased population also causes an overdraw on
   some town wells, resulting in salt-water intrusion,
   which contaminates many wells.

D. Salt and calcium used in snow removal add to the
   problem by entering the aquifer from surface runoff.

E. The effects of continuing pollution of the Cape's
   water table will be far-reaching.

   1. Drinking water will have to be piped in over a
      hundred miles from the Quabbin reservoir, at
      great expense.

   2. The Cape's beautiful fresh-water ponds will be
      unfit for swimming.

   3. All aquatic and aviary marsh life will be
      threatened.

FIGURE 15-1 (*Continued*)

4. The sensitive ecological balance of Cape Cod's
   environment will be destroyed.

F. Such damage would, in turn, lead to economic disaster for Cape Cod's major industry -- tourism.

III. CONCLUSION

A. In summary, from year to year, this problem becomes
   more real than theoretical.

B. The conclusion is obvious: If the Cape is to survive ecologically and financially, immediate steps
   must be taken to preserve the quality of our only
   water supply.

C. The following recommendations offer a starting point
   for effective action:

   1. Restrict population density in all Cape towns by
      creating larger lot requirements for private
      home building.

   2. Keep strict watch on proposed high-density
      apartment and condominium projects.

   3. Institute a committee in each town to educate its
      residents about the importance of conserving
      fresh water, thereby reducing the draw on town
      wells.

FIGURE 15-1 (*Continued*)

4. Prohibit the use of salt, calcium, and other
   additives in the sand spread on snow-covered
   winter roads.

5. Identify alternatives to land-fill dumps for
   solid waste disposal.

D. This crucial issue deserves the immediate attention
   of every Cape Cod resident.

E. Question-and-answer session.

FIGURE 15-1 (*Continued*)

audience to lose attention. The outline in Figure 15-1 is so designed. Time yourself in your first practice session to be sure of staying within bounds.

Practice Your Delivery

Hold several practice sessions to learn the geography of your report. Then you won't fumble your actual delivery.

Feedback

Try to practice at least once before friends. Otherwise, use a full-length mirror and a tape recorder. Assess your rate of speaking from your friends' comments or from your taped voice (which, by the way, will sound high to you) and adjust your pace if necessary. Revise any parts that your friends find unclear. Ask them about your organization and tone, as discussed in the next sections.

Organization

Is your delivery unified, coherent, and logically developed? How well does it hang together? Will your audience be able to follow your chain of reasoning? Do you use enough transitional statements to reinforce the logical connection between related ideas — statements beginning with *as a result, on the other hand,* and so on?

Tone

Maintain a conversational tone — the informal or semiformal manner of speaking that you use in relating to other people. Be sure not to confuse a conversational tone with a low level of language use and word choice. Everyone converses daily at varying levels of language use. For example, your level in a conversation with an old friend over a beer differs from that in a job interview — where you use less slang. Then again, your level of use in a conversation with your grandmother would differ from those two. Using the level of language most appropriate to the situation is comfortable and effective. But even in formal speaking situations you can use a conversational tone — that is, a tone that is not pompous, one that doesn't make you sound like a religious crusader or a circus barker.

Anticipate Audience Questions

Consider the parts of your report that might elicit questions and challenges from your audience. For example, you might need to clarify or justify information that is new, controversial, disappointing, or in any way surprising. Be prepared to give full factual support for all conclusions, recommendations, assertions, and statements of opinion. The podium or lectern is no place for guesswork. If you doubt the validity of any statement, leave it unsaid. By reviewing your report, you should be able to predict your audience's responses and be ready to field questions confidently and effectively.

DELIVERING THE EXTEMPORANEOUS REPORT

Capitalize on your good preparation by keeping the following guidelines in mind during your delivery.

Use Nervous Energy to Advantage

Like most people, you can expect to be nervous as you first face your audience. However, don't let your nervousness make you seem like a recording machine, droning on in monotone, eyes fixed on the lectern, counting the minutes until the cessation of your agony! Even experienced speakers often feel nervous before an audience. But they try to use their nervousness to advantage. After surviving your initial moment of panic, use your nervous energy to make yourself lively and enthusiastic. Obviously, if your delivery sounds like a medieval dirge, your audience will quickly lose interest.

Use Natural Body Movements and Posture

If you move and gesture as you normally would in a conversation, your audience will be more relaxed. Nothing seems more pretentious than a speaker who works through a series of rehearsed moves and artificial gestures. Also, maintain a reasonable posture: somewhere between that of a tin soldier and a buzzard hunkered over your lectern!

Speak with Confidence, Conviction, and Authority

Show your audience that you believe in what you say. Avoid the use of tentative qualifiers (*I suppose, I'm not sure, but . . . , maybe,* etc.). Also, try to clean up any verbal tics (*er, ah, uuh, mmm,* etc.) which do a poor job of filling in the blank spaces between statements. If you seem to be apologizing for your existence, you won't be very impressive. Speaking with authority, however, is not the same as speaking like an authoritarian. Neither the sheepish nor the dictatorial persona will get you very far.

Moderate Voice Volume, Tone, Pronunciation, and Speed

When using a microphone, people often speak too loudly. Conversely, without a microphone, they may speak too softly. Be sure that you can be heard clearly without shattering eardrums. You might ask your audience about the sound and speed of your delivery after speaking a few sentences. Your speaking tone should be confident, sincere, friendly, and conversational.

Because nervousness can cause too-rapid speech and unclear or slurred pronunciation, pay close attention to your pace and pronunciation. Usually, the rate you feel is a bit slow will be just about right for your audience.

Maintain Eye Contact

Eye contact is a key in relating to your audience. It makes you a more engaging speaker. If you stare at the ceiling, your notes, the rear wall, or your feet, your audience will feel that you are talking at them, not to them. Instead, look directly into your listeners' eyes to hold their interest. With a small audience, your eye contact is one of your best connectors. As you speak, establish eye contact with as many members of your audience as possible. In addressing a large group, maintain eye contact with those in the first few rows.

Read Audience Feedback

Addressing a live audience gives you the advantage of receiving immediate feedback on your delivery. Assess your audience's responses continually and make adjustments as needed. If, for example, you are laboring through a long list of facts, figures, specific examples, or elaborate statistical data, and you notice that people are dozing or moving restlessly, you might wish to summarize the point you are making. Likewise, if frowns, raised eyebrows, or questioning looks indicate confusion, skepticism, or indignation, you can backtrack a bit with a specific example or a more detailed explanation. By tuning in to your audience's reactions, you can avoid leaving them confused, hostile, or simply bored. Their nods of agreement, smiles, and looks of interest, on the other hand, will increase your confidence, making your talk a pleasure rather than an ordeal.

Be Concise

Say what you came to say, then summarize and close — politely and on time. Don't punctuate your speech with "clever" digressions that pop into your head. Unless a specific anecdote was part of your original plan to clarify a point or increase interest, avoid excursions. They usually harm the unity and coherence of your delivery and may cause you to drag on too long. Remember that each of us often finds what we have to say much more engaging and entertaining than our listeners do! Don't wear out your welcome.

Summarize Effectively

Before ending, take a brief moment to summarize the major points contained in the body of your delivery and to reemphasize any data of special importance to your audience. In other words, tell your audience, in abbreviated form, what you have just told them. As you conclude, thank your listeners.

Leave Time for Questions and Answers

As you begin, inform your audience that a question-and-answer period will follow. Announce a specific time limit (such as ten minutes) so you will not become embroiled in lengthy public debates over certain points. With an announced time limit you can conclude the session gracefully, without making anyone feel that he or she has been cut off abruptly or arbitrarily excluded from the discussion. Answer each question as fully as you can and don't be afraid to admit ignorance. If you can't answer a given question, say so, and move on to the next question. Terminate the session by saying "We have time for one more question," or something similar.

Planning and practice make oral reports pleasurable and rewarding. As in writing, *control* is central to speaking. On a basic level, just filling a page with words can be called *writing*. Similarly, the mere utterance of intelligible sounds can be called *speaking*. However, the effective speaker communicates with confidence, sophistication, and purpose. As with all skills, practice makes perfect. Therefore, instead of avoiding public speaking opportunities, seek them out.

CHAPTER SUMMARY

An oral report is any spoken factual statement that requires preparation and forethought. Compared to its written equivalent, an oral report elicits direct audience response, is more personalized, may have a greater effect, and saves time. In contrast, a written report is easier to refine and organize, can be more complex, can be studied by the reader at leisure, and can be easily reviewed.

Depending on your situation, you might give (1) an informal report, as in a discussion with a colleague; (2) a semiformal report, as in briefing work crews; or (3) a formal report, as in speaking at a convention or sales meeting. When you do prepare a formal report (in this case, based on a written equivalent), don't try to memorize the report, don't expect to read the report to your audience, and don't try to cook it up on stage because you think "it's all in your head." Your typical situation will be an extemporaneous one in which the report is by no means written out, but for which you have ample time for preparation and in which you have notes to rely on.

Follow these steps in preparing your delivery:

1. Know your subject matter so you can speak with authority.
2. Identify the technical level of your audience and plan accordingly.
3. Plan your report by writing a statement of purpose, doing your homework, constructing an introduction-body-conclusion sentence outline, and working out a reasonable delivery time span.
4. Practice your delivery before friends or using a mirror and tape recorder.
5. Try to anticipate the kinds of questions your audience might ask.

Follow these guidelines in delivering your report:

1. Use your nervous energy to lend vitality to your delivery.
2. Move and gesture as you normally would in a conversation; keep a good, natural posture.
3. Speak with confidence, conviction, and authority — as though you know what you are talking about.
4. Keep tabs on your voice volume, tone, pronunciation, and speed.
5. Maintain eye contact, talking to your listeners, not at them.
6. Read audience feedback for any adjustments you might need to make.
7. Be concise; say what you came to say, and close.
8. Near closing, summarize your main points.
9. Conclude gracefully leaving time for questions and answers.

REVISION CHECKLIST

Use this checklist during practice to refine your delivery.

1. Do I sound as though I know what I'm talking about?
2. Is the report content suited to the makeup and needs of my audience?
3. Are the introduction-body-conclusion sections of my report clearly differentiated and fully developed?
4. Can I follow my outline with only brief glances?
5. Do I begin with a clear statement of purpose?
6. Does my report hang together?
7. Does it achieve my stated purpose (i.e., does it deliver what title and purpose statement promise)?
8. Do I know what kinds of questions to expect from my audience, and am I prepared to answer them?
9. Is my delivery relaxed and personable?

10. During delivery, am I comfortable with my body movements and posture?
11. Do I speak with confidence and authority without sounding pretentious?
12. Do I pronounce all words distinctly?
13. Are the volume, tone, and speed of my delivery effective?
14. Do I maintain good eye contact with my audience/mirror reflection?
15. Do I stick to my purpose without digressing?
16. Do I summarize effectively, pulling everything together before concluding?
17. Is my delivery clear?

Now list those elements of your delivery that need practice.

EXERCISES

1. In a one- or two-paragraph memo to your instructor, identify and discuss the kinds of oral reporting duties you expect to encounter in the course of your career.

2. In a two-paragraph memo to your instructor, identify your biggest hang-up about oral reporting. Discuss the reasons for this anxiety, while describing it in detail. Finally, propose solutions to your problem.

3. In a one- or two-paragraph memo to your instructor, identify and discuss the advantages that one has as an effective speaker. What differences could a good speaking ability make in your life?

4. Design an oral report for presentation to your technical writing class. (The report may be based on one of your written reports.) Outline your presentation in sentence form. Practice at home with a tape recorder and mirror or a friend as audience. Evaluate your delivery according to the revision checklist.

5. Observe a lecture or speech at your college and evaluate it according to the revision checklist. Write a memo to your instructor (without naming the speaker) identifying any weak areas and making recommendations for improving the delivery. Identify the strong areas as well.

Appendix A

Review of Grammar, Usage, and Mechanics

If we can think of the fifteen chapters in this book as containing the tools for building effective messages, we might view this appendix as a collection of the nuts and bolts that hold messages together and provide repairs for weak parts and loose ends.

No matter how vital and informative a message may be, its credibility can be damaged by basic errors. Any of these errors — an illogical, fragmented, or run-on sentence; faulty punctuation; or a poorly chosen word — stands out and mars otherwise good writing. Not only do such errors confuse and annoy the reader, but they also speak badly for the writer's attention to detail and one's ability to do precise work. Your career will make the same demands for good writing that your English classes do. Quality begins at the level of the word, phrase, clause, and sentence.

None of the material here should be new to you. Everyone studies the ground rules of our language from the earliest grades onward. For reasons that are not yet fully understood, however, many writers continue to have trouble with "the basics." Although the material in this appendix offers no overnight solutions to long-standing writing problems, it does provide a simple and practical guide for making basic repairs. Spend an occasional few minutes reviewing sections that fit your needs, and you may discover that some troublesome writing problems are easier to solve than you had realized.

Table A-1 contains the standard correction symbols along with their interpretation and page references. When your instructor or proofreader marks a symbol on your paper, turn to the appropriate section for explanations and examples that will help you make corrections quickly and easily. This appendix is for your reference; you should use it when you need it, as you would a dictionary or thesaurus.

TABLE A-1   Correction Symbols and Their Meanings

Symbol	Meaning	Page	Symbol	Meaning	Page
ab	abbreviation	575–578	ro	run-on sentence	539–540
agr p	pronoun/referent agreement	544	seq	sequence of development in a paragraph	587–591
agr sv	subject/verb agreement	542–543	shift	sentence shift	552
			sl	sloppy phrasing	556
awk	awkward sentence	555–557	sp	spelling	580
ca	faulty pronoun case	546–547	sub	subordination	540–542
cap	capitalization	578–579	trans	transition	591–595
chop	choppy sentences	540	trite	triteness	557
coh	paragraph coherence	585–587	un	paragraph unity	585
cont	contraction	570–571	w	wordiness	558
cs	comma splice	538–539	wo	poor word order	549
dgl	dangling modifier	548–549	ww	wrong word	555–556
frag	sentence fragment	535–538	#	numbers	579–580
hs	hopeless statement	556–557	¶	begin new paragraph	580–582
il	illogical construction	553–554	no ¶	not a paragraph	580–585
jarg	jargon	21–22			
lev	level of technicality	14–20			
mod	misplaced modifier	549			
om	omitted word	555			
par	faulty parallelism	549–552			
pct	punctuation				
ap/	apostrophe	569–571			
[ ] /	brackets	573			
: /	colon	562–563			
, /	comma	563–569			
– – /	dashes	573–574			
... /	ellipses	572			
! /	exclamation point	561			
- /	hyphen	574–575			
ital	italics	572			
( ) /	parentheses	573			
. /	period	560–561			
? /	question mark	561			
" / "	quotation	571–572			
; /	semicolon	561–562			
red	redundancy	558			
rep	needless repetition	558–559			
ret	faulty reference	544–546			

SENTENCE PARTS AND TYPES

Sentence Parts

A sentence is a statement that contains a subject and a verb and expresses a complete idea. Much more important than this textbook definition of sentence, however, is our innate understanding of how groups of words function as sentences. As an illustration, consider this nonsense statement:

> In the cronk, the crat midingly pleted the mook smurg.

Although the only words we recognize in the example are "in" and "the," we can say that this is a sentence. Why? Because in some place, something did something to something else. Specifically, there is a subject, "crat," which did the doing; there is a verb, "pleted," which is in the past tense; there is an adverb, "midingly," which modifies the verb, telling us how the crat pleted; there is an adjective, "mook," which modifies "smurg"; there are three nouns, "cronk," "crat," and "smurg"; "cronk" is the object of the preposition "in," and "smurg" is the object of the verb, "pleted." So, without understanding the words, we can see that we already know something about language — how words work to make up a sentence. We don't know what the idea is but we do know that it is complete.

Let's look at these sentence parts, and others, in more detail.

Subject

The subject is the actor of the sentence — the noun or pronoun that usually precedes the predicate (the verb and other words that explain it) and about which we say something or ask a question.

> The **cat** eats too much.
> Why does the **cat** eat too much?
> **The big, fat, lazy cat sitting on the table** eats too much.

In this last sentence, the simple subject is "cat," and the complete subject (with all the words that explain the simple subject) is "The big, fat, lazy cat sitting on the table."

Predicate

The predicate is made up of the verb and any words that modify and explain it. The predicate usually denotes the subject's action or being. It is usually what is said about the subject.

The cat **eats.**
Who **is** a fat cat?
The cat **eats until he can no longer stand up.**

In this last sentence, the simple verb is "eats," and the complete predicate (with all the words that explain the simple predicate) is "eats until he can no longer stand up."

Object

An object is something that is acted on either directly or indirectly by a verb, or is governed by a preposition.

Direct Object.   A direct object is a noun or noun substitute that receives or is otherwise affected by the predicate's action.

The cat drank the **bowl of milk.**
Why did the cat eat **the mouse?**
I don't know **where the cat is.**
What did the cat eat?

Indirect Object.   An indirect object is a noun or noun substitute that states to whom or for whom (or to what or for what) the predicate acts.

I gave **the cat** a bowl of milk.
He built **his friend** a cat house.

Usually the indirect object could be replaced by a prepositional phrase beginning with *to* or *for*.

I gave a bowl of milk **to the cat.**
He built a cat house **for his friend.**

Object of the Preposition.   The object of the preposition is a noun or noun substitute that is joined to another part of the sentence by a preposition (*across, after, between, by, for, in, near, up, with,* and other "relationship" words). The words "cat" and "friend" in the previous sentences are objects of the preposition.

The fat cat collapsed on the **floor.**

Objective Complement

An objective complement is a word or group of words that further explains the subject's action on the direct object.

The cats elected Jack **president.**
I consider him **a villain.**

Subjective Complement

A subjective complement is a word or group of words that further explains the subject.

> Jack is **fat.**
> All cats appear **alert and vigilant.**

Phrase

A phrase is a group of related words that lacks either a subject or a predicate, or both. There are several kinds of phrases.

> *Infinitive Phrase*
> Jack likes **to be fat.** (*functions as direct object*)
>
> *Prepositional Phrase*
> Jack is content to sit **on the table.** (*functions as adverb*)
>
> *Verbal Phrase*
> Jack **will be eating** until his dying day. (*functions as verb*)
>
> *Gerund Phrase*
> **Eating constantly** can be damaging. (*functions as noun*)
>
> *Participial Phrase*
> **Hoping for more food,** Jack meowed loudly. (*functions as adjective*)

Clause

A clause is a group of related words that contains a subject and a predicate and is used in a sentence. It may be independent (main) or dependent (subordinate). An independent clause can stand alone as a sentence.

> The cat eats too much.

A dependent clause cannot stand alone as a sentence; it can serve as a noun, an adjective, or an adverb. A dependent clause always needs an independent clause to complete its meaning.

> *Noun Clause*
> Jack hopes **that he can eat forever.** (*as direct object*)
> **Whomever Jack meets** is a potential meal ticket. (*as subject*)
>
> *Adjective Clause*
> Jack, **who eats constantly,** is the fattest cat in town. (*modifies "Jack"*)

Adverb Clause

Jack is fat **because he eats too much.** (*modifies the subjective complement "fat"*)

Now let's look at the types of sentences that can be made by combining these sentence parts.

Sentence Types

Simple Sentence

A simple sentence contains one clause with one predicate.

> Jack eats.
> **Jack eats** too much.
> On any given day, **Jack eats** too much.
> On any given day, **Jack**, the fat, lazy cat, **eats** too much dry and canned food for any small animal.

Each of these sentences is a simple sentence. Although the subject and verb are gradually expanded, and objects, adjectives, adverbs, and prepositional phrases are added, the kernel sentence is still "Jack eats."

Compound Sentence

A compound sentence contains two or more main clauses, each with a subject and a predicate. The clauses are usually joined by coordinating conjunctions (*and, but, or, nor, for*) or by a semicolon or colon.

> Jack eats constantly **and** he gets fatter.
> Jack eats constantly; he gets fatter.

Ideas in a compound sentence are roughly equal in importance; therefore, they are expressed in equal (coordinate) grammatical form.

> Jack eats all morning, sleeps all afternoon, and prowls all night.

Complex Sentence

A complex sentence has two or more clauses that are not equal in importance. Instead, it has a dependent clause and an independent clause; the former depends on the latter for completion of its meaning.

> Because Jack eats too much, he is fat. (*second clause is independent*)
> Have you seen the cat who eats too much? (*first clause is independent*)

Because one clause depends on the other, they should not be separated by anything stronger than a comma. Words like *who, which, although, after, when,* and *because* (subordinating conjunctions), placed at the beginning of an independent clause, will make it dependent.

A complex sentence can have more than one dependent clause, as long as it has an independent clause.

> After Jack eats all morning, sleeps all afternoon, and prowls all night, he is ready to start all over again. (*final clause is independent*)

As we will see in the discussion of subordination, complex sentences show that some ideas should receive more emphasis than others.

Compound-Complex Sentence

A compound-complex sentence has at least two independent clauses and one dependent clause.

> Jack is unhappy because his bowl is missing and his girlfriend has left town. (*first and third clauses are independent*)

Now that we have discussed sentence parts and types, let's look at some of the things that go wrong in sentences, along with ways to avoid these mistakes.

COMMON SENTENCE ERRORS

Any piece of writing is only as good as each of its sentences. Sometimes, in haste to complete a writing assignment, you might overlook some weak spots. Here are some of the most common sentence errors, along with suggestions for easy repairs.

Sentence Fragment

As we said earlier, a sentence can be defined as the expression of a logically complete idea. Any complete idea must contain a subject and a verb and must not depend on another complete idea in order to make sense. Your sentence might contain several complete ideas, but it must contain at least one!

> Although he was nervous, he grabbed the line, and he saved the sailboat. (*incomplete idea*)   (*complete idea*)   (*complete idea*)

However long or short your sentence is, it should make sense to your reader. If the idea is not complete — if your reader is left wondering what you mean — you probably have left an essential element out of your statement (the subject, the verb, or another complete idea). Such a piece of a sentence is called a fragment.

Grabbed the line. (*a fragment because it lacks a subject*)

Although he was nervous. (*a fragment because — although it has a subject and a verb — it needs to be joined with a complete idea to make sense*)

The only exception to the rule for sentences is when we give a command (Run!) in which the subject (you) is understood. Because this is a logically complete statement, it can properly be called a sentence. So can this one:

Jack is a fat cat.

Again the idea is logically complete. Although your readers may have questions about who Jack is, and how fat he is, they cannot fail to understand your meaning: Somewhere there is a cat; the cat's name is Jack; the cat is fat.

Suppose instead we write:

Jack a fat cat.

This statement is not logically complete, therefore not a sentence. The reader is left asking, "What about Jack the fat cat?" The verb — the word that makes things happen — is missing. By adding a verb we can easily change this fragment to a complete sentence.

Simple Verb
Jack **is** a fat cat.

Verb plus Adverb
Jack, a fat cat, **runs fast.**

Dependent Clause, Verb, and Subjective Complement
Although he smiles often, Jack, a fat cat, **is neurotic.**

Do not, however, mistake the following statement — which seems to contain a verb — for a complete sentence:

Jack **being** a fat cat.

Such "ing" forms do not function as verbs unless they are accompanied by such other verbs as *is*, *was*, and *will be*. Again the reader is left in a fog unless you complete your idea by adding an independent clause.

Jack, being a fat cat, **was on a diet.**

Likewise, remember that the "to + verb" form does not function as a verb.

To be a fat cat.

The meaning is unclear unless you complete the thought.

To be a fat cat, **Jack must eat like a horse.**

Sometimes we can inadvertently create fragments by adding certain words — *because, since, if, although, while, unless, until, when, where,* and others — to an already complete sentence. We then change our independent clause (complete sentence) to a dependent clause.

> **Although** Jack is a fat cat.

Such words subordinate the words that follow them so that an additional idea becomes necessary to make the first statement complete. That is, they make the statement dependent on an additional idea, which must itself contain a subject and a verb and be a complete sentence. (See "Complex Sentences" and "Subordination.") Now we need to round off the statement with a complete idea (an independent clause).

> Although Jack is a fat cat, **he is athletic.**

Note: Be careful not to use a semicolon or a period, instead of a comma, to separate elements in the previous sentence. Because the incomplete idea (dependent clause) depends on the complete idea (independent clause) for its meaning, you need only a *pause* (symbolized by a comma), not a *break* (symbolized by a semicolon), between these ideas. In fact, many fragments are created when the writer uses too strong a mark of punctuation (period or semicolon) between a dependent and an independent clause, thereby severing the needed connection. (See our later discussion of punctuation.)

Here are some fragments from student reports. Each is repaired in several ways. Can you think of any other ways of making these statements complete?

> *Fragment*
>
> She spent her first week on the job as a researcher. **Selecting and compiling technical information from digests and journals.**

> *Correct*
>
> She spent her first week on the job as a researcher, selecting and compiling technical information from digests and journals.
>
> She spent her first week on the job as a researcher. She selected and compiled technical information from digests and journals.
>
> She spent her first week on the job as a researcher by selecting and compiling technical information from digests and encyclopedias.

> *Fragment*
>
> **Because the operator was careless.** The new computer was damaged.

> *Correct*
>
> Because the operator was careless, the new computer was damaged.

The operator's carelessness resulted in damage to the new computer.

The operator was careless; as a result, the new computer was damaged.

Fragment
When each spool is in place. Advance your film.

Correct
When each spool is in place, advance your film.

Be sure that each spool is in place before advancing your film.

Comma Splice

In a sentence fragment, an incomplete statement is isolated from items on which it depends for its completion by too strong a punctuation mark: A period or semicolon is mistakenly used in place of a comma. In a comma splice, on the other hand, two complete ideas (independent clauses), which should be separated by a period or a semicolon, are incorrectly joined by a comma, as follows:

Jack is a fat cat, he loves to eat.

There are several possibilities for correcting this error.

1. Substituting a period followed by a capital letter:

Jack is a fat cat. **He** loves to eat.

2. Substituting a semicolon to signal a close relationship between two complete ideas:

Jack is a fat cat; he loves to eat.

3. Using a semicolon with a connecting adverb (a transitional word):

Jack loves to eat; **consequently,** he is a fat cat.

4. Using a subordinating word to make one sentence incomplete and dependent on the other:

Because he loves to eat, Jack is a fat cat.

5. Adding a connecting word after the comma:

Jack is a fat cat, **and** he loves to eat.

Your choice of construction will depend, of course, on the exact meaning or tone you wish to convey. Here are some comma splices from student reports. Each can be repaired in the ways mentioned previously.

Comma Splice
This is a fairly new technique, therefore, some people don't trust it.

Correct

This is a fairly new technique. Some people don't trust it.

This is a fairly new technique; therefore, some people don't trust it.

Because this is a fairly new technique, some people don't trust it.

This is a fairly new technique, **so** some people don't trust it.

Comma Splice

Ms. Jones was a strict supervisor, she was well liked by her employees.

Correct

Ms. Jones was a strict supervisor. She was well liked by her employees.

Ms. Jones was a strict supervisor; **however,** she was well liked by her employees.

Although Ms. Jones was a strict supervisor, she was well liked by her employees.

Ms. Jones was a strict supervisor, **but** she was well liked by her employees.

Ms. Jones was a strict supervisor; she was well liked by her employees.

Comma Splice

A current is placed on the wires entering and leaving the meter, the magnetic field generated by the current moves the coil.

Correct

A current is placed on the wires entering and leaving the meter. The magnetic field generated by the current moves the coil.

A current is placed on the wires entering and leaving the meter; the magnetic field generated by the current moves the coil.

A current is placed on the wires entering and leaving the meter; **consequently** the magnetic field generated by the current moves the coil.

When a current is placed on the wires entering and leaving the meter, the magnetic field generated by the current moves the coil.

A current is placed on the wires entering and leaving the meter, **and** the magnetic field generated by the current moves the coil.

Run-on Sentence

The run-on sentence, a cousin to the comma splice, crams too many ideas together without providing needed breaks or pauses between thoughts.

> The hourglass is more accurate than the waterclock for the water in a water clock must always be of the same temperature in order to flow with the same speed since water evaporates it must be replenished at regular intervals thus not being as effective in measuring time as the hourglass.

Like a runaway train, such a statement is completely out of control. Here is a corrected version:

> The hourglass is more accurate than the waterclock because water in a water clock must always be of the same temperature to flow at the same speed. Also, water evaporates and must be replenished at regular intervals. These temperature and volume problems make the waterclock less effective than the hourglass in measuring time.

Choppy Sentences

It is possible to write grammatically correct sentences that, nonetheless, read like the Dick-and-Jane sentences in a third-grade reader. Short, choppy sentences cause tedious reading for your audience and bad publicity for you.

> *Choppy*
>
> Brass-plated prongs are not desirable. They do not always make a good contact in the outlet. They also rust or corrode. Some of the cheaper plugs also have no terminal screws. The conductors in the cord are soldered to the prongs. Sometimes they are just wrapped around them. These types often come as original equipment on small lamps and appliances. They are not worth repairing when a wire comes loose.

This problem can easily be corrected by combining related ideas within single sentences and by using transitional terms (see the section on transitions) to increase coherence.

> *Correct*
>
> Brass-plated prongs are not desirable because they do not always make a good contact in the outlet and they rust and corrode. Furthermore, some of the cheaper plugs, which often come as original equipment on small lamps and appliances, have no terminal screws: the conductors in the cord are either soldered to the prongs or just wrapped around them. Therefore, these plugs are not worth repairing when a wire comes loose.

Notice that the original eight sentences have been replaced by three.

Faulty Subordination

Subordination is the placing of less important clauses in a sentence in a dependent position. Through proper subordination, you can combine several related short sentences within one longer sentence and thereby emphasize the most important idea by making it an independent clause. Consider, for instance, these two ideas:

> Jack is still fat. Jack is attending Weight Watchers.

Because these ideas are expressed as simple sentences, they seem to be co-ordinate in value — neither one more important than the other. However, suppose we wanted to give more than just this basic information. Suppose, for example, that we wanted to express an opinion. By combining these ideas in a complex sentence, we could state one of two opinions, depending on which idea we chose to emphasize.

> Although Jack is still fat, he is attending Weight Watchers.
> *(dependent — or*   *(independent idea)*
> *subordinate — idea)*
>
> Although Jack is attending Weight Watchers, he is still fat.
> *(dependent — or subordinate — idea)*   *(independent idea)*

The first sentence suggests that Jack is doing something to solve his problem; the second suggests that Jack's solution is not working. The independent idea in a complex sentence is the one that receives the most emphasis, and the dependent idea is subordinated to it.

When you combine a string of ideas within one sentence, decide which is the most important and make the other ideas subordinate to it.

> This employee is often late for work, and he writes illogical reports, and he has poor management skills, and he should be fired.

The major emphasis in this sentence should fall on the last clause: "and he should be fired." Therefore, make the other clauses subordinate to it by adding a word like *who, which, because, since, if,* or *unless.*

> Because this employee is often late for work, writes illogical reports, and has poor management skills, **he should be fired.** *(last clause is independent)*

Be sure to place the idea you wish to emphasize in the independent position; don't write

> Although Joe studies diligently, he has a learning disability.

if you mean to suggest that Joe will succeed. Instead, write

> Although Joe has a learning disability, he studies diligently. *(last clause is independent, and therefore emphasized)*

Avoid excessive subordination.

> *Excessive*
> This job, which I took when I graduated from college, while I waited for a better one to come along, which is boring, where I have gained no useful experience, makes me anxious to quit.

Better

Upon graduation from college, I took this job while waiting for a better one to come along. Because I find it boring and have gained no useful experience, I am anxious to leave.

Faulty Agreement — Subject and Verb

Failure to make the subject of a sentence agree in number with the verb is one of the most common errors made by writers. Happily, it's an error easily corrected and avoided. We are not likely to use faulty agreement in short sentences, where subject and verb are not far apart. Thus we are not likely to say "Jack eat too much" instead of "Jack eats too much." However, in more complicated sentences — in which the subject is separated from its verb by other words — we sometimes lose track of the subject-verb relationship.

Faulty

The lion's **share** of diesels **are** sold in Europe.

Although "diesels" is the word closest to the verb, the subject here is "share," a singular subject which must agree with a singular verb.

Correct

The lion's **share** of diesels **is** sold in Europe.

Faulty Agreement

There **is** an estimated 29,000 **women** living in Barnstable County.

A **system** of lines **are** extended horizontally to form a grid.

Chiropractors believe that **interferences** within the nervous system **impairs** other bodily systems.

Despite the word order of a sentence, these agreement errors can be easily repaired when the subject and verb are identified.

Correct

There **are** an estimated 29,000 **women** living in Barnstable County.

A **system** of lines **is** extended horizontally to form a grid.

Chiropractors believe that **interferences** within the nervous system **impair** other bodily functions.

A second situation that causes us trouble in subject-verb agreement occurs when we use certain kinds of words. For instance, when indefinite pronouns like *each, everyone, anybody,* and *somebody* function as subjects, they usually take a singular verb.

> *Faulty Agreement*
> **Each** of the crew members **were** injured.
> **Everyone** in the group **have** practiced long hours.

> *Correct*
> **Each** of the crew members **was** injured.
> **Everyone** in the group **has** practiced long hours.

Another kind of word that sometimes causes agreement problems is the collective noun. Words like *herd, family, union, group, army, team, committee,* and *board* take either a singular or a plural verb, depending on your intended meaning. When denoting the group as a whole, use a singular verb.

> *Correct*
> The **committee meets** weekly to discuss new business.
> The editorial **board** of this magazine **has** high standards.

Conversely, to denote individual members of the group, use a plural verb.

> *Correct*
> The **committee have** voted unanimously to support the new personnel policy.
> The editorial **board are** all published writers.

A third problem occurs when we have two subjects joined by *either . . . or* or *neither . . . nor.* Here, the verb will be singular if both subjects are singular, and plural if both subjects are plural. If one subject is plural and one is singular, the verb agrees with the one that is closer.

> *Correct*
> Neither **John** nor **Bill works** regularly.
> Either **apples** or **oranges are** good sources of vitamins.
> Either the man or his **friends are** crazy.
> Neither the boys nor their **father likes** the home team.

If, on the other hand, two subjects (singular, plural, or mixed) are joined by *both . . . and,* the verb will be plural. Whereas *or* suggests "one or the other," *and* suggests a combination of the two subjects, thereby requiring a plural verb.

> *Correct*
> **Both** Joe and Bill **are** resigning.
> The **book and** the **briefcase appear** to be very expensive.
> The **manager and** the **foreman have** measles.

Faulty Agreement — Pronoun and Referent

A pronoun can be meaningful only if it refers to a specific noun (its referent or antecedent), with which it must agree in gender and number. It is easy enough to make most pronouns agree with their respective referents.

> *Correct*
> **Joe** lost **his** blueprints.
> The **workers** complained that **they** were treated unfairly.

Some cases, however, are not as obvious. For example, when an indefinite pronoun like *each, everyone, anybody, someone,* and *none* serves as the pronoun referent, the pronoun itself is singular.

> *Correct*
> **Anyone** can get **his** degree from that college.
> **Anyone** can get **his or her** degree from that college.
> **Each** candidate described **her** plans in detail.

Historically, the masculine pronoun has been used to represent both male and female, but that use is now unacceptable to many readers and writers. The consistent alternation of *his* and *her* is one way to treat the problem. Another way is to use *his or her*. But these can seem awkward and artificial if they are overused. The best solution is to avoid the construction by substituting an article, using the plural, or using the passive voice. In any case, don't use *their* when a singular pronoun is called for.

> *Faulty Agreement*
> **None** of the workers **were** satisfied with **their** wages.
> **Someone** forgot **their** briefcase.

> *Correct*
> **All** the workers **were** dissatisfied with **their** wages.
> **This** briefcase **was forgotten** by someone.
> **Someone** forgot a briefcase.

Faulty Pronoun Reference

Whenever a pronoun is used, it must refer to one clearly identified referent; otherwise, your message will be vague and confusing.

> *Ambiguous Reference*
> **Sally** told **Sarah** that **she** was obsessed with her job.

Does "she" refer to Sally or Sarah? The meaning of the message is obscured, giving rise to several possible interpretations:

1. Sally is obsessed with her job.
2. Sally thinks that Sarah is obsessed with her (Sally's) job. (Sarah is envious.)
3. Sally thinks that Sarah is obsessed with her own job.
4. Sally is obsessed with Sarah's job.
5. Sally thinks that someone else is obsessed with her (Sally's) job.
6. Sally thinks that someone else is obsessed with Sarah's job.
7. Sally thinks that someone else is obsessed with some other person's job.
8. Sally thinks that someone else is obsessed with her own job.

Corrections

Sally told Sarah, "I'm obsessed with my job."
Sally told Sarah, "I'm obsessed with your job."
Sally told Sarah, "You're obsessed with [your, my] job."
Sally told Sarah, "She's obsessed with [her, my, your] job."

Avoid using *this, that,* or *it* — especially to begin a sentence — unless the pronoun refers to a specific antecedent (referent).

Vague Reference

As he drove away from his menial **job**, boring **lifestyle**, and damp **apartment**, he was happy to be leaving **it** behind.

The problem with our **defective machinery** is only compounded by the new **operator's incompetence. That** makes me angry!

Correction

As he drove away, he was happy to be leaving his menial job, boring lifestyle, and damp apartment behind.

I am angered by the problem with our defective machinery as well as by the new operator's incompetence.

Vague Reference

Water boils at 212 degrees F. and freezes at 32 degrees F., which makes it usable as a coolant in most parts of the country. Antifreeze is required to prevent **this**. Some manufacturers recommend **this** on cars with air conditioning because of the possibility of the heater core freezing.

Notice that the first "this" has no specific referent, and the second seems to refer to "antifreeze" but is placed too far from its referent. The meaning of the message is obscured by such vague construction.

Vague Reference

Smog, congestion, and **noise** are ways of life in most big cities. **This** is not for me.

Correction
The smog, congestion, and noise which are ways of life in a big city are not for me.

Inaccurate Reference
Increased blood pressure is caused by the narrowing of the blood vessels, making the pressure higher as **it** attempts to flow through the blood vessels.

Here, "it" seems to refer to "pressure," which is absurd.

Correct
Increased blood pressure is caused by the narrowing of the blood vessels, making the pressure higher as the blood attempts to flow through the vessels.

Faulty Pronoun Case

The case of a pronoun — nominative, objective, or possessive — is determined by the role it plays in the sentence: as subject, as object, or as indicator of possession.

If the pronoun serves as the subject of a sentence (*I, we, you, she, he, it, they, who*), its case is *nominative*.

> **She** completed her graduate program in record time.
> **Who** broke the chair?

When a pronoun follows a version of the verb *to be* (a linking verb), it further explains (complements) the subject, and thus its case is nominative.

> It was **she**.
> The chemist who perfected our new distillation process is **he**.

If the pronoun serves as the object of a verb or a preposition (*me, us, you, her, him, it, them, whom*), its case is *objective*.

> *Object of the Verb*
> The employees gave **her** a parting gift.

> *Object of the Preposition*
> Several colleagues left with **him**.
> To **whom** do you wish to complain?

If a pronoun indicates possession (*my, mine, our, ours, your, yours, his, her, hers, its, their, theirs, whose*), its case is *possessive*.

> The brown briefcase is **mine**.
> **Her** offer was accepted.
> **Whose** opinion do you value most?

Here are some examples of the most frequent errors made in pronoun case:

> *Faulty Case*
>
> **Whom** is responsible to **who**? (*The subject should be nominative, and the object should be objective.*)
>
> The debate was between Marsha and **I**. (*As object of the preposition, the pronoun should be objective.*)
>
> **Us** board members are accountable for our decisions. (*The pronoun accompanies the subject, "board members," and thus should be nominative.*)
>
> A group of **we** managers will fly to the convention on a chartered plane. (*The pronoun accompanies the object, "managers," and thus should be objective.*)

Hint: By temporarily deleting the accompanying noun from each of the two last examples, we can immediately identify the correct pronoun case ("We ... are accountable ..."; "A group of us ... will fly ...").

> *Correct*
>
> **Who** is responsible to **whom**?
> The debate was between Marsha and **me**.
> **We** board members are accountable for our decisions.
> A group of **us** managers will fly to the convention on a chartered plane.

Close reading of your sentences will help you avoid these kinds of errors.

Faulty Modification

The word order (syntax) of a sentence determines its effectiveness and meaning. Certain words or groups of words are modified (i.e., explained or defined) by other words or groups of words. For example, prepositional phrases usually define or limit adjacent words:

> the foundation **with the cracked wall**
> the repair job **on the old Ford**
> the journey **to the moon**
> the party **for our manager**

As do phrases with "ing" verb forms:

> the student **painting the portrait**
> **Opening the door**, we entered quietly.

Or phrases with "to + verb" form:

> **To succeed**, one must work hard.

Or certain clauses:

> the man **who came to dinner**
> the job **that I recently accepted**

Clearly, word order is important.

When using modifying phrases to begin sentences, we can get into trouble unless we read our sentences carefully.

> *Dangling Modifier*
> **Answering the telephone,** the cat ran out the open door.

Here, the introductory phrase signals the reader that the noun beginning the main clause (its subject) is what or who is answering the telephone. The absurd message occurs because the opening phrase has no proper subject to modify; in effect it *dangles.*

> *Correct*
> As Mary answered the telephone, the cat ran out the open door.

A dangling modifier can also obscure the meaning of your message.

> *Dangling Modifier*
> **After completing the student financial aid application form**, the Financial Aid Office will forward it to the appropriate state agency.

Who completes the form — the student or the financial aid office? Here are some other dangling modifiers that make the message confusing, inaccurate, or downright absurd:

> *Dangling Modifier*
> **While walking down the stairs**, a cold chill ran through my body.
> **After a night of worry**, the lights came on.
> Impurities have entered our bodies **by eating chemically processed foods.**
> **After being watered**, place manure around the base of the tree.
> **By planting different varieties of crops**, the pests were unable to adapt.

Correct these by giving an explicit subject to the dangling clause or phrase, as follows:

> *Correct*
> While **I** walked down the stairs, a cold chill ran through my body.
>
> After **we** worried all night, the lights came on.
>
> Impurities have entered our bodies by **our** eating chemically processed foods.
>
> After **you** water the tree, place manure around its base.
>
> By planting different varieties of crops, **farmers** prevented the pests from adapting.

The word order of adjectives and adverbs in a sentence is as important as the order of modifying phrases and clauses. Notice how changing word order affects the meaning of these sentences:

I **often** remind myself of the need to balance my checkbook.
I remind myself of the need to balance my checkbook **often**.

Be sure that modifiers and the words they modify follow a word order that reflects your meaning.

Misplaced Modifier

Harry typed another memo on our new electric typewriter **that was useless.** (*Was the memo or the typewriter useless?*)

He read a report on the use of nonchemical pesticides **in our conference room.** (*Are the pesticides to be used in the conference room?*)

Ms. Smith is the newest executive to join our company **in blue tennis shorts.** (*Do executives join the company in blue tennis shorts?*)

She **only** expects basic courtesy. (*No one else does?*)

She volunteered **immediately** to deliver the radioactive shipment. (*Volunteering immediately, or delivering immediately?*)

John ordered his materials from an out-of-state lumber mill **which cost only $850.** (*Did the mill cost $850?*)

Correct

Harry typed another useless memo on our new electric typewriter.
or
Harry typed another memo on our new, useless electric typewriter.

In our conference room, he read a report on the use of nonchemical pesticides.

Ms. Smith, in blue tennis shorts, is the newest executive to join our company.

She expects only basic courtesy.

She immediately volunteered to deliver the radioactive shipment.
or
She volunteered to immediately deliver the radioactive shipment.

John ordered his materials, which cost only $850, from an out-of-state lumber mill.

Faulty Parallelism

Parallel statements are two or more statements of the same importance that are constructed in the same way. To ensure a consistent message, any *series* of words, phrases, clauses, or other expressions that are related in meaning and are used within the same sentence must be written in identical grammatical form.

Correct

We here highly resolve . . . that government **of the people, by the people, and for the people** shall not perish from the earth.

That statement describes the government in terms of three modifiers that clearly are related in meaning. Because the first modifier is a prepositional phrase, the others must also be. Otherwise, the sentence might read as follows:

Faulty Parallelism

We here highly resolve . . . that government **of the people, which the people created and maintain, serving the people** shall not perish from the earth.

Lack of parallel structure garbles the message. All items in a series, within a sentence, must be phrased consistently. If you begin the series with a noun, use nouns for all other items in the series; if you begin with an adjective, use adjectives; if you begin with a clause or phrase, use the same type of clause or phrase.

Faulty Parallelism

The new apprentice is **enthusiastic, skilled,** and **you can depend on him.**

My car needs an **oil change, a grease job,** and **the carburetor should be adjusted.**

Diesels have a **high price, potential emission problems,** and **do not perform well.**

I hope **to be finished** with the survey by noon and **that I will be** on the return flight by 2 P.M.

Her weekend chores included **painting the garage, waxing the car, mowing the lawn, walking the dog,** and **she had a report to write by Monday morning.**

Correct

The new apprentice is **enthusiastic, skilled,** and **dependable.** (*all subjective complements*)

My car needs an **oil change, a grease job,** and a **carburetor adjustment.** (*all nouns*)

Diesels have a **high price, potential emission problems,** and **poor performance.** (*all nouns*)

I hope **to be** finished with the survey by noon and **to be** on the return flight by 2 P.M. (*all infinitive phrases*)

Her weekend chores included **painting the garage, waxing the car, mowing the lawn, walking the dog**, and **writing a report** by Monday morning. (*all "ing" phrases*)

Because parallelism is sometimes a troublesome issue, here are additional examples:

Faulty Parallelism

In her new job, she felt **lonely** and **without a friend.**

She plans **to study** all this month and **on scoring** well in her licensing examinations.

He **sleeps well** and **jogs daily, as well as eating** high protein foods.

Most service technicians are hesitant to discuss the TV set with the owner. More often, it has been a case of **doing the repair, collect the money**, and **on to the next service call.**

Correct

In her new job, she felt **lonely** and **friendless.** (*both adverbs*)

She plans **to study** all this month and **to score** well in her licensing examinations. (*both infinitive phrases*)

He **sleeps** well, **jogs** daily, and **eats** high-protein food. (*all verbs*)

. . . . More often, it has been a case of **doing** the repair, **collecting** the money, and **moving** on to the next service call. (*all "ing" phrases*)

To increase the coherence of long sentences, repeat words that introduce parallel expressions.

Faulty Parallelism

Before buying this property you should decide whether you plan to settle down and raise a family, travel for a few years, or pursue graduate study in your field.

Correct

Before buying this property you should decide whether you plan **to settle** down and raise a family, **to travel** for a few years, or **to pursue** graduate study in your field.

Be sure that all headings in your outline, table of contents, and report text are expressed in parallel grammatical form.

Faulty Parallelism

A. Picking the Fruit
   1. When to pick
   2. Packing
   3. Suitable temperature
   4. Transport with care

The logical connection between steps in that sequence is obscured because each heading is phrased in a different grammatical form.

Correct

A. Picking the Fruit
   1. Choose the best time
   2. Pack the fruit loosely
   3. Store at a suitable temperature
   4. Transport with care

Other forms of phrasing would also be correct here, as long as each item is expressed in a form parallel to all other items in the series.

Sentence Shifts

Shifts in point of view will damage coherence. If you begin a sentence or paragraph with one subject or person, don't shift courses.

Shift in Person
When **you** finish such a great book, **one** will have a sense of achievement.

Shift in Number
One should sift the flour before **they** make the pie.

Correct
When **you** finish such a great book, **you** will have a sense of achievement.
One should sift the flour before **one** makes the pie.

Don't begin a sentence in the active voice and then shift to the passive voice.

Shift in Voice
He delivered the plans for the apartment complex, and the building site **was also inspected by him.**

Correct
He delivered the plans for the apartment complex and also **inspected** the building site.

Don't shift tenses without good reason.

> *Shift in Tense*
> She **delivered** the blueprints, **inspected** the foundation, **wrote** her report, and **takes** the afternoon off.

> *Correct*
> She **delivered** the blueprints, **inspected** the foundation, **wrote** her report, and **took** the afternoon off.

Don't shift from one mood to another (e.g., from imperative to indicative mood in a set of instructions).

> *Shift in Mood*
> **Unscrew** the valve and then steel wool **should be used** to clean the rubber ring.

> *Correct*
> **Unscrew** the valve and then **use** steel wool to clean the rubber ring.

Don't shift from indirect to direct discourse within the same sentence.

> *Shift in Discourse*
> Jim wonders **if he will get the job** and **will he like it?**

> *Correct*
> Jim wonders **if he will get the job** and **if he will like it.**
> Will Jim get the job, and will he like it?

Illogical Construction

Each sentence must make sense to your reader. If you begin a sentence with one direction of grammatical expression or development and change directions in the middle, your message will probably be illogical.

> *Illogical*
> Some manufacturers **are not as worried about** high prices **than** government policy.

> *Correct*
> Some manufacturers **are not as worried about** high prices **as they are about** government policy.
> Some manufacturers **are less worried about** high prices **than about** government policy.

Again, in the next example, the second part of the sentence seems to have forgotten the direction taken by the first part.

> *Illogical*
>
> A lobster's large claws yield tender meat, **and** can also be obtained by sucking and squeezing its small appendages.

The conjunction, "and," refers grammatically to the "lobster's large claws." Accordingly, this statement tells us that the large claws — not the tender meat — can be obtained by sucking and squeezing.

> *Correct*
>
> A lobster's large claws yield tender meat, **which** can also be obtained by sucking and squeezing its small appendages.

Here, the relative pronoun, "which," clearly refers to "tender meat."

In the following example, the writer fails to develop the initial idea relating to temperature, and instead shifts to an idea relating to location:

> *Illogical*
>
> The best temperature for growing pears is a warm and sheltered area.

An area cannot be a temperature!

> *Correct*
>
> The best temperature for growing pears can be found in a warm and sheltered area.

In the following sentence, the writer tries to take a grammatical shortcut:

> *Illogical*
>
> The diesel can satisfy antipollution standards by installing exotic hardware.

The diesel cannot *install* anything!

> *Correct*
>
> The diesel can satisfy antipollution standards if its manufacturers install exotic hardware.

A slight oversight in singular and plural usage can destroy logic:

> *Illogical*
>
> The twenty-five technical writing students were asked to choose their own **subject** for their analytical reports.

All students are not choosing the same subject for their individual reports.

> *Correct*
>
> The twenty-five technical writing students were asked to choose their own **subjects** for their analytical reports.

Awkward Construction

Sometimes a sentence just doesn't deliver the clear message that it should deliver, for one or more of the following reasons:

1. Key words have been left out.
2. The word order of the sentence is incorrect.
3. The word choice is inaccurate.
4. The phrasing is sloppy.
5. The statement is hopeless and needs an overhaul.

You can avoid most of these errors by proofreading your sentences aloud.

Omission of a Necessary Word
The film container is your first step.

Obviously, a container cannot be a step because it is not an action.

Correct
Opening the film container is your first step.

Do not omit the necessary articles (*a, an, the*) from your sentences.

Omission of an Article
Open door and place newspaper on floor.

Correct
Open **the** door and place **a** newspaper on **the** floor.

Faulty Word Order
Pour into the eight-inch pan **the oil**.
Nonsmokers are affected harmfully by tobacco smoke **as well as smokers**.

Correct
Pour **the oil** into the eight-inch pan.
Nonsmokers, **as well as smokers**, are affected harmfully by tobacco smoke.

Inaccurate Word Choice
The diesel engine is not without fault and **skepticism**. (*Can an engine be skeptical?*)

Prices **hope** to be held down by **building** a smaller engine. (*Can prices hope or build?*)

When a plug is **pushed in** the outlet, it connects the cord to the power supply. (*Does one have to be inside of the outlet in order to push the plug? Do we "push" a plug as we push a door?*)

Anaerobic fermentation **is used** in this report. (*Can a report ferment?*)

Correct

The diesel engine is not without fault, and skepticism exists among manufacturers and consumers.

Manufacturers hope to hold prices down by building a smaller engine.

When a plug is inserted into the outlet, it connects the cord to the power supply.

Anaerobic fermentation is discussed in this report.

Sloppy Phrasing

Your rate of interest is higher than the First National Bank. (*Can an interest rate be higher than a bank?*)

Aging in the bottle for six months is desirable before drinking. (*Should you age in the bottle before you drink?*)

Knowing what a nonfilter cigarette is and its appearance will facilitate your understanding of this report. (*Will the cigarette have to appear in order to aid your understanding? This is also an error in parallelism.*)

One great advantage of diesel engines is that they are low on fuel. (*Are they almost out of gas?*)

Our outlet does more business than San Francisco. (*Can a store do more business than a city?*)

Correct

Your rate of interest is higher than that of the First National Bank.

The brew should be aged in the bottle for six months before it is drunk.

Knowing what a nonfilter cigarette is and what it looks like will facilitate your understanding of this report.

One great advantage of diesel engines is their low fuel consumption.

Our outlet does more business than the San Francisco outlet.

Hopeless Statements (taken from actual reports)

This design may become a possibility because of no other choices rather than a decision.

Duress is similar to blackmail which is to force a man to do something as if by threats.

Whatever golf posture and alignment will be sought at the address of the ball, his body must be open and square. By this, which means legs aligned with shoulders in a standing stance, is the only proper way to address a swing.

The best remedy for these last statements is to discard them completely and to begin anew. Because most awkward constructions result from writers' failure to read the sentences they have written, they can be easily corrected. Left uncorrected, such statements are interpreted as expressions of incompetence, or, at best, blatant disregard for the reader's needs. This kind of shoddy writing is an insult to your reader. (See Chapter 2 for related discussions.)

Triteness

Avoid the easy-to-use but tired old sayings that make you sound like a person with little imagination and even less of a vocabulary. The following expressions are just a few of many that may have sounded witty and colorful once, but have become worn out through overuse. Now, persons who use such trite expressions seem either too lazy or verbally incompetent to formulate original ways of saying what they mean.

Trite Expressions

work like a dog	burning your bridges behind you
easy come, easy go	don't put all your eggs in one basket
doing a bang-up job	bite the bullet
it never rains but it pours	almighty dollar
give it the old college try	fly off the handle
never say die	heavy as a ton of bricks
cash on the barrelhead	a stitch in time saves nine
hard as a rock	get with the program
dry as a bone	the whole ball of wax
tough as nails	waste not, want not
nerves of steel	don't give up the ship
holding the bag	a needle in a haystack
water over the dam	slow as molasses
water under the bridge	

These are just a few of thousands of such prefabricated responses. As a general rule, if you think it sounds familiar or "cute," don't say it.

Dead Wood

Whenever you can economize without compromising the quality of your message, do so. After writing your first draft, lean heavily on your red pencil to strike out wordiness, redundancy, and needless repetition.

Wordiness

The following sentences all contain unnecessary words. Much better sentences would result if the words in boldface were omitted.

At this time I would like to say that I am delighted to be here.

In the case of the larger glands, **they are the glands which** secrete **their products** into the intestine through a common duct.

Each and every member was concerned.

I most certainly do feel that in my own mind there can be no question about the need for a day-care center on our campus.

If there is a change in the patient's blood or urine chemistry, **this** could mean that rejection of the kidney is occurring.

Redundancy

Redundancy is the using of different words to needlessly repeat the same message. The words in boldface in these examples repeat ideas already contained in the sentences, and can be eliminated.

The room was too narrow **in width** for our file cabinet.

The reason for this safety regulation is **due to the fact** that several accidents have occurred.

The upstairs dining room was reserved for executives, **and no other personnel were admitted.**

In my own personal experience I have seen **extremely** extensive damage caused by termites.

Needless Repetition

Much of the repetition in the following passage can be eliminated by combining ideas within larger sentences and by trimming.

Repetitious

Breathing is restored by artificial respiration. Artificial respiration means that breathing is being maintained by artificial means. Techniques of artificial respiration are mouth-to-mouth and mouth-to-nose. Artificial respiration must always be performed when external cardiac massage is being carried out.

Correct

Breathing is restored by artificial respiration through either the mouth-to-mouth or mouth-to-nose technique. Artificial respiration must always be performed if external cardiac massage is being given.

The same information is now given in 40 percent fewer words.

EFFECTIVE PUNCTUATION

Punctuation marks are like road signs and traffic signals: They govern reading speed and provide clues for navigation through a network of ideas; they mark intersections, detours, and road repairs; they draw attention to points of interest along the route; and they mark geographic boundaries. In short, punctuation marks provide us with a practical and simple way of making ourselves understood. They take up the slack created when the spoken message (made clear by the speaker's tone, pitch, volume, speaking rate, pauses, body movements, and facial expressions) is transposed into a written message (silent, static words on a page). In fact, effective punctuation can often make the written message clearer than its spoken equivalent.

As an experiment, copy a paragraph — without the punctuation — from any book, and try to read it clearly.

Before we discuss individual punctuation marks in detail, a commonsense review of the relationship among the four used most often (period, semicolon, colon, and comma) might help. These marks can be ranked in order of their relative strengths.

1. *Period.* The strongest mark. A period signals a complete stop at the end of an independent idea (independent clause). The first word in the idea following the period begins with a capital letter.

> Jack is a fat cat. His friends urge him to diet.

2. *Semicolon.* Weaker than a period but stronger than a comma. A semicolon signals a brief stop after an independent idea, but does not end the sentence; instead, it provides advance notice that the independent idea that follows is *closely related* to the previous idea.

> Jack is a fat cat; he eats too much.

3. *Colon.* Weaker than a period but stronger than a comma. A colon usually follows an independent idea and, like the semicolon, signals a brief stop but does not end the sentence. The colon and semicolon, however, are never interchangeable. A colon provides an important cue: it symbolizes "explana-

tion to follow." Information after the colon (which need not be an independent idea) explains or clarifies the idea expressed before the colon.

> Jack is a fat cat: he weighs forty pounds. (*The information after the colon answers "How fat?"*)
>
> *or*
>
> Jack is a fat cat: forty pounds worth! (*The second clause is not independent.*)

Note: As long as any two adjacent ideas are independent they may correctly be separated by a period. Sometimes, a colon or a semicolon may be more appropriate for illustrating the logical relationship between two given ideas. However, when in doubt, use a period.

4. *Comma.* The weakest of these marks. A comma does not signal a stop at the end of an independent idea, but only a pause within or between ideas in the sentence. A comma often indicates that the word, phrase, or clause set off from the independent idea cannot stand alone, but must rely on the independent idea for its meaning.

> Jack, **a fat cat**, is jolly. (*In that sentence, the phrase within commas depends on the independent idea for its meaning.*)
>
> **Although he diets often**, Jack is a fat cat. (*Because the first clause depends on the second, any stronger mark would create a fragment.*)

A comma is rarely appropriate between two independent clauses.

> *Comma Splice*
> Jack is a fat cat, he eats too much.

So we see that punctuation marks, like words, convey specific meanings to the reader. These meanings are further discussed in the sections that follow.

End Punctuation

The three marks of end punctuation — period, question mark, and exclamation point — work like a red traffic light by signalling a complete stop.

Period

A period ends a sentence. Periods end some abbreviations.

> Ms.
> M.D.
> Assn.
> Inc.
> N.Y.
> B.A.

Periods serve as decimal points for figures.

$15.95
21.4%

Question Mark

A question mark ends a sentence asking a direct question.

Where is the balance sheet?

Do not use a question mark to end a sentence that contains an indirect question.

Faulty
He asked if all students had failed the test?

Correct
He asked if all students had failed the test.
or
He asked, "Did all students fail the test?"

Exclamation Point

Because exclamation points mean that you are excited or adamant, don't overuse them. Otherwise you might seem hysterical or insincere.

Correct
Oh, no!
Pay up!
My pants are missing!

Use an exclamation point only when the expression of strong feeling is appropriate.

Semicolon

A semicolon usually works like a blinking red traffic light at a deserted intersection by signalling a brief but definite stop.

Semicolons Separating Independent Clauses

Most commonly, semicolons separate independent clauses (logically complete ideas) whose contents are closely related.

The project was finally completed; we had done a good week's work.

The semicolon can replace the conjunction/comma combination that joins two independent ideas.

> The project was finally completed, and we were elated.
> The project was finally completed; we were elated.

The second version emphasizes the sense of elation.

Semicolons Used with Adverbs as Conjunctions, and Other Transitional Expressions

Semicolons must accompany adverbs and other expressions that connect related independent ideas (*besides, otherwise, still, however, furthermore, moreover, consequently, therefore, on the other hand, in contrast, in fact*, etc.).

> The job is filled; however, we will keep your résumé on file.

> Your background is impressive; in fact, it is clearly superior to your opponent's.

Semicolons Separating Items in a Series

When items in a series contain internal commas, semicolons provide clear separations for the elements in the series.

> We are opening branch offices in the following cities: Santa Fe, New Mexico; Albany, New York; Montgomery, Alabama; and Moscow, Idaho.

> Members of the survey crew were John Jones, a geologist; Hector Lightweight, a draftsman; and Mary Shelley, a graduate student.

Colon

A colon works like a flare in the middle of the road: It signals you to stop and then proceed paying close attention to the situation ahead, the details of which will be revealed as you move ahead. Usually, a colon follows an introductory statement that requires a follow-up explanation.

> We need the following equipment immediately: a voltmeter, a portable generator, and three pairs of insulated gloves.

> She is an ideal colleague: honest, reliable, and competent.

> Two candidates are clearly superior: John and Marsha.

In most cases — with the exception of *Dear Sir:* and other salutations in formal correspondence — colons follow independent statements (logically and grammatically complete). Because colons, like end punctuation and semicolons, signal a full stop, they are never used to fragment a complete statement.

Faulty

My plans include: finishing college, traveling for two years, and settling down in Boston.

No punctuation should follow "include."

Colons can introduce quotations.

The supervisor's message was clear enough: "You're fired."

As shown on page 560, a colon normally replaces a semicolon in separating two related, complete statements, when the second statement directly explains or amplifies the first.

His reason for accepting the lowest-paying job offer was simple: he had always wanted to live in the Northwest.

The statement following the colon explains the "reason" mentioned in the statement preceding the colon.

Comma

The comma is the most frequently used — and abused — punctuation mark. Unlike the period, semicolon, and colon, which signal a full stop, the comma signals a *brief pause*. Thus, the comma works like a blinking green traffic light for which you slow down without coming to a dead stop. As we said earlier, a comma should never be used to signal a *break* between independent ideas; it is not strong enough.

Comma as a Pause between Complete Ideas

In a compound sentence where a coordinating conjunction (*and, or, nor, for, but*) connects equal (independent) statements, a comma is usually placed immediately before the conjunction.

This is a high-paying job, but the physical and emotional stresses are unbearable.

This vacant shop is just large enough for our boutique, and the location is excellent for walk-in customer traffic.

Without the conjunction, each of the above statements would suffer from a comma splice, unless the comma were changed to a semicolon or a period.

Comma as a Pause between an Incomplete and a Complete Idea

In most cases, a comma is placed between a complete and an incomplete statement in a complex sentence to show that the incomplete statement depends for its meaning on the complete statement (i.e., that the incomplete statement cannot stand alone, separated by a break symbol such as a semicolon, colon, or period).

> **Because he is a fat cat,** Jack diets often.
> **When he eats too much,** Jack gains weight.

In each example, the first idea is made incomplete by a subordinating conjunction (*since, when, because, although, where, while, if, until,* etc.) which here connects a dependent with an independent statement. The first (incomplete) idea depends on the second (complete) for wholeness of message. When the order is reversed (complete idea followed by incomplete), the comma can be omitted in most cases.

> Jack diets often **because he is a fat cat.**
> Jack gains weight **when he eats too much.**

Because commas take the place of speech signals, reading a sentence aloud should tell you whether or not to pause (and use a comma).

Commas Separating Items (Words, Phrases, or Clauses) in a Series

> **Sam, Joe, Marsha,** and **John** are joining us on the hydroelectric project.
>
> The office was **yellow, orange,** and **red.**
>
> He works hard **at home, on the job,** and even **during his vacation.**
>
> The new employee complained **that the hours were long, that the pay was low, that the work was boring,** and **that the foreman was paranoid.**
>
> **She came, she saw,** and **she conquered.**

Do not use commas when *or* or *and* is used between all items in the series.

> She is willing to work in San Francisco or Seattle or even in Anchorage.

Add a comma when *or* or *and* is used only before the final item in the series.

> Our luncheon special for Thursday will be coffee, rolls, steak, beans, and ice cream.

Without the comma, that sentence might cause the reader to conclude that beans and ice cream is an exotic new dessert.

Commas Setting off Introductory Phrases

When infinitive, prepositional, or verbal phrases introduce a sentence, they are usually set off by commas.

Infinitive Phrase
To be or not to be, that is the question.

Prepositional Phrase
In Rome, do as the Romans do.
In other words, you're fired.
In fact, the finish work was superb.

Verbal Phrase
Being fat, Jack was a slow runner.
Moving quickly, the army surrounded the enemy.

When an interjection introduces a sentence, it is set off by a comma.

Oh, is that the final verdict?

When a direct address introduces a sentence, it is set off by a comma.

Mary, you've done a great job.

Commas Used to Avoid Ambiguity

By signalling a pause that you would make in speaking, a comma can increase the clarity of your statement.

Ambiguous
Outside the office building was colorful. (*Was the exterior of the building or the area surrounding the building colorful?*)

Clear
Outside, the office building was colorful.

Ambiguous
For Bill Smith's advice was a lifesaver. (*Was Bill Smith's advice a lifesaver, or was Smith's advice to Bill a lifesaver?*)

Clear
For Bill, Smith's advice was a lifesaver.

Read your sentences aloud to reveal any such ambiguities in your own writing.

Commas Setting off Nonrestrictive Elements

A restrictive phrase or clause describes, defines, or limits its subject in such a way that it could not be deleted without affecting the essential meaning of the sentence.

All candidates **who have work experience** will receive preference.

The clause, "who have work experience," defines "candidates" and is essential to the meaning of the sentence. Without this clause, the meaning of the message would be entirely different.

All candidates will receive preference.

The following sentence also contains a restriction.

All candidates **with work experience** will receive preference.

The phrase, "with work experience," defines "candidates" and thus specifies the meaning of the sentence. Because these elements *restrict* the subject by limiting the category, "candidates," each forms an integral part of the sentence and is thus not separated from the rest of the sentence by commas.

In contrast, a nonrestrictive phrase or clause does not limit or define the subject; such an element is optional because it could be deleted without changing the essential meaning of the sentence.

Our new draftsperson, **who has only six weeks' experience,** is highly competent.

This house, **riddled with carpenter ants,** is falling apart.

In each of those sentences, the modifying phrase or clause does not restrict the subject; each could be deleted as follows:

Our new draftsperson is highly competent.
This house is falling apart.

Unlike a restrictive modifier, the nonrestrictive modifier does not supply the essential meaning to the sentence; therefore, it is set off by commas from the rest of the sentence.

To appreciate how the use of simple commas can affect meaning, consider the following statements:

Restrictive

Office workers **who drink martinis with lunch** have slow afternoons.

Because the restrictive clause limits the subject "office workers," we interpret that statement as follows: Some office workers drink martinis with lunch, and these have slow afternoons. In contrast, we could write

Nonrestrictive

Office workers, **who drink martinis with lunch,** have slow afternoons.

Here the subject, "office workers," is not limited or defined. Thus we interpret the statement as follows: All office workers drink martinis with lunch and have slow afternoons.

Commas Setting off Parenthetical Elements

Items that interrupt the flow of a sentence are called parenthetical and are enclosed by commas. Phrases and words like *of course, as a result, as I recall,* and *however* are parenthetical and may denote emphasis, afterthought, clarification, or transition.

> *Emphasis*
> This deluxe model, **of course**, is more expensive.
>
> *Afterthought*
> Your report format, **by the way**, was impeccable.
>
> *Clarification*
> The loss of my job was, **in a way**, a blessing.
>
> *Transition*
> Our warranty, **however**, does not cover tire damage.

So is a direct address.

> Listen, **my children**, and you shall hear . . .

A parenthetical statement at the beginning or the end of a sentence is set off with a comma.

> **Naturally**, we will expect a full guarantee.
> **My friends**, I think we have a problem.
> You've done a good job, **Jim**.
> **Yes**, you may use my name in your advertisement.

Commas Setting off Quoted Material

Quoted items included within a sentence are often set off by commas.

> The customer said, **"I'll take it,"** as soon as he laid eyes on our new model.

Commas Setting off Appositives

An appositive, a word or words explaining a noun and placed immediately after it, is set off by commas.

> Martha Jones, **our new president**, is overhauling all personnel policies.
>
> The new Mercedes, **my dream car**, is priced far beyond my budget.
>
> Alpha waves, **the most prominent of the brain waves**, are typically recorded in a waking subject whose eyes are closed.

Please make all checks payable to Sam Sawbuck, **company treasurer.**

Sarah, **my colleague,** has arrived.

Notice that the commas clarify the meaning of the last sentence. Without commas, the sentence would be ambiguous.

Sarah my colleague has arrived.

Are you telling Sarah that your colleague has arrived?

Sarah, my colleague has arrived.

Or are you saying that your colleague, Sarah, has arrived (as in the first version)?

Commas Used in Common Practice

Commas are used to set off the day of the month from the year, in a date.

May 10, 1984

They are used to set off numbers in three-digit intervals.

11,215
6,463,657

They are also used to set off street, city, and state in an address.

The bill was sent to John Smith, 184 Sea Street, Albany, New York 01642.

However, when the address is written vertically, the commas that are omitted are those that would otherwise occur at the end of each address line.

John Smith
184 Sea Street
Albany, New York 01642

If we put "Albany" and "New York" on separate lines, we wouldn't have a comma after "Albany" either.

Use commas to set off an address or a date from its following elements in a sentence.

Room 3C, Margate Complex, is the site of our newest office.
December 15, 1977, is my retirement date.

Use them to set off degrees and titles from proper names.

Roger P. Cayer, M.D.
Gordon Browne, Jr.
Marsha Mello, Ph.D.
Lon Cheney, B.A., M.A., C.P.A.

Commas Used Erroneously

Don't be a comma philanthropist. Avoid sprinkling commas where they are not needed or simply do not belong. In fact, you are probably safer using too few commas than using too many. Again, the overuse of commas generally can be avoided if you read your sentences aloud. Here are a few examples of the ways in which commas are used incorrectly:

> *Faulty Comma Use*
>
> As I opened the door, he told me, that I was late. (*separates the indirect from the direct object*)
>
> The most universal symptom of the suicide impulse, is depression. (*separates the subject from its verb*)
>
> This has been a long, difficult, project. (*separates the final adjective from its noun*)
>
> John, Bill, and Sally, are joining us on the design phase of this project. (*separates the final subject from its verb*)
>
> An employee, who expects rapid promotion, must quickly prove his worth. (*separates a modifier that should be restrictive*)
>
> I spoke in a conference call with John, and Marsha. (*separates two words linked by a coordinating conjunction*)
>
> The room was, eighteen feet long. (*separates the linking verb from the subjective complement*)
>
> We painted the room, red. (*separates the object from its complement*)

Apostrophe

Apostrophes are used for three purposes: to indicate the possessive, to indicate a contraction, and to indicate the plural of numbers, letters, and figures.

Apostrophe Indicating the Possessive

At the end of a singular or plural word that does not end in *s*, add an apostrophe plus an *s* to indicate the possessive.

> The people's candidate won.
> The chain saw was Bill's.
> The men's locker room burned.
> The car's paint job was ruined by the hail storm.

Do not use an apostrophe to indicate the possessive form of either singular or plural pronouns.

Correct

The book was hers.
Ours is the best sales record.
The fault was theirs.

At the end of a singular or plural word that ends in *s*, add an apostrophe only.

the cows' water supply
Mr. and Ms. Jacksons' wine cellar

In some cases, pronunciation will require that you add an *s*.

Charles's tools

At the end of the last word of a compound noun, add an apostrophe plus an *s*.

my father-in-law's false teeth

At the end of the last word in nouns of joint possession, add an apostrophe plus *s* if both own one item.

Joe and Sam's lakefront cottage

and an apostrophe plus *s* to both nouns if each owns specific items.

Joe's and Sam's passports

Apostrophe Indicating a Contraction

An apostrophe shows that you have omitted one or more letters in a phrase that is usually a combination of a pronoun and a verb.

I'm	they're
he's	you'd
we'll	who's
you're	who'll

Don't confuse *they're* with *their* or *there*.

Faulty	*Correct*
there books	their books
their now leaving	they're now leaving
living their	living there

Remember the distinction this way:

Their boss knows they're there.

Don't confuse *it's* and *its*. *It's* means "it is." *Its* is the possessive.

> It's watching its reflection in the pond.

Don't confuse *who's* and *whose*. *Who's* means "who is," whereas *whose* indicates the possessive.

> Who's interrupting whose work?

Other contractions are formed from the verb and the negative.

> isn't   can't
> don't   haven't
> won't

Apostrophe Indicating the Plural of Numbers, Letters, and Figures

> There are no but's about it: The 6's on this new typewriter look like smudged G's, 9's are illegible, and the %'s are unclear.

Quotation Marks

Quotation marks set off the exact words borrowed from another speaker or writer. At the end of a quotation the period or comma is placed within the quotation marks.

> "Hurry up," he whispered.
> She told me, "I'm depressed."

The colon or semicolon is always placed outside the quotation marks:

> Our contract clearly defines "middle-management personnel"; however, it does not clearly state the promotional procedures for this group.

> You know what to expect when Honest John offers you a "bargain": a piece of junk.

Sometimes a question mark is used within a quotation that is part of a larger sentence.

> "Can we stop the flooding?" inquired the foreman.

When the question mark or exclamation point is part of the quote, it is placed within the quotation marks, thereby replacing the comma or period.

> "Help!" he screamed.
> He asked John, "Can't we agree about anything?"

If, however, the question mark or exclamation point is meant to denote the attitude of the quoter instead of the quotee, it is placed outside the quotation marks.

Why did he wink and tell me, "It's a big secret"?
He actually accused me of being an "elitist"!

When quoting a passage of fifty words or longer, indent the entire passage five spaces and single space between the lines of the passage to set it off from the text. Do not enclose the passage in quotation marks.

Use quotation marks around the titles of articles, paintings, book chapters, and poems.

The enclosed article, "The Job Market for College Graduates," should provide some helpful insights.

The title of a bound volume — book, journal, or newspaper — should be underlined to represent italics.

Finally, use quotation marks to indicate your using a word ironically.

He is some "friend"!

Ellipses

Use three dots in a row (...) to indicate that you have left some material out of a quotation. If the omitted words come at the end of the original sentence, a fourth dot indicates the period. Use several dots centered in a line to indicate that a paragraph or more has been left out. Ellipses help you save time and zero in on the important material within a quote.

"Three dots ... indicate that you have left some material out. ... A fourth dot indicates the period. Several dots centered in a line ... a paragraph or more. ... Ellipses help you ... zero in on the important material. ..."

Italics

In typing or longhand writing, indicate italics by underlining. Use italics for titles of books, periodicals, films, newspapers, and plays; for the names of ships; for foreign words or scientific names; for emphasizing a word (used sparingly); for indicating the special use of a word.

The Oxford English Dictionary is a handy reference tool.

The *Lusitania* sank rapidly.

He reads *The Boston Globe* often.

My only advice is *caveat emptor*.

Bacillus anthracis is a highly virulent organism.

Do not inhale these spores, under any circumstances!

Our contract defines a *full-time employee* as one who works a minimum of thirty-five hours weekly.

Parentheses

Use commas normally to set off parenthetical elements, dashes to give some emphasis to the material that is set off, and parentheses to enclose material that defines or explains the preceding statements.

> An anaerobic (airless) environment must be maintained for the cultivation of this organism.

> The cost of manufacturing our Beta II transistors has increased by ten percent in one year (see Appendix A for full cost breakdown).

> This new three-colored model (made by Ilco Corporation) is selling well.

Notice that material between parentheses, like all other parenthetical material discussed earlier can be deleted without harming the logical and grammatical structure of the sentence.

Also, use parentheses to enclose numbers or letters that segment items of information in a series.

> There are three basic steps to this process: (1) ..., (2) ..., and (3)....

Brackets

Use brackets within a quotation to add material that was not in the original quote but that is needed for clarification. Sometimes a bracketed word will provide an antecedent (or referent) for a pronoun.

> "She [Jones] was the outstanding candidate for the job."

Brackets can enclose information taken from some other location within the context of the quotation.

> "It was in early spring [April 2, to be exact] that the tornado hit."

Use brackets to correct a quotation.

> "His report was [full] of mistakes."

Use *sic* ("thus so") when quoting accurately a mistake in spelling, usage, or logic.

> His secretary's comment was clear: "He don't [sic] want any of these."

Dashes

Dashes are effective — as long as they are not overused. Make dashes on your typewriter by placing two hyphens side by side.

Used selectively, dashes can provide dramatic emphasis for a statement.

However, they should not be used flagrantly as a substitute for all other forms of punctuation. In other words, when in doubt, do not use a dash!

Dashes can be used to denote an afterthought.

> Have a good vacation — but don't get sunstroke.

Or to enclose an interruption in the middle of a sentence.

> The designer of this building — I think it was Wright — was, above all, an artist.

> Our new team — Jones, Smith, and Brown — is already compiling outstanding statistics.

Although they can often be used interchangeably with commas, dashes dramatize a parenthetical statement more than commas do.

> Mary, a true friend, spent hours helping me rehearse for my interview.
> Mary — a true friend — spent hours helping me rehearse for my interview.

Notice the added emphasis in the second version.

Hyphens

Use a hyphen to divide a word at your right-hand margin. Consult your dictionary for the correct syllable breakdown:

> com-puter
> comput-er

Actually, it is best to avoid altogether this practice of word division at the ends of lines in your text.

Use a hyphen to join compound modifiers (two or more words preceding the noun as a single adjective).

> the rough-hewn wood
> the well-written report
> the all-too-human error

Do not hyphenate these same words if they *follow* the noun.

> The wood was rough hewn.
> The report is well written.
> The error was all too human.

Hyphenate an adverb-participle compound preceding a noun.

> the high-flying glider

Do not hyphenate compound modifiers if the adverb ends in *ly*.

> the finely tuned engine

Hyphenate all words that begin with the prefix *self*.

> self-reliance
> self-discipline
> self-actualizing

Hyphenate to avoid ambiguity.

> re-creation (*a new creation*)
> recreation (*leisure activity*)

Hyphenate words that begin with *ex* only if *ex* means "past."

> ex-foreman
> expectant

Hyphenate fractions used as adjectives and preceding the noun.

> a two-thirds majority
> In a four-to-one vote they defeated the proposal.

Do not hyphenate fractions if they do not immediately precede the noun.

> four fifths of the voters
> The proposal was voted down four to one.

Hyphenate compound numbers from twenty-one through ninety-nine.

> Thirty-eight windows were broken.

Hyphenate a series of compound adjectives preceding a noun.

> The subjects for the motivation experiment were fourteen-, fifteen-, and sixteen-year-old students.

EFFECTIVE MECHANICS

Correctness in abbreviation, capitalization, use of numbers, and spelling is an important sign of your attention to detail. Don't ignore these conventions. (See Chapter 8 for format conventions.)

Abbreviation

(For correct abbreviation in footnotes and bibliography, see pages 163–167.)

In using abbreviations consider your audience; never use one that might confuse your reader. Often, abbreviations are not appropriate in formal writing. When in doubt, write the word out in full.

Abbreviate certain words and titles when they precede or immediately follow a proper name.

Mr. Jones   Raymond Dumont, Jr.
Dr. Jekyll   Warren Weary, Ph.D.
St. Simeon

However, do not write abbreviations like the following:

Faulty
He is a Dr.
Pray, and you might become a St.

In general, do not abbreviate military, religious, and political titles.

Reverend Ormsby   President Carter
Captain Hook

Abbreviate time designations only when they are used with actual times.

400 B.C.   5:15 A.M.

Do not abbreviate these designations when they are used alone.

Faulty
Plato lived sometime in the B.C. period.
She arrived in the A.M.

In the text of a piece of formal writing, don't abbreviate days of the week, individual months, words like *street* and *road* or names of disciplines, like *English*. Other abbreviations to avoid include those for states, such as *Me.* for *Maine;* countries, such as *U.S.* for *United States;* and book items, such as *Chap.* for *Chapter, pg.* for *page,* and *fig.* for *figure.*

Use *no.* for *number* only when the actual number is given.

Check switch No. 3.

Abbreviate units of measurement only when they are used often in your report and are written out in full on first use. Use only those abbreviations which you are sure your reader will understand. Abbreviate items in a visual aid only if you need to save space.

Here is a list of common technical abbreviations for units of measurement:

ac	alternating current	cps	cycles per second
amp	ampere	cu ft	cubic foot
A	angstrom	db	decibel
az	azimuth	dc	direct current
bbl	barrel	dm	decimeter
BTU	British Thermal Unit	doz	dozen
C	Centigrade	dp	dewpoint
Cal	calorie	F	Farenheit
cc	cubic centimeter	f	farad
circ	circumference	fbm	foot board measure
cm	centimeter	fl oz	fluid ounce

FM	frequency modulation	min	minute
fp	foot pound	ml	milliliter
fpm	feet per minute	mm	millimeter
freq	frequency	mo	month
ft	foot	mph	miles per hour
g	gram	no	number
gal	gallon	oct	octane
gpm	gallons per minute	oz	ounce
gr	gram	psf	pounds per square foot
hp	horsepower	psi	pounds per square inch
hr	hour	qt	quart
in	inch	r	roentgen
iu	international unit	rpm	revolutions per minute
j	joule	rps	revolutions per second
ke	kinetic energy	sec	second
kg	kilogram	sp gr	specific gravity
km	kilometer	sq	square
kw	kilowatt	t	ton
kwh	kilowatt hour	temp	temperature
l	liter	tol	tolerance
lat	latitude	ts	tensile strength
lb	pound	v	volt
lin	linear	va	volt ampere
long	longitude	w	watt
log	logarithm	wk	week
m	meter	wl	wavelength
max	maximum	yd	yard
mg	milligram	yr	year

Here are some common abbreviations for reference in manuscripts:

anon.	anonymous	fig.	figure
app.	appendix	i.e.	that is
b.	born	illus.	illustrated
bull.	bulletin	jour.	journal
©	copyright	l., ll.	line(s)
c., ca.	about (c. 1963)	ms., mss.	manuscript(s)
cf.	compare	n.	note
ch.	chapter	no.	number
col.	column	p., pp.	page(s)
d.	died	pt., pts.	part(s)
diss.	dissertation	rev.	revised or review
ed.	editor	rep.	reprint
e.g.	for example	sec.	section
esp.	especially	sic	thus, so (to cite an
et al.	and others		error in the quote)
etc.	and so forth	trans.	translation
ex.	example	viz.	namely
f. or ff.	the following page or pages	vol.	volume

For abbreviations of other words, consult your dictionary. Most dictionaries have a list of abbreviations at the front or rear or include them alphabetically with the appropriate word entry.

Capitalization

Capitalize the following: proper names, titles of people, books and chapters, languages, days of the week, the months, holidays, names of organizations or groups, races and nationalities, historical events, important documents, and names of structures or vehicles. In titles of books, films, etc., capitalize the first word and all those following except articles or prepositions.

> Joe Schmoe
> *A Tale of Two Cities*
> Protestant
> Wednesday
> the *Queen Mary*
> the Statue of Liberty
> April
> Chicago
> the Bill of Rights
> the Chevrolet Vega
> Russian
> Labor Day
> Dupont Chemical Company
> Senator John Pasteur
> France
> The War of 1812
> Daughters of the American Revolution
> The Emancipation Proclamation
> Jewish
> *Gone With the Wind*

Don't capitalize the seasons, names of college classes (*freshman, junior*), or general groups (*the younger generation*, or *the leisure class*).
Capitalize adjectives that are derived from proper nouns.

> Newtonian Physics

Capitalize titles preceding a proper noun, but not those following.

> State Senator Marsha Smith
> Marsha Smith, state senator

Capitalize words like *street, road, corporation, college* only when they accompany a proper name.

> Bob Jones University
> High Street
> The Rand Corporation

Capitalize *north, south, east,* and *west* when they denote specific locations, not when they are simply directions.

> the South
> the Northwest
> Turn east at the next set of lights.

Begin all sentences with capitals.

Use of Numbers

As a general rule, write out numbers that can be expressed in two words or less.

> fourteen   five
> eighty-one   two million
> ninety-nine

Use numerals for all others.

> 4364   2,800,357
> 543   3¼

Use numerals to express decimals, precise technical figures, or any other exact measurements.

> 50 kilowatts   15 pounds of pressure
> 14.3 milligrams   4000 rpm

Express the following in numerals: dates, census figures, addresses, page numbers, exact units of measurement, percentages, ages, and times with A.M. or P.M. designations, monetary and mileage figures.

> page 14   1:15 P.M.
> 18.4 pounds   9 feet
> 115 miles   12 gallons
> the 9-year-old tractor $15
> 15.1 percent

Do not begin a sentence with a numeral.

> Six-hundred students applied for the 102 available jobs.

If your figure consumes more than two words, revise your word order.

> The 102 available jobs brought 780 applicants.

Do not use numerals to express approximate figures, time not stated with A.M. or P.M. designations, or streets named by numbers below 100.

> about seven hundred and fifty
> four-fifteen
> 108 East Forty-second Street

If one number immediately precedes another, spell out the first and use a numeral to express the second:

> Please deliver twelve 18-foot rafters.

Only in contracts and other legal documents should a number be stated both in numerals and in words:

> The tenant agrees to pay a rental fee of three hundred and seventy-five dollars ($375.00) monthly.

Spelling

As you should already know, spelling problems will not cure themselves. If you are bothered by certain spelling weaknesses, take the time to use your dictionary, *religiously,* for all writing assignments. As you read, note carefully the spelling of the words that have given you trouble in the past. You might even compile a list of troublesome words. Moreover, your college may have a learning laboratory or a skills resources center where you can get professional assistance with spelling problems. If not, your instructor may be willing to suggest several self-teaching books with instructions and practice exercises for spelling improvement.

EFFECTIVE PARAGRAPHS

The Purpose of Paragraphs

A paragraph is an orderly and logical arrangement of sentences designed to express an idea and to explain it with supporting details. Most well-written paragraphs should be able to stand alone as complete and meaningful messages. In fact, a good deal of your job-related writing will likely consist of one- or two-paragraph messages (as shown in the memo examples in Chapter 11).

Effective paragraphs help you stay in control of your writing. They provide individual spatial units for discussing a main idea in detail. For example, if you begin your paragraph by describing a work accident you can easily stay on course. All words, phrases, and sentences within that paragraph can be tailored to tell your readers what they need to know about the accident. Thus, if you find yourself arguing for longer lunch breaks by the third sentence you know that you have strayed.

Effective paragraphs also make your message more readable. Visually, they segment a whole page into smaller units that your reader can easily digest. Logically, they help your reader follow your reasoning. The indentation on your page provides a breathing space. It is a signal that one "central-idea block" has ended and another is beginning.

To appreciate how paragraph structure affects readability, try reading the following version of this section, written as one single block, without breathing space.

> A paragraph is an orderly and logical arrangement of sentences designed to express an idea and to explain it with supporting details. Most well-written paragraphs should be able to stand alone as complete and meaningful messages. In fact, a good deal of your job-related writing may consist of one- or two-paragraph messages (as shown in the memo examples in Chapter 11). Effective paragraphs help you stay in control of your writing. They provide individual spatial units for discussing a main idea in detail. For example, if you begin your paragraph by describing a work accident you can easily stay on course. All words, phrases, and sentences within that paragraph can be tailored to tell your readers what they need to know about the accident. Thus, if you find yourself arguing for longer lunch breaks by the third sentence you know that you have strayed. Effective paragraphs also make your message more readable. Visually, they segment a whole page into smaller units that your reader can easily digest. Logically, they help your reader follow your reasoning. The indentation on your page provides a breathing space. It is a signal that one "central-idea block" has ended and another is beginning. To appreciate how paragraph structure affects readability, try reading the following version of this section, written as one single block, without breathing space.

Because four major ideas are all lumped together in this second version, reading is much more difficult, and skimming is nearly impossible. Paragraphs *do* make a difference!

Paragraph Length

There is no rule to tell you how long a specific paragraph should be. We can only say that a paragraph should be long enough to tell the readers what they need to know and to reflect the content and emphasis the writer wants to achieve. However, a few general guidelines are worth keeping in mind.

1. A series of short paragraphs (one or two sentences each) makes your writing seem choppy and poorly organized. Imagine, for example, the beginning of this section divided into eight or ten paragraphs instead of four. However, a series of short paragraphs *is* effective in a set of step-by-step instructions.

2. A series of long paragraphs can make your material difficult to follow, as shown earlier in this section. A paragraph that is too long can easily obscure an important idea buried somewhere in the middle.

3. A single-sentence paragraph can be a good way of calling your reader's attention to an important idea by setting it off from the rest of your text.

> In summary, we can avoid further damage from mud slides only by building a retaining wall around our #3 construction site immediately.

4. Unless your paragraph is patterned as a list (like this one) in general it should be no longer than fifteen lines. A combination of shorter and longer paragraphs can be quite effective, if your subject lends itself to this kind of arrangement.

Paragraph Structure

In technical writing, paragraphs are usually best structured in an introduction-body-conclusion fashion. With this structure you move from the general to the specific by (1) stating your central idea in a topic sentence, (2) supporting and explaining your idea with specific details and examples, and (3) tying your paragraph together with a concluding statement. Each part is discussed in detail below.

Introduction

Your topic sentence introduces your reader to your central idea. It sets boundaries by promising what your paragraph will deliver — no more and no less. Before you can write a useful topic sentence you need to identify your purpose in writing the paragraph. Narrow your focus as much as you can. For instance, if you are writing about whales you need to ask, "What point do I wish to make about whales in this paragraph?" What do you intend to discuss about whales: their breeding habits, migratory habits, threatened extinction, by-products, level of intelligence, or something else? Answer this question before you write your first word.

Assume that you know something about the whale's level of intelligence and you choose to discuss that topic. Here is a rough topic sentence:

Whales have a high level of intelligence.

Now you can think about ways of making this sentence more specific and informative. Because a whale is a mammal, you decide to relate its level of intelligence to that of other mammals. Here is how your finished topic sentence might read:

Whales are among the most intelligent mammals ever to inhabit the earth.

With your central idea clearly stated, you have a clear plan of attack for developing the body section of your paragraph.

Body

The body of your paragraph contains the supporting details that clarify, explain, and otherwise support your central idea. Develop this section by answering the following question: What does my reader need to know in order to understand the central idea stated in my topic sentence? Or you might ask,

"What questions will my reader have about my topic sentence?" Here are some questions that your reader might ask:

Says who?
How do you know that whales are so intelligent?
What proof do you have to support this claim?
Can you give me some examples?

You can answer these implied questions by brainstorming your topic (as discussed in Appendix B), making a list of everything you know about whale intelligence. Your list might look like this:

— whales help wounded fellow whales
— communication through sonar clicks and pings
— scientists have studied whales
— exhibit complex group behavior
— they teach and discipline their young
— scientists compare whales' intelligence with that of higher primates
— elaborate sexual foreplay
— they play in game-like patterns
— they have a sophisticated communications system

By thinking about your subject before writing, you will probably find that you have more to say than you thought you did.

After identifying the full inventory of facts that support your topic sentence you can arrange them in categories (as discussed in Chapter 5). In reviewing your brainstorming list you notice that items 3, 4, and 9 are more general than the others. Therefore, because each item relates to whale intelligence, the more specific items should fit into the categories formed by the general items.

scientific studies
scientists compare whales' intelligence with that of higher primates

complex group behavior
they help wounded fellow whales
they teach and discipline their young
they engage in elaborate sexual foreplay
they play in game-like patterns

sophisticated communications system
they communicate through sonar clicks and pings

You now have three categories of general evidence further supported by specific details and explanations. When these supporting ideas have been combined within sentences your paragraph might look like this:

Whales are among the most intelligent mammals ever to inhabit the earth. Scientists studying whales rate their intelligence on a level with higher primates because of their complex group behavior. For example, these impressive mammals have been seen teaching and disciplining their young, helping wounded fellow whales, engaging in elaborate sexual foreplay, and playing in definite game-like patterns. They are able to coordinate such complex group activities because of their apparently effective communications system of sonar clicks and pings.

With your topic sentence and supporting details clearly expressed, you are ready to write your concluding statement.

Conclusion

Your concluding statement signals your reader that the discussion of the central idea stated in your topic sentence is ending. It usually ties the paragraph together by summarizing the preceding information. If the paragraph is part of a longer essay, your conclusion can also prepare your reader for the subject of the following paragraph. Assume, for example, that your paragraph on whale intelligence is to be followed by a paragraph describing abuses in the whaling industry. Here is an effective conclusion for the first paragraph:

> All in all, scientific evidence shows that whales have a high level of social organization. Unfortunately, the whales' intelligence is ignored by an industry that threatens them with extinction.

The final statement in this conclusion serves as a transition to the next major idea.

This introduction-body-conclusion structure should serve most of your paragraph needs in report writing. Begin each paragraph with a solid topic sentence and you will stay on target.

Sometimes a central idea that needs detailed definition might call for a topic statement of two or more sentences (as shown in the needle-description paragraph in the "Spatial Sequence" section). On the other hand, your central idea might be made up of several distinct parts, which would result in an excessively long paragraph. In this case you might break up the paragraph, letting your topic statement stand as a brief introductory paragraph and serve the separate subparts, which are set off as independent paragraphs for the readers' convenience.

> **The most common types of strip-mining procedures are open-pit mining, contour mining, and auger mining. The specific type employed will depend on the type of terrain covering the coal.**
>
> Open-pit mining is employed in the relatively flat lands in Western Kentucky, Oklahoma, and Kansas. Here, draglines and scoops operate directly on the coal seams. This process produces long, parallel rows of packed spoil banks, ten to thirty feet high, with steep slopes. Between the spoil banks are large pits which soon fill with water to produce pollution and flood hazards.

Contour mining is most widely practiced in the mountainous terrain of the Cumberland Plateau and Eastern Kentucky. Here, bulldozers and explosives cut and blast the earth and rock covering a coal seam. Wide bands are removed from the mountain's circumference to reach the embedded coal beneath. The cutting and blasting form a shelf along with a man-made cliff some sixty feet high at a right angle to the shelf. The blasted and churned earth is pushed over the shelf to form a massive and unstable spoil bank which creates a danger of mud slides.

Auger mining is employed when the mountain has been cut so thin that it can no longer be stripped. It is also used in other difficult-access terrain. Here, large augers bore parallel rows of holes into the hidden coal seams in order to extract the embedded coal. Among the three strip-mining processes, auger mining causes the least damage to the surrounding landscape.

Each paragraph begins with a clear statement of the part of the central idea to be discussed. The reader can then easily follow the discussion.

Paragraph Unity

A paragraph is unified when all of its parts work toward the same end — when every word, phrase, and sentence explains, illustrates, and clarifies the central idea expressed in the topic sentence. Paragraph unity is destroyed when you drift away from your stated purpose by adding details that fall outside the domain of your central idea. Here is an example of how the paragraph on whaling intelligence could become disunified:

A Disunified Paragraph

Whales are among the most intelligent mammals ever to inhabit the earth. Scientists studying whales rate their intelligence on a level with higher primates because of their complex group behavior. For example, these impressive mammals have been seen teaching and disciplining their young, helping wounded fellow whales, engaging in elaborate sexual foreplay, and playing in definite game-like patterns. **Whales continually need to search for food in order to survive. As fish populations decrease because of overfishing, the whale's quest for food becomes more difficult.**

This paragraph is not unified because it begins by discussing whale intelligence and drifts off into a discussion of food problems. Stay on the track determined by your topic sentence.

Paragraph Coherence

A paragraph is coherent when it hangs together and flows smoothly in a clear direction — when all sentences are logically connected like links in a chain, leading toward a definite conclusion.

One way to damage paragraph coherence is to use too many short, choppy sentences without subordinating your ideas. Two other ways to damage coherence are (1) to place sentences in the wrong order, and (2) to use insufficient transitions and other connectors to link related ideas. Here is how the paragraph on whaling intelligence could become incoherent:

An Incoherent Paragraph

Whales are among the most intelligent creatures ever to inhabit the earth. Scientists rate their intelligence on a level with higher primates. Whales exhibit complex group behavior. **The whaling industry ignores the whales' intelligence and threatens them with extinction.** Whales have been seen teaching and disciplining their young, helping wounded fellow whales, engaging in elaborate sexual foreplay, and playing in definite game-like patterns. **Scientific evidence shows that whales have a high order of social organization.** They are able to coordinate such complex group activities because of their apparently effective communication system of sonar clicks and pings.

This paragraph is not coherent because it fails to progress logically. For instance, the fourth sentence (in boldface) does not logically follow from the first two; it should be the last sentence. Also, the second-to-last sentence should follow the sentence that is now last. Finally, more transitions and connectors should be added to help the sentences flow smoothly from idea to idea. Here is the same paragraph with sentences written in correct sequence and with enough transitional expressions and other connectors (in boldface):

Whales are among the most **intelligent** creatures ever to inhabit the earth. Scientists studying **whales** rate **their intelligence** on a level with higher primates **because** of **their** complex group behavior. **For example, these huge and impressive mammals** have been seen teaching and disciplining **their** young, helping wounded fellow whales, engaging in elaborate sexual foreplay, and playing in definite game-like patterns. **They** are able to coordinate complex group activities **because** of **their** apparently effective communications system of sonar clicks and pings. **All in all**, scientific evidence shows that **whales** have a high order of social organization. **Unfortunately**, the **whales' intelligence** is ignored by an industry that threatens **them** with extinction.

The paragraph is now much tighter and moves in a logical sequence. The sequence of development here can be called a *reasons sequence,* because reasons are given to support an observation and to lead to a recommendation. The logical sequence in the paragraph can be expressed like this:

1. A topic sentence about whale intelligence.
2. Scientific documentation to support the thesis.
3. Specific examples and explanations of the scientific claims.

4. A statement that sums up and interprets the earlier evidence.

5. A concluding statement that provides a bridge to the next part of the discussion: abuses by the whaling industry.

Paragraphs Developed in Logical Sequence

Following a logical sequence within a paragraph simply means that you make a choice about which idea to discuss first, which second, and so on. This ordering technique will help you maintain paragraph unity and coherence by giving you a sense of direction. The sequence you select for any paragraph will depend on your subject and your purpose. Some possibilities follow.

Spatial Sequence

A spatial order of development begins at one location and ends at another. This order is most useful in a paragraph that describes a physical item or a mechanism. Simply describe the item and its parts in the order that makes most sense to your reader: left to right, inside to outside, etc. This writer has chosen a spatial order that proceeds from the needle's base (hub) to its point:

> A hypodermic needle is a slender, hollow, steel instrument used to introduce medication into the body (usually through a vein or muscle). It is a single piece composed of three parts, all considered sterile: the hub, the cannula, and the point. The hub is the lower, larger part of the needle that attaches to the neck-like opening on the syringe barrel. Next is the cannula (stem), the smooth and slender central portion. Last is the point, which consists of a beveled (slanted) opening, ending in a sharp tip. The diameter of a needle's cannula is indicated by gauge number; commonly, a 24-25 gauge needle is used for subcutaneous injections. Needle lengths are varied to suit individual needs. Common lengths used for subcutaneous injections are ⅜, ½, ¾, and ⅝ inches. Regardless of length and diameter, all needles have the same functional design.

Explanation Sequence

Sometimes a paragraph can be arranged according to the order of details used to explain the topic sentence (or an earlier paragraph). Here is the paragraph that explains the preceding one. The writer has wisely chosen to move from the point backward because the needle's function begins at the point.

> Functionally, the needle serves as a passage for the flow of medication. First, the firm, sharp point penetrates the vial for withdrawal of medication. Next, the cannula provides a channel from the vial, through the hub attachment, to the syringe. In turn, the sharp point permits rapid penetration of the skin and tissue while the slender cannula provides a smooth surface,

reducing the body's resistance to entrance. Finally, the entire needle works as a unit to allow passage of solution from the syringe barrel into the subcutaneous tissue during the injection.

Chronological Sequence

A paragraph describing a series of events or giving instructions is most effective when its details are arranged according to a strict time sequence: first step, second step, etc.

> When you have collected all needed ingredients, prepare your cake batter. Begin by sifting 3½ cups of flour. Then measure the flour and sift it again, along with 2½ cups of granulated sugar, 5 teaspoons of baking powder, and 1 teaspoon of salt into a mixing bowl. To this mixture add ¾ cup of shortening, 4 eggs, 1½ cups of milk, and 2 teaspoons of vanilla extract. Finally, blend the ingredients by hand until the batter is mixed well enough to divide.

Examples Sequence

Often, a topic sentence can best be supported by specific examples.

> Although strip mining is safer and cheaper than conventional mining, it is highly damaging to the surrounding landscape. Among its effects are scarred mountains, ruined land, and polluted waterways. Strip operations are altering our country's land at the rate of 5,000 acres per week. An estimated 10,500 miles of streams have been poisoned by silt drainage in Appalachia alone. If strip mining continues at its present rate, 16,000 square miles of United States land will eventually be stripped barren.

Effect to Cause Sequence

A paragraph that first identifies a problem and then discusses its causes is typically found in problem-solving reports.

> Modern whaling techniques have brought the whale population to the threshold of extinction. In the nineteenth century the invention of the steamboat increased hunters' speed and mobility. Shortly afterward, the grenade harpoon was invented so that whales could be killed quickly and easily from the ship's deck. In 1904 a whaling station opened on Georgia Island in South America. This station became the gateway to Antarctic whaling for the nations of the world. In 1924 factory ships were designed that enabled 'round-the-clock whale tracking and processing. These ships could reduce a 90-foot whale to its by-products in roughly thirty minutes. After World War II, more powerful boats with remote sensing devices gave a final boost to the whaling industry. The number of kills had now increased far above the whales' capacity to reproduce.

Cause and Effect Sequence

In a cause and effect sequence the topic sentence identifies the cause(s) and the remainder of the paragraph discusses its effects.

The state prisoner furlough program was devised primarily to help ex-offenders stay out of jail after their release. It was believed that short periods of societal exposure would help inmates prepare for their eventual reintegration. According to figures compiled by the State Corrections Department, the program is working.

Definition Sequence

For adequate definition, a term may require a full paragraph (as discussed in Chapter 4).

The prisoner furlough program permits inmates to leave a state or county institution, unescorted, for no less than twelve hours and no more than seven consecutive days. The state corrections commissioner or the administrator of a county jail may grant furloughs to inmates for the following purposes: attending the funeral of a relative; visiting a critically ill relative; obtaining medical, psychiatric, or counseling services when such services are not available within the institution; contacting prospective employers; finding a suitable residence for use on permanent release; or for any other purpose that will help the inmate's reintegration into the community. Inmates released in 1973 after receiving at least one furlough had a one-year recidivism[1] rate of 17 percent. In contrast, inmates released in the same year after receiving no furloughs had a one-year recidivism rate of 25 percent. These figures are significant because convicts from all crime categories have been furloughed.

[1] For the purpose of the study, a recidivist was defined as an ex-convict who was returned to any federal, state, or county jail for thirty days or more.

Reasons Sequence

A paragraph that provides detailed reasons to support a specific viewpoint or recommendation is often used in job-related writing.

The Wankel Engine has obvious advantages over the conventional V-8 engine. Its simplicity of design and operation add to its efficiency and adaptability. The Wankel's lack of valves and camshaft — parts found in all conventional engines — increases its breathing abilities making for a smooth running engine on low octane gas. Because of its high power-to-weight ratio the Wankel allows more passenger room in large automobiles, while providing better power and performance in smaller ones. Even the cost of manufacturing and maintaining the Wankel should be lower because of its few moving parts.

Problem-Causes-Solution Sequence

The problem-causes-solution paragraph is used in daily-activity or progress reports.

> The unpainted wood exteriors of all waterfront buildings had been severely damaged by the high winds and standstorms of the previous winter. After the damage was repaired, the following protective steps against further storms were taken. First, all joints, edges, and sashes were treated with water-repellent preservative to protect against water damage. Next, three coats of nonporous primer were applied to all exterior surfaces to prevent paint blistering and peeling. Finally, two coats of wood-quality latex paint were applied over the nonporous primer. To avoid future separation between coats of paint, the first coat was applied within two weeks of the priming coats and the second within two weeks of the first. As of two weeks after completion, no blistering, peeling, or separation has occurred.

Comparison/Contrast Sequence

A paragraph discussing the similarities or differences (or both) between two or more related items is often used in job-related writing assignments.

> The ski industry's quest for a binding that ensures both good performance and safety has led to the development of two basic binding types. The first type consists of two units (one at the toe, another at the heel) that are spring-loaded. These units apply their retention forces directly to the boot sole. In contrast, the second type has one spring-loaded unit located at either the toe or the heel. From this unit extends a boot plate, which travels lengthwise under the boot to a fixed receptacle attached to the opposite end. With this plate-type binding, the boot plays no part in release or retention effectiveness. Instead, retention force is applied directly to the boot plate. On the whole, the double-unit binding performs better, but the plate-type is safer.

For the comparison and contrast of specific data on each of these bindings, two lists would be most effective.

> The Salomon 555 offers the following features.
>
> 1. Upward release at the heel and lateral release at the toe. *Note:* Lack of a lateral release at the heel causes 80% of all leg injuries.
> 2. Lateral anti-shock capacity of 15 millimeters with the highest available return-to-center force.

3. Two methods of reentry to the binding: for hard and deep powder conditions.

4. Five adjustments.

5. Maximum hold-down power for racers and experts.

6. The necessity of boot alteration.

7. Release torque applied to the boot sole, which, under stress of normal use, alters its release characteristics necessitating readjustment and eventual replacement of boots.

8. High durability and a combined weight of 74 ounces for $80.

9. The most endorsements among alpine racers today.

The Americana offers these features:

1. Upward release at the toe as well as upward and lateral release at the heel.

2. Lateral antishock capacity of 30 millimeters with a moderate return-to-center force.

3. Two methods of reentry to the binding.

4. Two adjustments, one for boot length and another comprehensive adjustment for all angles of release and elasticity.

5. Hold-down power that is slightly compromised at the heel to provide a lateral release potential.

6. A boot plate that eliminates the need for boot alterations, wear on boots, and danger due to friction potentials when the boot is included in the release system.

7. The durability of two moving parts and a combined weight of 56 ounces for $54.50.

Instead of this block-type structure (in which one binding is discussed and then the other) the writer might have chosen a point-by-point structure (in which related points about each item are listed together: e.g., "Reentry methods").

Transitions and Other Connectors

After selecting the most logical sequence for developing your paragraph, link your sentences by using transitional words and phrases. These work like hinges to signal a specific relationship between ideas and to make a paragraph coherent. Here are some sample transitions.

To Signal an Added Idea

I have a bachelor's degree in naval architecture; **furthermore**, I spent three years as a crew member on a racing yawl.

To Signal an Opposing Idea

Jack worked hard; **however**, he was never promoted.

To Signal a Result
Jack worked hard; **consequently**, he was promoted.

To Signal an Illustration
Local competition is too heavy; **for example**, five competing businesses have opened in the past year alone.

To Signal a Comparison
Our town reservoir is drying up because of the long drought; **similarly**, water resources throughout the state are dangerously low.

To Signal a Time Relationship
The crew will pour the foundation on Tuesday; **immediately afterward**, we will deliver the framing lumber.

To Signal a Space Relationship
Here is the lever that controls the blade pitch. **To the right** is the lever that controls the shovel height.

To Signal a Conclusion
Our credit is destroyed, our bank account is empty, and our debts are piling up; **in short**, we are bankrupt.

A list of transitional expressions follows. Learn them well and write practice sentences using each one.

To Signal an Addition

moreover	and
in addition	furthermore
also	

To Signal Place

beyond	inside
over	to the right
under	nearby
opposite to	adjacent to

To Signal Time

first	later
next	now
second	the next day
finally	in the meantime
meanwhile	in turn
at length	subsequently

To Signal a Comparison

likewise	in comparison
similarly	

To Signal a Contrast

however	but
nevertheless	on the other hand
yet	to the contrary
still	notwithstanding
in contrast	conversely
otherwise	

To Signal Results

thus	accordingly
hence	thereupon
therefore	as a result
because of this	so
consequently	

To Signal an Example

for example	namely
for instance	specifically

To Signal an Explanation

in other words	simply stated
that is	in fact

To Signal a Summary or a Conclusion

in closing	in short
to conclude	all in all
to summarize	on the whole
in brief	in retrospect

Besides these expressions, which link independent ideas, there are other words designed to make one clause dependent on another (as discussed on page 537). These connectors increase the coherence *within* sentences as well as between them.

To Signal a Contrast
Although Jack worked hard, he was never promoted.

To Signal Cause and Effect
Since he had no job prospects in the East, he decided to move West.

To Signal a Time Relationship
While she waited, it began to rain.

To Signal a Conditional Relationship
If he arrives late, he will be fired.

To Signal a Space Relationship
Where there is smoke, there is fire.

Here are some other subordinating words that serve as transitions:

besides	until
unless	before
when	after
though	because

Pronouns also serve as connectors, because a pronoun refers back to a noun that you have used in a preceding clause or sentence.

> As the **crew** neared the end of the project, **they** were all willing to work overtime to get the job done.

> **Low employee morale** is damaging our productivity. **This** problem needs immediate attention.

Synonyms (words meaning the same as other words) can also be effective connectors. In the whaling intelligence paragraph earlier, for example, "huge and impressive mammals" (a synonym for "whales") helps tie the ideas together.

Repetition of key words or phrases is another good connecting device — as long as it is not overdone. Too much repetition is boring. The word "whales" is repeated effectively in the earlier paragraph. Here is another example of effective repetition:

> Overuse and drought conditions have depleted our water supply to a critical level. Because of our **depleted water supply**, we will need to enforce strict **water**-conservation measures.

Here, the repetition also emphasizes a critical problem.

The following paragraph lacks adequate transitions, and the sentences seem choppy and awkward:

> Technical writing is a difficult but important skill to master. It requires long hours of work and concentration. This time and effort are well spent. Writing is an indispensable tool that will help determine one's level of professional success. Good writers derive great pride and satisfaction from their effort. A highly disciplined writing course should be a part of every student's curriculum.

Here is the same paragraph rewritten to improve coherence:

> Technical writing is a difficult but important skill to master. **Thus** it requires long hours of work and concentration. **This** time and effort, **however**, are well spent **because writing** is an indispensable tool that will help determine one's level of professional success. **Moreover**, good **writers** derive great pride and satisfaction from their effort. A highly disciplined **writing** course, **therefore**, should be a part of every student's curriculum.

Transitions and connectors not only emphasize the logical connection between related ideas but also improve the writing style. They are both an aid to clarity and coherence and a mark of sophistication.

Besides increasing coherence *within* a paragraph, transitions and other connectors can underscore relationships *between* paragraphs by linking related groups of ideas. Here are two transitional sentences that could serve as the concluding sentences for certain paragraphs or as topic sentences for paragraphs that would follow; or they could stand alone for emphasis as single-sentence paragraphs:

> Because the A-12 filter has decreased overall engine wear by 15 percent, it should be included as a standard item in all our new models.

> With the camera activated and the watertight cover sealed, the diving bell is ready to be submerged.

These sentences look both ahead and back, thereby providing a clear direction for continuing discussion.

Topic headings, like those used in this book, are another device for increasing coherence. A topic heading is both a link and a separation between related, yet distinct, groups of ideas.

Finally, a whole paragraph can serve as a connector between major sections of your report. Assume, for instance, that you have just completed a section of a report on the advantages of a new oil filter and are now moving to a section on selling the idea to the buying public. Here is a paragraph you might write to link the two sections:

> Because the A-12 filter has decreased overall engine wear by 15 percent, it should be included as a standard item in all our new models. However, because tooling and installation adjustments will add roughly $100 to the list price of each model, we need to explain the filter's long-range advantages to the customers. Let's look at ways of explaining these advantages.

The effective use of transitional devices in your revisions is one way of transforming a piece of writing from adequate to excellent.

Appendix B

The Brainstorming Technique

Brainstorming is based on the well-proven thesis that we cannot make something from nothing. Its purpose is to get ideas down *on paper* so that they may be used and so that relationships among them may be recognized. You can hold a brainstorming session alone or with a group. All you need is a quiet room, an alarm clock, and pencil and paper. The procedure is simple: just think about a chosen subject and write down every idea that pops into your head within a given period. The technique was devised years ago by Alex Osborne as a way of attacking a problem or question from all sides. Here are his guidelines for a brainstorming session:

1. Don't criticize or evaluate any ideas during the session. Simply write down every idea that emerges. Save the criticism and evaluation until later.

2. Use your imagination for "free wheeling." The wilder the idea the better, because it might lead to some valuable insights later.

3. Strive for quantity. The more ideas, the better chance for a winner to emerge.

4. Combine and improve ideas as you proceed. As your list grows, someone may suggest ways of combining two or more ideas into a better idea, or of improving on some of the ideas already listed.[1]

The point is to write down all your ideas immediately!

The brainstorming procedure can be applied to just about any question or problem. Imagine, for instance, that you are having trouble balancing your budget. Begin by formulating the problem as a question: How can I make ends meet? Now follow these steps:

1. Lock yourself in a quiet room with an alarm clock, a pencil, and a stock of paper.

---

[1] Alex F. Osborne, *Applied Imagination* (New York: Charles Scribner's Sons, 1957), p. 84. Reprinted by permission of Charles Scribner's Sons.

2. Set the alarm to ring in thirty minutes.

3. Empty your mind of anxieties — about the bills, studies, the football team, and everything else. Sit with your eyes closed for two minutes, thinking about *absolutely nothing.*

4. Now, begin thinking about ways to solve your problem. Repeat this question: How can I make ends meet?

5. As the ideas begin to flow, write *every one* of them down. Don't make judgments about relevance or value and don't worry about complete sentences. Just *get them down on paper* — all of them!

6. Continue this pushing and sweating until the alarm goes off, thinking of nothing but the universal question.

7. And if the ideas are still flowing, reset the alarm clock and go on.

8. At the end of this time you should have an impressive mixture of gibberish, irrelevancies, and *pure gold.*

9. Take the rest of the day off!

10. On the next day confront your list. Strike out the gibberish and irrelevancies and organize related items into categories. As you work on your list, other ideas will surely come to mind; put *them* down too. Out of your list, the best solution to your problem should emerge.

Here is how your brainstorming list might read:

> get more roommates for the apartment
> move to a cheaper place
> sell car
> get part-time job
> apply for a loan
> drink less beer
> do less partying
> find rich girlfriend/boyfriend
> buy used books
> apply for work-study
> cook at home
> wash and iron own shirts
> sell my stereo
> apply for a scholarship
> quit school and work full time
> transfer to a tuition-free institution
> help from home
> write to rich aunt
> make a strict budget
> sell skis and surfboard
> turn in credit cards
> lock checkbook in closet
> do less dating
> work two jobs during summer
> live on peanut-butter sandwiches

> buy a van and live in it
> have telephone removed
> no weekend trips

As the next step, cross out the ideas that seem less practical and realistic than the others and add any new ideas. Now organize related items within broader categories (as discussed in Chapter 5). The six classes that seem to emerge from this list are:

> Selling Things
> Asking for Help
> Changing Lifestyle
> Making a Physical Move
> Getting a Job
> Managing Money

As you ponder these categories, which cover all sides of the problem, you should come up with a practical solution.

The same technique can be applied to your job-hunting campaign, especially to making up your résumé. Simply modify items 4 and 10 in the earlier list.

4. Now, reach back into your personal, educational, and work experience for specific items to answer your prospective employer's *big* question: What do you have to offer? Especially dig for items that separate you from the herd.

10. On the next day, review your list and strike out the irrelevancies. On separate sheets of paper headed Career Objectives; Educational Background; Work Experience; and Personal Interests, Activities, Awards, and Special Skills, arrange the remaining items along with any new ones that pop into your head.

Now you have the raw material for your résumé.

You will find the brainstorming technique handy for achieving the depth of concentration needed for coming up with good ideas — ideas which otherwise you might never realize you had. This technique may well be your most essential prewriting step.

Index

Abbreviations, 163–166, 575–578
Abstracts
    descriptive, 48
    informative, 48, 204, 206 (*see also*
        Summaries)
    placement in reports, 48–49
Active voice, 24–26
    in instructions, 388
Agreement
    noun-pronoun, 542–543
    subject-verb, 542–543
Analytical reports. *See also* Formal reports
    body in, 449–451
    conclusion in, 451–453
    definition, 433–434
    elements of, 438–441
    evidence in, 442–443
    flexible approach to, 445
    introduction in, 447–449
    outline for, 446
    purpose, 434–435
    reasoning in, 444–445
    revision checklist, 508
    sources for, 441–442
    supplements to, 453
    typical analytical problems, 435–438
Apostrophe, 569–571
Appendix. *See* Supplements, to reports
Audience
    background of, 13–14
    for definitions, 58, 59
    for descriptions, 347–348
        expectations, 20
        for informal reports, 299–300
        for instructions, 384
        for letters, 256, 259–260
        level of technicality, 14–17, 18
        needs, 9, 17–19
        for oral reports, 517
        for process analyses, 396
        sample situations, 19–20
        for summaries, 37–39

Bibliography. *See* Documentation
Brackets, 573
Brainstorming, 598–599
Business license application, 321, 323. *See
        also* Informal reports

Capitalization, 578–579
Cause-and-effect sequence, 114, 589
Charts, 230–234
Chronological sequence, 113, 354, 588
Classification
    applications, 93–95
    definition, 79–80
    guidelines, 87–93
    revision checklist, 96
    uses, 80–82
    visual aids in, 88–92
Coherence, in paragraphs, 585–587
Colon, 559–560

Comma, 560, 563–569
Comma splice, 538–539
Comparison/contrast sequence, 114, 435–
    436, 590–591
Conciseness, 26–27
  in oral reports, 525–526
  in summaries, 37, 39
Correction symbols, 530

Dangling modifiers, 548
Dashes, 573–574
Definition
  of abstract and general terms, 58, 59
  audience for, 58, 59
  basic properties of, 60
  of concrete and specific terms, 58, 59
  expanded, 59, 63–65
  expansion methods, 65–68
  objectivity in, 60–61
  parenthetical, 59, 61
  placement of, 72–73
  plain English in, 60
  purpose, 57–59
  revision checklist, 74–75
  sentence definition, 59, 62–63
Description
  body in, 361–362
  conclusion in, 363
  definition, 341
  elements of, 351–353
  introduction in, 361
  objectivity in, 347–351
  outline of, 355
  precise language in, 349–351
  purpose, 342–346
  revision checklist, 376
  sequences in, 353–355, 356–360
  visual aids in, 352
Diction, 22–23
Documentation. *See also* Research;
    Supplements, to reports
  alternative documentation systems
    list of parenthetical numbers, 167
    parenthetical author/year designation,
      167
  MLA bibiliography format, 165–166
  MLA footnote format, 163–165
  purpose, 162–163
Dossier, 284, 286

Ellipses, 572
Exclamation points, 561

Figures, 233–235
Footnotes. *See* Documentation
Formal reports, 181–182, 432–511. *See
    also* Analytical reports
Format, 180–192, 251

Glossary. *See* Supplements, to reports
Graphs, 223–230

Headings, 190–192, 193
  in outlines, 112–113
  as transitions, 595 (*see also* Transitions)
Hyphen, 574–575

Informal reports, 181–182, 298–339
  audience needs in, 300–301
  definition, 299
  as letters, 310–315, 316–319
  as memoranda, 301–310, 311
  in miscellaneous forms, 321–334
  on prepared forms, 315, 320–321, 322–
    325
  purpose, 299–300
  revision checklist, 335
Instructions. *See also* Process explanation
  letters of, 266–268
Interviews
  informative, 143–149
  job, 286–287
Italics, 572

Jargon, 21–22, 252, 255–256
Job hunting, 268–270, 280. *See also* Letters

Letters
  of acceptance, 287, 289
  accepted form, 252, 253–254
  clear purpose in, 259, 260
  of complaint, 264–266
  definition, 243
  dossier, 284, 286
  of follow-up, 287, 288
  format, 251 (*see also* Format)
  of inquiry, 246, 260–264
  of instruction, 266–268

introduction-body-conclusion in, 245
of job application, 278–284 (*see also*
    Job hunting)
job interviews (*see* Interviews)
plain English in, 252–255, 256, 257–258
    (*see also* Jargon)
purpose, 244
of refusal, 290–291
required parts
    closing, 249
    heading, 245, 248
    inside address, 248
    salutation, 248
    signature, 249
résumé, 268–278
revision checklist, 292
specialized parts
    distribution notation, 250
    enclosure notation, 250
    postscript, 250
    typist's initials, 250
of transmittal, 196–198, 200, 201 (*see
    also* Supplements, to reports)
"you" perspective in, 256, 259
Library
    card catalog, 133–138
    periodical indexes, 138-142
    reference books, 142
    reference librarian, 143
    vertical file, 142–143

Minutes, of meetings, 326, 327, 328
Misplaced modifiers, 549

Note taking, 155–158
Numbers, use of, 579–580

Objectivity, 6, 27–28
    in analytical reports, 439, 440
    in classification, 90
    in definitions, 60–61
    in descriptions, 347–351
Operational sequence, 354
Oral reports
    audience needs, 517
    definition, 513–514
    extemporaneous delivery, 517–524
    formal reports, 515

informal reports, 515
    purpose, 514–515
    revision checklist, 527–528
    semiformal reports, 515
    sentence outline for, 518, 519–522
    techniques for delivery, 524–526
Outline
    for analytical reports, 446
    construction of, 114–118
    coverage in, 109
    definition, 101–102
    for a description, 355
    formal sentence outline, 106–109
    formal topic outline, 104–106
    headings in, 112–113
    informal outline, 103–104
    for instructions, 390–391
    logical sequence, 113–114
    notation in, 104–106, 110–111
    parallelism in, 112
    partitioning in, 109
    for process analysis, 416
    for process narrative, 405–406
    purpose, 102
    revision checklist, 124

Paragraphs
    cause-and-effect sequence, 589
    chronological sequence, 588
    coherence, 585-587, 594–595
    comparison/contrast sequence, 590–591
    definition sequence, 589
    effect-to-cause sequence, 588
    examples sequence, 588
    explanation sequence, 587–588
    length, 581–582
    logical sequences, 587–591
    problem-causes-solution sequence, 590
    purpose, 580–581
    reasons sequence, 589
    spatial sequence, 587
    structure, 582–585
    transitions in, 591–595
    unity, 585
Parallelism, 549–552
    in classifications, 90
    in headings, 191–192
    in instructions, 389–390
    in outlines, 112
    in partitions, 84

Parentheses, 573
Partition
  applications, 93–95
  definition, 79–80
  guidelines, 82–87
  in outlines, 109
  use of, 80–82
  visual aids in, 86–87
Passive voice, 24–26
Periodic activity reports, 321, 324–325. *See*
      also Informal reports
Pretentious prose, 20–21
  in letters, 252, 255–256, 257–258
Problem-causes-solution sequence, 113, 436,
      590
Process explanation, 380–431
  definition, 381
  instructions, 382–383, 384–396, 397–404
    body in, 393–395
    conclusion in, 395
    elements of, 384, 390
    introduction in, 391–393
    outline for, 390-391
  process analysis, 383, 406, 415–427
    elements of, 406–415
    outline for, 416
  process narrative, 383, 396, 405–406,
      407–414
    elements of, 396, 405–406
    outline for, 405–406
  purpose, 381, 382
  revision checklist, 429
Progress reports, 310, 311, 332, 333–334.
      See also Informal reports
Pronouns, 344–347
Proofreading, 28
Proposals, 305, 307–309, 315, 316–317. *See*
      also Informal reports
Punctuation
  apostrophe, 569–571
  brackets, 573
  colon, 559–560, 562–563
  comma, 560, 563–569
  dashes, 573–574
  ellipses, 572
  end punctuation, 560–561
  hyphen, 574–575
  parentheses, 573
  purpose of, 559
  quotation marks, 571–572

relative strength of, 559–560
  semicolon, 559, 561–562
Purchase requisitions, 321, 322. *See also*
      Informal reports

Question marks, 561
Quotation marks, 571–572

Readers. *See* Audience
Redundancy, 558
Report design worksheet, 118–122
Reports
  formal, 181–182, 432–511 (*see also*
      Analytical reports)
  informal, 181–182, 298–339
Research
  bibliography, 165–166
  definition, 129–130
  footnotes, 163–165
  information gathering, 160–161
  information sources, 132
  informative interviews, 143–149
  inquiry letters, 151 (*see also* Letters)
  library use, 132–143
  note taking, 155–158
  organizational records, 151
  other systems of documentation, 165, 167
  personal experience, 132
  personal observation, 154
  planning and writing the report, 158–173
  preparation, 159–160
  primary research, 129–130
  purpose of, 130–132
  questionnaires, 150–153
  secondary research, 129–130
  writing and documentation, 162–174
Résumé, 268–278. *See also* Letters
Revisions, 28–29
  of letters, 282

Semicolon, 559, 561–562
Sentences. *See also* Punctuation
  awkward construction, 555–557
  choppiness, 540
  comma splice, 538–539
  complexity of, 23–24
  dangling modifiers, 548
  dead wood, 557–559
  fragments, 535–538

illogical construction, 553–554
misplaced modifiers, 549
noun-pronoun agreement, 542–543
parallelism, 549–552
parts of, 531–534
pronoun case, 546–547
pronoun reference, 544–546
run-on, 539–540
shifts, 552–553
subject-verb agreement, 542–543
subordination, 540–542
triteness, 557
types of sentences, 534–535
Site inspection reports, 310, 312–315. *See also* Informal reports
Spatial sequence, 113, 353–354, 587
Summaries. *See also* Abstracts
accuracy of, 37
conciseness in, 37, 39
definition, 35
essential message in, 38
meaning in, 38
placement in reports, 48–49
purpose of, 35–37
revision checklist, 50
sample procedure, 41–47
steps in writing, 39–41
structure of, 39
style in, 38
Supplements, to reports
appendix, 212–214
bibliography, 212
cover, 192, 194
definition, 182
footnotes, 212
glossary, 206, 211
informative abstract, 204, 206, 207–210
(*see also* Abstracts; Summaries)
letter of transmittal, 196–198, 200, 201
(*see also* Letters)
purpose, 183, 188
table of contents, 199, 202–203
table of illustrations, 204, 205
title page, 194–196

Survey results, 301, 302, 304–305, 306, 326, 329–332. *See also* Informal reports

Table of contents. *See* Supplements, to reports
Tables, 221–223
Technical writing
definition, 3
example of, 3–6
uses of, 8–9
value of, 8–9
Transitions, 591–595. *See also* Semicolon
in instructions, 388–389
in summaries, 46–47
Triteness, 557

Unity, in paragraphs, 585

Visual aids
charts
flow charts, 233–234
organizational charts, 231–232
pie charts, 230–231
in a classification, 88–92
definition, 219
in a description, 352
diagrams, 234–235
graphs
bar graphs, 224–226
line graphs, 226–230
in a partition, 86–87
photographs, 235
in process narration, 405
purpose, 219, 221
revision checklist, 237
samples, 235
tables, 221–223

Wordiness, 558
Work estimates, 315, 318–319. *See also* Informal reports